WORLD®
AIR POWER
J O U R N A L

Aerospace Publishing Ltd
Airtime Publishing Inc.

Published quarterly by
Aerospace Publishing Ltd
179 Dalling Road
London W6 0ES
UK

Copyright © Aerospace Publishing Ltd

Cutaway drawings copyright
© Mike Badrocke/Aviagraphica

ISSN 0959-7050

Aerospace ISBN   1 874023 43 3
                 (softback)
                 1 874023 44 1
                 (hardback)
AIRtime ISBN   1-880588-07-2
                (hardback)

Published under licence in USA and
Canada by AIRtime Publishing Inc.,
10 Bay Street, Westport,
CT 06880, USA

Editorial Offices:
WORLD AIR POWER JOURNAL
Aerospace Publishing Ltd
3A Brackenbury Road
London   W6 0BE   UK

Publisher: Stan Morse
Managing Editor: David Donald
Editor: Jon Lake
Editorial Assistants:
    Robert Hewson
    Soph Moeng
    Tim Senior
Sub Editor: Karen Leverington
Origination and printing by
    Imago Publishing Ltd
Printed in Singapore

Europe Correspondent:
    Paul Jackson
Washington Correspondent:
    Robert F. Dorr
USA West Coast Correspondent:
    René J. Francillon
Asia Correspondent:
    Pushpindar Singh

The editors of WORLD AIR
POWER JOURNAL welcome
photographs for possible publication,
but cannot accept any responsibility for
loss or damage to unsolicited material.

The publishers gratefully acknowledge
the assistance given by the following
people:

Rostislav A. Belyakov, Valery V.
Novikov, Pavel N. Vlasov, Marat
Alykov and Nikolai Buntin of the
Mikoyan Design Bureau, Mikoyan
retirees Mikhail P. Waldenburg and
Valery Menitsky, and Fedor M.
Timofeyev, Alexander F. Dmitriyev
and Victor P. Trifonov of the Moscow
Aircraft Production Organisation for
their enthusiastic help with the MiG-29
feature. Also to Dr Ezio Bonsignore,
Editor of *Military Technology* and
Editorial Director of Mönch Publishing
Group for his kind assistance with the
same article.

Jahn Ahlgren, Asa Holm and Eva-Li
Asplund of Saab for their considerable
assistance with the Draken Variant
Briefing.

Colonel William Manire, Commander
55th Wing, Colonel David Wolfe,
Commander 55th OG, Major Scott
Hackney, 55th OSS, and Major Mark
Lewis, 55th OSS, for their invaluable
contributions to 'Offutt's White-tops'.

**World Air Power Journal is a
registered trademark in the United
States of America of AIRtime
Publishing Inc.**

**World Air Power Journal is
published quarterly and is available
by subscription and from many fine
book and hobby stores.**

**SUBSCRIPTION AND BACK
NUMBERS:**

**UK and World (except USA and
Canada) write to:**
**Aerospace Publishing Ltd
FREEPOST
PO Box 2822
London
W6 0BR
UK**

**(No stamp required if posted in the
UK)**

USA and Canada, write to:
**AIRtime Publishing Inc.
Subscription Dept
10 Bay Street
Westport
CT 06880
USA**
**Toll-free order number in USA:
1-800-359-3003**

**Prevailing subscription rates are as
follows:**
**Softbound edition for 1 year:
    $58.00**
**Softbound edition for 2 years:
    $108.00**
**Softbound back numbers (subject
to availability) are:**
**$17.95 each. All rates are for
delivery within mainland USA,
Alaska and Hawaii. Canadian and
overseas prices available upon
request. American Express,
Mastercard and Visa accepted.
When ordering please include your
card number, expiration date and
signature.**

**Publisher, North America:
    Melvyn Williams**
**Subscription Director:
    Linda de Angelis**
**Retail Sales Director:
    Jill Brooks**
**Charter Member Services
Managers:
    Janie Munroe
    Monica A. Virag**

WORLD AIR POWER®

AIR POWER

J O U R N A L

CONTENTS

Military Aviation Review

International

NATO membership proposals

A new 'limited privileges' membership class of NATO was being considered late in 1993 to meet interest expressed by Hungary, Poland and the Czech Republic in joining the alliance. Associate status was devised by existing members wary of extending the guarantee of 'an attack upon one is an attack upon all' to areas of Europe which have still to prove their stability. However, new members – which could also include Austria, Finland, Sweden and Switzerland – would enrich NATO and permit better collaboration in military programmes, joint exercises and peacekeeping operations. Russia has declined to participate.

Eurofighter 2000 stays grounded

Following a start to taxiing trials on 31 July and finalisation on 16 August of flight control software for the Eurofighter 2000, the much-delayed (since late 1991) maiden sortie was pencilled in for the end of October. However, a few weeks before German-built DA1 (serial number 9829) was expected to begin trials, a further postponement until the spring of 1994 was announced. The aircraft's protracted grounding is ascribed to the need to ensure that the flight control software is, according to a Eurofighter spokesman, '1,000 per cent' error free, a requirement which can only have been underscored by the very public crash of a second SAAB Gripen on 8 August. Having narrowly averted a German financial pull-out in 1992, Eurofighter appears to consider the embarrassment of further grounding preferable to the minute risk of TV pictures of a Eurofighter running amok in the air being beamed into every German taxpayer's home. German support of the project was further eroded in October when the Bundesrechnungshof (federal audit office) published a report claiming that the Eurofighter would be no better than existing aircraft when it entered service. The report, which had been commissioned by arch Eurofighter rival Volker Rühe, the Defence Minister, was dismissed as 'stupid' by a UK source.

Responsibility for the delay in flying the Eurofighter was laid at Germany's door in the same month that the consortium's directors agreed to deprive DASA of design leadership in the flight control system. BAe was brought in to share the programme with DASA in the hope that its expertise would speed progress towards flight trials. Germany's armaments certification agency, the Bundesamt für Wehrtechnik und Beschaffung, was also implicated in the delay, it having allegedly underestimated the time required to conduct its own confirmatory tests of the software. At the same time, however, there were concerns that the flight control computer's processing capacity was too small and could become swamped.

During the October meeting it was also decided that DASA would have to share design responsibility for the Eurofighter's ECR90 radar with BAe. That programme was then on schedule, so the step appeared

26 November was the 30th anniversary of the SE.316B Alouette III with No. 3 Support Wing, Irish Air Corps. This scheme was the first 'special' ever applied to an Air Corps aircraft.

to have been taken to forestall possible future problems.

One of the few recent items of good news associated with the Eurofighter 2000 was released at the end of October when the Eurojet EJ200 reheated turbofan was given preliminary flight certification. Rated at 90 kN (20,230 lb st), the EJ 200 will be installed in the third and subsequent Eurofighters, the first two machines having the Tornado's RB.199.

Russia looks down on Europe

Russia flew its first Open Skies reconnaissance flights over Germany between 23 and 26 August, using an An-30 'Clank'. Operating out of Bremen, the aircraft overflew Berlin, Leipzig and Frankfurt. The NATO/WEU countries are entitled to reciprocal flights over the CIS, for which an interim fleet of surveillance aircraft has been assembled.

The UK has assigned an Andover C.Mk 1(R) until 1995 and Germany a Tu-154; Benelux countries use Belgian Hercules fitted with the SAMSON underwing sensor pod. Canada also favours the C-130 pod, but the USAF has launched a more ambitious programme involving conversion of three Boeing reconnaissance/weather aircraft to OC-135B standard. It is hoped that the West can agree on a unified fleet for reasons of standardisation and economy, perhaps even forming a unit similar to the NAEWF Sentry force at Geilenkirchen. All the 16 NATO nations are involved in Open Skies, together with Russia/Byelorussia, Bulgaria, Poland, Czech Republic, Slovakia, Romania and Ukraine.

Participants are allowed to make their flights only from specified bases, those for the UK being Brize Norton, Scampton and Leuchars. Entitled aircraft can conduct sorties of up to 715 miles (1150 km) from each of these stations (increasing to 930 miles/1500 km if the Shetlands or Scillies are included). US centres are Washington/Dulles (3,045 miles/4900 km), Travis AFB (2,485 miles/4000 km), Elmendorf AFB (1,865 miles/3000 km) and Lincoln Municipal (2,980 miles/4800 km). Signatories are allowed a specified number of sorties per year over designated countries, but may not have access to other signatories not on their list. As an example, Poland has the allocation of one flight each over Germany, Byelorussia, the Russian Federation and Ukraine, while the USA can fly eight sorties over Byelorussia or the Russian Federation and one joint flight with Canada over Ukraine.

Denmark's Fennec anti-tank helicopters took part in their first operational deployment during the NATO exercise Action Express. The aircraft are designated AS 550C-2 with ESCO HeliTOW system.

Western Europe

BELGIUM:

Fighting Falcon surplus

Aircraft made surplus as the result of defence cuts began entering storage on 18 October when the first Lockheed F-16 Fighting Falcon arrived at the NATO reserve airfield of Weelde. Located between Antwerp and Turnhout, and normally the base of nothing more dynamic than Air Cadets' sailplanes, the airfield will eventually hold 30 F-16s as well as the Mirage 5s withdrawn from 42 Squadron at the end of 1993. Hitherto, Koksijde/Coxyde has been the resting place of retired aircraft. F-16s have been made surplus by Belgium's decision to cut its contribution to NATO from 144 to 72 fighters. The F-16-equipped 1 Wing at Beauvechain/Bevekom is to disband and contribute 36 aircraft to the surplus, but its two squadrons are to be saved. Nos 349 and 350 Squadrons were Belgian components of the RAF during World War II and are to be shared between the two existing fighter wings, which will have three squadrons of 12 aircraft each, instead of two with 18. At Florennes, 2 Wing is to comprise 1, 2 and 350 Squadrons, while 10 Wing at Kleine Brogel gains No. 349 to add to 23 and 31.

DENMARK:

Drakens disband

Eskadrille 729, the last of Denmark's two Draken squadrons, was reduced to six aircraft in the autumn prior to disbandment at Karup on 31 December. Formed with F-84G Thunderjets at Karup on 1 September 1953, Esk 729 moved to Skrydstrup on 1 January 1954 and disbanded there on 1 March 1960. Simultaneously, the FR/PR Flight at Karup was redesignated Esk 729 and its RF-84F Thunder-

flashes equipped the squadron until the first RF-35 Draken arrived on 25 May 1971. When co-located Draken squadron Esk 725 disbanded on the last day of 1991, 729 Squadron became a joint recce/attack squadron with a mixed fleet of A-35s and RF-35s plus, of course, the two-seat TF-35s which had been in service since June 1971. Sweden, Finland and Austria continue to fly the distinctive 'double delta'.

FINLAND:

Hornet plans

Re-equipment plans for the McDonnell Douglas F/A-18 Hornet were announced during the autumn, revealing that the Satakunnan Fighter Wing (HävLLv 21), currently flying Drakens from its base at Tampere, will be the first operator. It is to be followed by the Lapland Wing (HävLLv 11, another Draken unit) at Rovaniemi and the MiG-21bis-equipped Karalian Wing (HävLLv 31) at Kuopio. Finland is acquiring 57 F/A-18Cs and seven tandem-seat F/A-18Ds, of which the former will be assembled locally by Valmet from US kits. The sale documents were signed on 5 June 1992, and on 22 July the first batch of four F-18Ds was ordered from McDonnell Douglas. The remaining three US-built trainers were ordered on 28 April 1993, together with the first 11 F/A-18C kits, all of which are due for completion by August 1997.

FRANCE:

1994 defence budget

Aircraft orders to be placed by the French armed forces during 1994 were announced to the National Assembly in October. They confirmed the continuation of current programmes, although the 1994 defence law is riddled with stretch-outs

The French C-135FRs are in the process of gaining wingtip pods.

and slow-downs. Main items comprise three Rafales, 16 Mirage 2000s, six Eurocopter AS 365 Panthers, eight Super Etendard rebuilds, 28 EMB-312F Tucanos and two Airbus A310-300s. The Rafale order – for both air force and naval versions – augments one of each type ordered in 1993, but the effect of contracting for such small numbers means that service entry has again been postponed. It will now be July 1999 before the Rafale M is considered 'operational', although with just six aircraft delivered. Only in mid-2000 will a full squadron (12) be available to the navy, the first service to receive the aircraft. As recently as last year, it had been hoped to have 10 Rafale Ms operational by 1998.

Mirage 2000 orders will bring no new aircraft. One of the 16 to be bought in 1994 is the first conversion from 2000C to 2000-5, a further 36 reworks of late production aircraft being scheduled to follow. The balance of 15 represents earlier cancellations (five 2000Bs and 10 2000Cs) being reordered as 2000Ds to bring the totals to 27 2000Bs, 126 2000Cs, 75 2000Ns and 90 2000Ds.

Tucano commitments now total 50, following earlier batches of two (delivered in June 1993) and 20 (due July 1994 to July 1995). The 28 to be ordered in 1994 are to be supplied between July 1995 and July 1996 and all will go to the Ecole de l'Air at Salon de Provence to replace Magisters. EMBRAER expects a further two batches of 15 each to increase procurement to 80, but these are unlikely to

emerge. They had been intended to replace those Magisters used as light transports and continuation trainers by fighter wings until re-equipment was cancelled as an economy measure. The two Airbuses were to have been delivered in 1993 for replacement of McDonnell Douglas DC-8 Srs 72s until they fell victim to the almost 'non-event' of the 1993 defence budget. The navy gains Panthers and upgraded Super Etendards to complement earlier orders. As previously announced, there are no orders for the Atlantic 2 following the decision to terminate production at 30 aircraft, instead of the planned 40.

Squadron traditions maintained

No less than six wing headquarters were disbanded on 31 July as the Armée de l'Air initiated its policy of removing one level of the chain of command and allowing squadrons to report directly to their command. Those affected were the 4th (Mirage 2000N at Luxeuil), 8th (Alpha Jet at Cazaux), 33rd (Mirage F1CR at Strasbourg), 36th (E-3F at Avord), 91st (Mirage IVP at Mont-de-Marsan and Cazaux) and 93rd (C-135FR at Mont-de-Marsan and Istres) Wings. At the same time, the air force continued with squadron disbandments to meet the new force structure.

To keep alive the traditions of two famous squadrons disbanded on 31 July, a pair of existing units of Mirage F1CTs at Colmar was renamed on 1 August. EC 3/13 'Auvergne' became EC 3/13 'Alsace' (ex-EC 3/2 with Mirage 2000Cs) and EC 1/13 'Artois' is now EC 1/13 'Normandie-Niémen' (ex-Mirage F1C). The

sole flying unit in Air Defence Command (CAFDA), 36 Escadre de Détection Aéroportée, operating four Boeing E-3Fs from Avord, became a squadron on 1 August. Now known as 36 Escadron de Détection et de Controle Aéroportée, it has two component E-3 flights that were formerly squadrons: Escadrilles 1/36 'Berry' and 2/36 'Nivernais'. In support are Escadron de Préparation de Mission et de Simulation 10/036 and the aircraft technical unit, GERMaS 15/036.

On 1 September, the 65th VIP transport wing at Villacoublay was reduced to a squadron, becoming Escadron de Transport, d'Entrainement et de Calibration 65. Its two components are now Escadrille 1/65 'Vendome' with five Nord 262s and three Twin Otters, and Escadrille 2/65 'Rambouillet' with eight Falcon 20s and four TBM700s.

Although not part of the regular air force, the Centre d'Expériences Aériennes Militaires (CEAM) trials unit at Mont-de-Marsan was also involved in an administrative streamlining. On 29 July, the internal organisation was revised so that the two flying squadrons (Escadron de Chasse 5/330 'Côte d'Argent' and Escadron d' Expérimentations et de Transport 6/330 'Albret') are no longer subordinate to the now-disbanded Division Avions 02/330. Instead, they report to the Direction des Expérimentations which controls the non-flying Escadron Electronique (EEL 04/330), Escadron d'Expérimentations et de Soutien Technique (EST 03/330), Laboratoire d'Etudes Médico-Physiologiques (LEMP 16/330) and five out-stations: Annexe Cazaux 00/331, Annexe Brétigny 00/332, Annexe Istres 00/333, Annexe Metz 00/334 and Annexe Avord 00/336.

Navigator training changes

More realistic navigation training is being undertaken as the result of the transfer of five MS.760 Paris light jet transports to the Weapon System Operators' School at Toulouse. Previously known as GE 316 and equipped with five Nord 262AENs (radar-equipped), three loaned Alpha Jets of EC 8 and eight Jodel D.140Es, the unit was renamed Ecole des Navigateurs Opérationels Systèmes d'Armes on 1 July and traded in its Jodels for the faster Paris during the autumn.

Army aircrew training to be streamlined

ALAT – French Army Light Aviation – revealed plans to combine its two major training schools, the Ecole d'Application at Luc/Le Cannet and the Ecole de Spécialisation at Dax, before mid-1994. It is unlikely there will be base closures, as it is planned to maintain the two mountain training detachments at Gap and Saillagousse as part of the combined operation. At a later stage, the organisation will parent a joint Franco-German training school to be established at Rennes/St Jacques for Eurocopter Tiger conversion. The school at Luc currently has 32 Gazelles, 14 Alouette IIs, 12 Pumas and 10 Fennecs which, in wartime, would constitute the 2nd Combat Helicopter Regiment (2 RHC).

Upgraded tanker trials

First of the 11 C-135FR tankers to receive Flight Refuelling Ltd Mk 32 wingtip pods (63-12736 '93-CH') was completed by Boeing at Wichita in October and undertook two months of flight testing in the USA before delivery. The remaining upgrades are being undertaken by Air France. Because France uses the probe-and-drogue system, C-135FRs previously had their 'flying booms' augmented by a short length of hose trailing a 'basket'. Now booms are free to refuel E-3F SDAs (Sentries) via their USAF-style receptacle (although the E-3 also has a probe) while two fighters can be replenished simultaneously from the Mk 32s, thereby speeding up operations.

Super Etendards move

Concentration of naval aviation's Super Etendard force was achieved on 13 September when 17 Flottille completed its move (begun on 19 July) from Hyères to Landivisiau. Redeclared operational on 15 September, the squadron partners 11F and replaces 14F, which disbanded with the 'SuE' on 10 July 1991 and will become the first Rafale M unit.

GERMANY:
Wings disbanded

Alpha Jet-equipped JBG 43 disbanded at Oldenberg on 30 September, having decorated one of its aircraft (4080) in a special blue, white and yellow colour scheme for the occasion. Jagdbombergeschwader 43 formed on 1 October 1964 with F-86 Sabres and began converting to Fiat G91Rs in May 1966, adopting the new designation Leichtenkampfgeschwader 43 in May 1967. On 1 October 1979 the wing became a JBG again in preparation for the delivery of Alpha Jets, begun in January 1981. Operational from 1 April 1981, it had reduced to half strength by April 1992.

At Leck, Aufklärungsgeschwader 52 prepared for running down and eventual disbandment with a last beer call for its NATO colleagues on 26 August. The wing is the second and final RF-4E Phan-

Six Mirage 2000Ds were declared operational on 29 July with EC 5/330, part of the CEAM.

tom operator in the Luftwaffe. Its companion, AG 51, stood down a year previously and began conversion to ex-naval Tornados on 1 April 1993. By July, training flights were being conducted from the Marineflieger base at Schleswig/Jagel with Tornados transferred from Marinefliegergeschwader 1, although the official disbandment of MFG 1 (and achievement of operational status by AG 51) was not due to take place until 1 January 1994.

Deliveries proceeded during the second half of the year of surplus McDonnell Douglas RF-4E Phantoms withdrawn from AGs 51 and 52. From 88 of the reconnaissance version delivered, 76 remained in 1993, including one earmarked for the Luftwaffen Museum, soon to be relocated from Uetersen to Berlin/Gatow. The others were being supplied to Turkey (46, including 13 for breaking down as spares) and Greece (27, including seven).

In army aviation, the first disbandment of a Western-based major unit took place at Neuhausen-ob-Eck on 28 September when Heeresfliegerregiment 20 ceased to be a UH-1D Iroquois operator. The wing, comprising two squadrons, had formed with UH-1s at Roth-bei-Nürnberg on 1 April 1971 and transferred to Neuhausen on 1 October 1979. Also on 28 September, co-located Heeresfliegerstaffel 10, with BO 105M (VBH) observation helicopters, also disbanded.

Composite wing being assembled

At the eastern base of Laage, a detachment of F-4F Phantoms took up QRA alert on 1 October in preparation for the installation of interceptor wing JG 73 one year later. One squadron of the wing is to be provided by MiG-29s currently based at Preschen, where the JG 73 title was bestowed on 1 June 1993. The MiGs will transfer to Laage on 1 October 1994. The other component of the Laage-based JG 73 will be provided by Phantoms. At Pferdsfeld, JBG 35 dropped its attack tasking on 1 January 1994 to become JG 35, before being reduced to squadron strength and transferring to Laage on 1 October. Also on the latter date, all Luftwaffe Phantoms will lose their secondary attack role.

Helicopter force diffused

Distribution of the Luftwaffe's transport helicopter force was completed on 1 October when HTG 64 disbanded at Ahlhorn following an official ceremony on 22 September. Previously with three squadrons of Dornier-built Bell UH-1D Iroquois, the wing has now added one squadron to each of the three Transall C.160D wings. The first transfer, to LTG 61 at Landsberg/Penzing, took place on 1 April 1979 when 641 Squadron became No. 613. More recently, 642 Staffel moved its 24 UH-1Ds to LTG 63 at Hohn in June 1993, while 643 Squadron has joined LTG 62. The latter move is effective from 1 October 1993, but on that day LTG 62 established a helicopter detachment at Holzdorf, in the east, and is to transfer slowly all its 24 Bells to the former NVA base. The wing's C.160Ds will follow when the infrastructure is complete. However, in order to overcome a shortfall of helicopters in west-central Germany, a squadron of 20 UH-1Ds was scheduled for formation at Nörvenich in April 1994.

Skyservant out of service

Disposal agency VEBEG was advertising a batch of 35 Dornier Do 28D-2 Skyservants for sale during the autumn, repre-

This aircraft was 3º Stormo's last Starfighter, seen prior to its move from Villafranca to 20º Gruppo, 4º Stormo at Grosseto.

senting some of the last in Luftwaffe service. The final machine, 5825, was retired on 11 July, having been a 'hack' with Phantom-equipped recce wing AG 52. The navy, which received 20 Skyservants, plans to withdraw the aircraft in October 1994.

'Fulcrums' stand aside

Once again, the annual round of NATO exercises was without participation by Germany's MiG-29 'Fulcrums'. Their absence was explained as resulting from an agreement with Russia which prohibits them from such joint training until 1995. That has not prevented them from undertaking one-to-one air combat assessment with allied fighters and occasionally travelling as far afield as RAF Valley. On such occasions the MiGs have kept a low profile, to the extent of remaining locked in a hangar while their hosts were holding a public air display.

NETHERLANDS:

Helicopter happenings

In a controversial decision on 29 October, the Netherlands government signed an agreement for purchase of 17 Eurocopter AS 532U2 Cougar transport helicopters as part of the re-equipment programme for its air transport force. The Cougar had earlier been placed lower than the competing Sikorsky S-70 Black Hawk in an assessment and allegations were made that Fokker had been promised a French airline contract for F100 aircraft if the Cougar were to be chosen. Nevertheless, the KLu appears to have obtained a financial bargain, for Eurocopter has agreed to provide 120 per cent industrial offsets and buy back the Cougars when they are replaced by the international NH90.

Cougar deliveries will begin to 298 Squadron at Eindhoven in January 1996. There, they will partner the 13 Chinooks (seven ex-Canadian, six new) that are to replace the Alouette IIIs of 300 Squadron. Arrival of NH90s is scheduled for 2003. Next to be selected is an attack helicopter, the current contenders being the McDonnell Douglas AH-64 Apache, Bell AH-1W SuperCobra, Eurocopter Tiger, Agusta A 129 Mangusta and Boeing/Sikorsky RAH-66 Comanche. It is suggested that the cheapest solution may be ex-US Army Apaches.

Equipment retirements begin

Following withdrawal of its first SAR-tasked Alouette III in May, the KLu retired the initial pair of these helicopters (A-319 and A-391) from the army-assigned Groep Helikopters two months later. After removal of useful spares at Woensdrecht, they were assigned to the LETS (electrical and technical school) at Schaarsbergen. A further 12 Alouette IIIs will be withdrawn in 1994.

Phasing out of the venerable Fokker

One of the Lossiemouth Buccaneer squadrons – No. 12 – disbanded on 1 October. The other follows in March.

F27 Friendship and Troopship began on 15 October when No. 334 Squadron's C-10 (the all-white 1993 display season aircraft) was placed in storage at Eindhoven, to be followed by C-12 in 1994. Partial replacements are two Lockheed C-130H-30 Super Hercules, of which the first was due for delivery in January 1994.

PORTUGAL:

Lynx delivered

Following their official hand-over on 29 July, the first two Westland Lynx Mk 95s for Portugal's navy departed the UK inside a Shorts Belfast on 24 August. The two, which are both ex-Royal Navy helicopters, are being followed by three more from new production.

Ex-German Alpha Jets

No less than 50 Alpha Jet As have been promised to Portugal by Germany as replacements for Fiat G91s from the same source, the last of which was withdrawn by Esquadra de Ataque 301 at Montijo on 17 June. Included in the total will be 20 aircraft armed with a centreline Mauser 27-mm cannon and five fitted for electronic warfare. Some will come from the German training detachment that disbanded on 31 December 1993 at Beja, where 301 Squadron is being reformed. The Luftwaffe requested permission to base a Tornado detachment at Beja, but this has not been granted.

SPAIN:

Fourth Boeing 707

Work was under way in Spain during the latter part of 1993 to convert a Boeing 707-351C (c/n 19164) as a combined tanker and Elint aircraft. This will augment three tanker/transports already in service with the local designation T.17. The Elint programme is known as Santiago and based on the Israeli Elta Electronic L-8300 Sigint suite, including intercept, analysis and direction-finding systems, plus datalinks and ground processing equipment, for a total package price of about $100 million.

SWEDEN:

New air force structure

The re-organisation of the Flygvapen that took place on 1 July proved to be slightly less drastic than at first planned and did not result in complete disbandment of the 1st Tactical Group, with its three wings of AJ 37 Viggens. This attack force is, nevertheless, considerably reduced, having lost F15 (wing) to one of the new regional air commands and F6 to disbandment. Its sole element after 1 July was F7, which at that time was just about to receive – and then lose in an accident – its first Saab JAS 39 Gripen. The three (reduced from four) regional commands are thus Northern Air Command (F4 and F21, both with JA 37 Viggens), Central Air Command (F15 with AJ 37s and F16 with JA 37s), and Southern Air Command (F10 and the AJ, SF and SH 37s of F17). F10 at Angelholm, which had earlier disbanded one of its three J 35J Draken squadrons, more recently reformed the unit to receive AJS 37 Viggens. The squadron, believed to be

RAF old and new: the Victor tanker has been retired from service, while the Tornado is the new equipment of No. 12 Squadron.

3/F10, is the first to operate this upgraded version of the first-generation Viggen. It is planned to convert all AJ, SF and SH 37 Viggens to AJS standard.

Following disbandment of F13 at Norrköping on 30 June, its related Malflygdivision was redesignated from F13M to F16M. Based at Malmslätt, Malflygdivisionen, equipped with target-facilities Lansens and special-duties Sabreliners and Caravelles, continues to operate semi-autonomously, but its 'parent' unit is now the Viggen-equipped F16 at Uppsala.

SAR cover increased

A further two Eurocopter Cougars (still described by the manufacturer as Super Pumas) were ordered for SAR duties by the air force in the autumn. The service already has 10 SA 332M1s in service under the local designation Hkp 10.

TURKEY:

Surprise order...

Despite its commitment to 95 Sikorsky S70A-28 Black Hawks, Turkey proceeded on 8 October to confirm an order for 20 Eurocopter AS 532UL Cougars. Deliveries will begin in the first half of 1995 and continue at the rate of two per month. Sales of the Cougar/Super Puma total 425 in 34 countries, including 23 air forces, seven armies and four navies.

...and surprise cancellation

The THK decided not to refurbish its Grumman S-2 Trackers with turboprop engines, having reached the stage of assessing bids from companies interested in undertaking the work. The aircraft are operated from Topel on the Black Sea coast by 103 Squadron.

UNITED KINGDOM:

RAF to lose nuclear role

Long-running speculation was ended on 18 October when Defence Secretary Malcolm Rifkind confirmed that there would be no replacement for the Tornado GR.Mk 1's WE177 nuclear bomb when it is withdrawn early in the next century. Instead, some Trident missiles aboard four submarines coming into service will be armed with tactical nuclear warheads, allowing them to take over the role.

The RAF has had a nuclear strike capability since strategically-tasked Valiants first carried Blue Danube atomic bombs in 1955. By mid-1958, Bomber Command's Vulcans and Victors were receiving the Yellow Sun Mk 1 hydrogen bomb, which also formed the basis of the Blue Steel stand-off missile carried by three squadrons of Vulcan B.Mk 2s and two of Victor B.Mk 2Rs. V-Force QRA ended on 30 June 1969 when the navy's Polaris submarines took over the strategic deterrent. Meanwhile, tactical strike had been assigned to Valiants and Canberras which, because they were under the control of NATO's SACEUR, were issued with American B43 bombs. A British equivalent was also developed under the code-name of Red Beard for use by Canberras, Buccaneers and the ill-fated TSR.2.

Red Beard appears to have been one of a family of weapons developed to meet Operational Requirement 1177 and known by the generic name of WE177. The large, strategic version of WE177 was issued to Vulcan B.Mk 2s at Cottesmore in September 1966 and would also have been an option on the TSR.2, which was intended to carry four Red Beards or two strategic WE177s. Nimrods were believed to be capable of carrying a depth-charge version of WE177, until these and equivalent US nuclear weapons for use under NATO auspices were withdrawn in 1992. The Tornado's weapon is reported to be designated WE177B.

Staff Requirement (Air) 1244 was formulated for a WE177 replacement, the prime requirement being stand-off capability. Three potential systems examined in detail were the Martin TASM, Boeing SRAM 2 and Aérospatiale ASLP (an extended-range development of ASMP carried by Mirage IVPs and 2000Ns). These options having been abandoned, the UK will rely on a missile that is pooled with the US Navy's stocks and serviced in the US, placing it in hock to changes of political support in Washington.

The UK is already being restricted in testing by a US moratorium on use of its underground facilities, although a global 'understanding' on tests was broken on 5 October when China exploded a device below the Lop Nor desert. Up to this time, the UK had made 44 tests (in Australia, the Pacific and USA), of which 23 were underground, compared with 954 (217 above/737 below) by the USA, 936 (214/722) in the former USSR, 192 (50/142) French, 39 (23/16) Chinese and one (underground) Indian.

Lynx run faster

Two modification programmes for Army Air Corps Lynx AH.Mk 7s were gathering momentum in the latter part of the year, the most noticeable being the retrofit with BERP (British Experimental Rotor Programme) main blades with their wide-chord tips. Introduced on the new-build

No. 12 Sqn reformed as a Tornado user with the renumbering of No. 27 Sqn. The famous fox's head badge is carried on the fin.

Lynx AH.Mk 9, the blades are of the same design as those that won the Lynx a world speed record in 1986. Additionally, in a separate but parallel programme, Lynx were gaining GEC (Ferranti) AWARE-3 (ARI23491) radar warning receiver system, evidenced by four small, circular antennas: two on the nose and two forward of the tailboom/cabin joint. Upgrading of 124 Mk 1 Lynx to Mk 7 is due to end in September 1994, but these helicopters do not always carry exhaust-diffuser boxes, as these reduce permitted speed from 156 to 145 kt (179 to 166 mph; 288 to 268 km/h).

Several changes in Army Air Corps squadron establishments were effected during the second half of 1993, the most profound being withdrawal of all Lynx from 651, 652 and 661 Squadrons at Hildesheim, Germany (1 Regiment) and their transfer to 4 Regiment at Detmold. Gazelles continue to operate at Hildesheim. At Dishforth, 9 Regiment's 664 Squadron lost all its Lynx AH.Mk 9s in August, with transfers to co-located 672 Squadron and No. 653 at Wattisham. Establishment at Netheravon later in the year of a third volunteer Territorial Army flight of four Gazelle AH.Mk 1s was due to complete a moderate Army Air Corps expansion in time for the units to be declared operational on 1 January. First two to form were 3 Flight (V) at Edinburgh/Turnhouse on 18 May 1993 and 6 Flight (V) at RAF Shawbury on 3 June.

Victors stand down

Begun with an Operational Requirement of 1946, the era of the RAF's V-bombers closed on 15 October as No. 55 Squadron retired its final seven Victor K.Mk 2 tankers. Withdrawn from (stand-off) nuclear bombing in 1968, the Victor had a long and distinguished second career in tanking, its operations including the Falklands War and Desert Storm. Four Victor K.Mk 2 sorties (two each by XL161 and XL231) were flown from Bahrain to support Tornado GR.Mk 1s in the January 1993 raids on Iraq by coalition aircraft. The Bahrain detachment was handed over to VC10s on 8 September 1993 and the last Victor to return home to Marham was XM715 on the following day. In all, Operation Jural, the southern Iraqi patrol by Tornados, involved 202 sorties (557.50 hours) from Bahrain between 9 December 1992 and 8 September 1993. No. 55 Squadron stood down from NATO on 30 September, its sole flying between then and disbandment being for ferrying to museums and fire-training dumps. All the aircraft retired were over 30 years old, XH672 having been delivered on 26 May 1960 and XM717 (the penultimate Victor) on 14 March 1963.

Squadron changes

On disbandment as a Victor unit on 15 October, No. 55 Squadron passed its title to the VC10 conversion unit (previously

A rarely-seen Lynx variant is the HAS.Mk 3ICE, two of which are assigned to HMS Endurance from No. 815 Squadron, Royal Navy. The high conspicuity panels are for operations in the Antarctic region.

No. 241 OCU) at Brize Norton. Also based at Marham, Tornado GR.Mk 1-operating No. 27 Squadron was transformed into No. 12 Squadron on 1 October when the Lossiemouth-based Buccaneer S.Mk 2B unit of this designation was disbanded. The new No. 12 was due to move to Lossiemouth on 1 January 1994 after working up in the anti-shipping role, but did so with the old No. 27 Squadron aircraft, as conversions to the Sea Eagle missile-carrying Tornado GR.Mk 1B have only recently begun.

No. 15 (Reserve) Squadron, the Tornado Weapons Conversion Unit, departed Honington en masse on 1 November for Lossiemouth as the first of the three-squadron Tornado wing forming there. Withdrawal of flying units from Honington was due to be complete on or about 1 February 1994 when No. 13 Squadron moves to Marham, thereby placing all the UK's reconnaissance assets at one base.

The No. 27 'number plate' was transferred to Odiham on 24 September when No. 240 OCU became No. 27 (Reserve) Squadron with Puma HC.Mk 1s and Chinooks. The OCU was relegated to borrowing Chinook HC.Mk 1Bs during 1993, as many of the fleet were then with Boeing at Ridley undergoing conversion to HC.Mk 2. The second refurbished helicopter, ZA681, arrived at Odiham from Liverpool Docks on 10 September and was due to receive No. 27's markings on one side and the operational No. 7 Squadron's on the other after trials at Boscombe Down.

More Chinooks

In the week that the second Chinook HC.Mk 2 upgrade was delivered to the RAF, it was announced that a further three of the type had been ordered from new production. Deliveries will begin from the second half of 1995 onwards, following on from the last conversion, due for completion in July of that year. Shortly before, it had been revealed that damage to one Chinook had resulted in the number of rebuilds being reduced from 33 to 32.

The Chinook reorder appears to have been connected with the Parliamentary announcement on 26 July that a decision was imminent to end the protracted uncertainty over the future composition of the RAF's transport helicopter force. Although expected to comprise Chinooks and EH.101s, plus a lighter helicopter chosen in a separate competition, the new structure still had not been revealed five months later. In the last-mentioned connection, the RAF was considering the possibility of obtaining Westland Lynx AH.Mk 7s from the Army Air Corps as a replacement for the ageing Westland Wessex HC.Mk 2. However, unless the AAC is reduced in size, it will be early the next century before delivery of a new attack helicopter makes the Lynx available.

Air defence developments

Tornado F.Mk 3s had their first QRA(I) scrambles for two years when a Russian 'Cub' and a 'Coot' approached the UK Air Defence Region (UKADR) on 9 and 17 September. Although aircraft from Leuchars were assigned to intercept, the Russians, both believed to be intelligence-gathering versions of transport aircraft, turned for home while being escorted by Norwegian F-16s. Probing flights into the

No. 27 (Reserve) Sqn is the new unit designation for the Puma and Chinook OCU.

UKADR virtually ceased with the collapse of the USSR, the immediately previous one having been on 6 September 1991.

With an inaudible whimper, rather than a bang, a relic of Cold War air defence bowed out slowly and gracefully. The Type 84 radar at RAF Neatishead, Norfolk, was withdrawn from full-time use on 19 July, but remained on stand-by for several months. During the bedding-down period of its replacement, a mobile Type 93, the T84 was operated for a few hours every four weeks to confirm its serviceability. Neatishead's radar was the last of the 80-series equipment introduced during the 1950s and 1960s, the main being the complementary Types 84 and 85 at central sites. These were backed by Types 80 and the unique 88/89 at peripheral stations. The Type 85 at Boulmer was the last of its genre when switched off in October 1990, the Type 80 following on 7 April 1993 when Buchan's equipment was decommissioned. (Types 82, 83, 86 and 87 were associated with the Bloodhound SAM and Type 81 was not built.)

Integration of radar sites into the Improved UK Air Defence Ground Environment (I-UKADGE) network was completed on 2 September when the unit at Saxa Vord, Shetland Islands, controlled its last fighter interception. Co-ordination of intercepts is now the sole responsibility of the underground Sector Operations Centres at Neatishead and Buchan, to where signals from ground radars such as Saxa Vord are transmitted by I-UKADGE datalink. The next stage in the modernisation process of UK air defence will be installation of JTIDS datalink terminals in the Tornado F.Mk 3s of Nos 5 and 29 Squadrons at Coningsby.

Civilian calibrators

Hunting Aviation Services at East Midlands Airport formally assumed operation of four RAF Andover E.Mk 3 navaids calibration aircraft on 19 October, following disbandment of No. 115 Squadron on 1 October. The ex-No. 115 aircraft have been loaned to Hunting for three years. Provision of crews and engineering support is the contractor's responsibility, while liaison with the RAF is provided by the 11-man No. 38 Group Flight Checking Operations Cell. Hunting takes over the calibration of 200 radar and radio aids (including ILS, TACAN and air defence radars) within an area bounded by Cyprus, Gibraltar, Belize, Shetland Islands and Germany. Only the Falkland Islands are not calibrated by the Andover, these being the responsibility of specially equipped Hercules C.Mk 1 XV292.

Last, last JP show

Positively the last 'farewell to the JP' was held at No. 6 FTS, Finningley, on 18 September when four Jet Provost T.Mk 5s (XW206, XW287, XW302 and XW307) took part in the station flypast for Battle of Britain Day. By then, most of the other No. 6 FTS Jet Provost Mk 5/5As – used for navigator training, rather than pilot instruction – had been delivered to Shawbury, only six having remained when

Finningley held a private ceremony for ex-JP aircrew on 14 August. Jet Provosts, including the T.Mk 3As withdrawn from No. 1 FTS at Linton-on-Ouse in June, found a ready market in the USA until the FAA placed a a six-month moratorium on the award of 'experimental' category airworthiness permits to uncertificated designs of foreign aircraft.

Air base news

Bentwaters, former home of the USAF 81st TFW A-10A Thunderbolt IIs, was formally handed back to the RAF on 28 September, the last USAF personnel leaving two days later. Studies have been launched into possible uses for Upper Heyford after the departure of 20th FW F-111s, one prospect being the Brüggen Tornado wing (Nos IX, 14, 17 and 31 Squadrons) which is likely to be withdrawn from Germany in 1995. Consideration has been given to abandonment of the facilities (hardened shelters and operations block) on Stornoway, built during the early 1980s for forward-basing of Tornado F.Mk 3 interceptors.

Nimrod replacement plans

By the late summer, Shorts and Beriev appeared to have dropped their interesting offer of Be-40 'Mermaid' jet flying-boats to the RAF. The aircraft was not among the three proposals put forward for a Nimrod MR.Mk 2 replacement when the MoD's request for information lapsed on 31 August. For service entry in 2000, Dassault is offering the Atlantique 2, and Lockheed is proposing the P-3C Update III. BAe, with the third and last proposal, is suggesting a Nimrod update to keep the aircraft operational until 2015 and to postpone the arrival of first replacements until 2012. Dassault's chances of success are rated slim, as the RAF's preference is for four engines. The Nimrod MR.Mk 2 fleet has been reduced to 26, while it has been suggested that the three Nimrod R.Mk 1 Elint aircraft could be replaced by a smaller aircraft in the Gulfstream series.

Hercules replacement considerations

The question of replacing the RAF's 60 Lockheed C-130K Hercules received consideration when Lockheed promoted the 'C-130J' and BAe urged adoption of the multi-national EuroFLA transport. A third option for replacement is the Antonov An-77 (a 'Westernised' An-70T, the prototype of which will fly in 1994). Ukrainian officials made a presentation on the An-77 to the RAF, yet no further steps can be taken until the UK government makes a policy decision on military equipment purchases from the CIS. EuroFLA is handicapped by the lack of a firm agreement for its manufacture, but this shortcoming was addressed when talks began on the possibility of Airbus Industrie becoming the industrial base. Hercules replacement studies were due for completion early in 1994 and include a further option of upgrading the existing aircraft for a further 15 years of service. Marshall Aerospace of Cambridge estimates this would cost £3-4 million per aircraft if 'glass cockpit' instrumentation is excluded.

Eastern Europe

CIS:

V-PVO revival?

Concerned by weaknesses in their mutual defence caused by hasty dismemberment of the USSR, defence ministers of the CIS states met on 24 August to sign an agreement which will attempt to put the V-PVO back together. Voyska Protivovozdushnoy Oborony (Troops of Air Defence) once administered the world's densest concentration of ground radars and interceptor aircraft, but its structure was splintered when peripheral republics of the USSR went their own ways. There are no inputs to the V-PVO's Moscow HQ from the Baltic States and Transcaucasia, while contributions by the Asian republics are below standard. Revitalisation of the V-PVO is all that remains of farther-reaching plans to establish a CIS joint defence command.

HUNGARY:

MiGs delivered

Re-equipment of the 'Szentgyörgyi Dezsö' Wing of the Hungarian air force began on 15 October when eight MiG-29 'Fulcrums' arrived at Kecskemét from Krasnodar, Russia, where their pilots had undergone conversion. Eight more aircraft were delivered on 26 October, with the balance following in November. The contract for 28 includes six tandem-seat MiG-29UBs, one of which was lost in a pre-delivery crash on 30 August. Hungary also received at least 20 ex-German L-39ZO Albatros advanced trainers, the first four of which had been accepted by early October.

Arrival of the 'Fulcrums' has not diminished the requirement for replacement of about 80 MiG-21 'Fishbeds', which the defence minister revealed would be "worn-out in a couple of years." The older MiG-21MF 'Fishbed-Js' may be replaced by a Western fighter, but some 40 MiG-21bis 'Fishbed-Ns' could be the subject of an upgrade programme for which an Israeli consortium of IAI and Elbit is bidding.

POLAND:

More Sokols

Polish helicopter deliveries have included six PZL W-3 Sokols to the 47 Szkolny Pluk Smiglowcow (Helicopter Training Regiment) at Nowe Miasto, where they augment and/or replace Mi-2s, and a single VIP W-3 Salon to the 36th Special Air Transport Regiment at Warsaw/Okecie IAP. Four more are on order, but of six W-3RM Anacondas reported to have been supplied to the navy earlier in 1993 only four are of this variant, the others being unarmed W-3s.

Huzar under development

A development of the Sokol, designated W-3WB Huzar, is under development for combat support duties in collaboration with Dennel of South Africa. The latter has provided the navigation system and weaponry, most significantly the Grot laser-guided anti-tank missile which the Huzar is believed to have tested during African trials. Though lacking the purposeful appearance of some other tank-killing helicopters, the Huzar will have day/night all-weather capability and is pursuing a potential order for 100 machines, this amount representing the difference between Poland's 30 Mil Mi-24 'Hinds' and the 130 combat helicopters it is permitted under CFE agreements.

Battlefield aircraft sought

During the latter part of 1993, Poland was preparing the ground for a decision on a small, agile battlefield attack (SABA) aircraft which would represent the next stage up from the Huzar. First inclinations have been to assess the PZL-22 Iryda jet trainer for the role but, if this proves unsuitable, two contenders are waiting in the wings. To the PZL-230F Skorpion, revealed in 1990, has been added the PZL Kobra, unveiled in project form on 11 September. This has two thrust-vectoring turbofans based on the PZL D-18, drawing air from an intake behind the cockpit. Poland requires between 60 and 100 SABAs to be in service by 2005.

Air force withdrawals

Survivors of local production in the late 1950s, Poland's last MiG-17 'Frescos' – in Lim-5 guise – were reduced to scrap at the Mierzecice/Zendek maintenance unit between 27 September and 2 October. Poland's first mass scrapping under CFE treaty provisions involved 54 Lim-5s, similar Lim-6s and MiG-21PF/PFMs. The final airworthy Lim-5, 1717, made its last sortie on 12 July, having just outlived SBLim-2 522543, retired on 19 May. Despite its designation, the latter was gen-

Above: This ex-Luftwaffe LET-410 is now operated by the Latvian air force, seen visiting Denmark.

Right: Emerging from overhaul at Novosibirsk is this Su-24MR 'Fencer-E', complete with new fuselage chaff/flare dispensers.

uinely a Czech-built CS-102, more easily recognised as a MiG-15UTI 'Midget'. A further retirement, on 25 May, was the last Polish military PZL-104 Wilga 35A, 74204, while a forthcoming departure, by 1998, will be the Su-20 'Fitter'. Later Su-22s, of which Poland received 76 Su-22M4Ks and 15 Su-22U3Ms, will remain in service at least until 2010.

RUSSIA:

Sukhoi supreme

By August, the Russian navy had taken delivery of 12 Sukhoi Su-27K (Su-33) 'Flanker Ds' for operation from the carrier *Admiral Kuznetsov*, and eight more of the type were in production. The rate of assembly had slowed, however, as sufficient aircraft are available for immediate needs following the abandonment of the carrier-building programme. Apparently, a related casualty has been the plan to convert 10 Sukhoi Su-25UB 'Frogfoots' for carrier training under the designation Su-25UBP (*Palubnyi* – shipborne) as complements to the four surviving Su-25UTGs (*Gak* – hook) at Severomorsk.

Slow progress was also reported with the Su-35 'Flanker', at least 10 of which had been built by August. The programme is experiencing funding shortages, yet it is hoped to have the first aircraft operational in two years' time. In the longer term, design is proceeding of the T-60 intermediate-range bomber to replace Tu-16 'Badgers', Tu-22M 'Backfires' and strategically-tasked Su-24s. Despite having redi-

rected half its business to commercial ventures, Sukhoi continues to seek new business opportunities. The latest proposal is for a joint fighter development programme with Mikoyan and/or an American company, either of which would have been unthinkable as partners a few years ago. Chief designer Mikhail Simonov discussed US collaboration with President Yeltsin, but does not consider that the political will to carry this through yet exists in either camp.

Mixed fortunes for MiG

A joint venture with Sukhoi may also appeal to MiG, which has been less than successful in promoting its designs for local use in recent years. The shipborne version of the MiG-29 'Fulcrum' appears to have been abandoned after two folding-wing prototypes were built (Sukhoi's Su-27K was successful in the competition) and work has been halted on the fly-by-wire MiG-29M, at least six prototypes of which were flight tested.

The MiG-MAPO company has comparatively little production work on hand, but the bureau was able to confirm at the Moscow Aerosalon in August that it is proceeding with design of the 1-42 project, the proposed counterpart to Lockheed's F-22. This had been placed in doubt by financial constraints and problems with suitable engines, but the prototype will now fly with off-the-shelf engines. In a separate programme, the bureau is designing a follow-on to the

This Polish air force Tu-154M visited England to collect the remains of General Wladyslaw Sikorski, Polish leader-in-exile during World War II. The aircraft was escorted by Tornado F.Mk 3s.

MiG-31 'Foxhound', this apparently to be based on the MiG-31M 'Foxhound-B' variant. MiG-31Ms are currently testing new AAM armament in the form of an upgraded R33 (AA-9 'Amos') with forward fins resembling those of the AIM-9P Sidewinder and the new active-radar Vympel X-37.

SLOVAKIA:

More MiGs

Under the terms of a bilateral defence treaty signed on 26 August, five more MiG-29 'Fulcrums' are due to be bought from Russia to augment the dozen inherited when the Czechoslovak federation was broken up.

TAJIKSTAN:

Air force formed

An initial order was placed during the late summer by the newly-formed Tajik air force for at least 10 Mil Mi-8MTB 'Hip-C' helicopters.

(former) YUGOSLAVIA:

Food drops continue

The US-led food airdrop to Bosnia was widened on 24/25 August when starving citizens of Mostar received dehydrated MRE rations by parachute. This 146th mission (each of between eight and 10 aircraft) since 28 February increased the total of aid delivered to nearly 7,500 tonnes of

Seen prior to delivery is one of six AH-64As diverted from US Army production to the UAE Air Force.

food and 144 tonnes of medical supplies in over 11,140 bundles. Defying earlier predictions of hopeless inaccuracy because of the 10,000 ft (3050 m) drop height, the force of mainly USAF Hercules operating out of Frankfurt has achieved precision through use of satellite navigation. It is estimated that 90 per cent of the loads have been recovered on the ground. The US is supported by RAF Hercules and French and German Transall C.160s.

Risks to aircraft and crew in the food airlift and other humanitarian operations have been reduced by the fitment of cockpit armour to some Hercules. The USAF fitted 13 C-130s with Aero Consultants Ltd (UK) cockpit floor armour between March and August and was planning another six installations before the end of 1993. The RAF equipped six Hercules to accept the system and bought three kits, each weighing 1,080 lb (490 kg) and capable of stopping a 7.62-mm bullet fired from close range. Other Hercules operators have obtained cockpit armour for Bosnia, and the USAF was planning to equip 17 more Hercules and 13 C-141B StarLifters in the USA. Netherlands Fokker F27 Troopships and German Transall C.160Ds are equipped with integrated missile warning and chaff/flare dispensing systems designed by Elta of Israel, and USAF C-130s have Loral AN/AAR-47 missile approach sensors.

UN enforcement effort

French naval forces of Task Force 470 patrolling the Adriatic as Operation Balbuzard were embarked on the carrier *Foch*. They comprised Super Etendards of 16F, Etendard IVPs of 16F, Alizés of 4F, planeguard Dauphins of 23S and Super Frelon transport helicopters of 32F. Absent were the Crusaders of 12F, currently in the process of a major upgrading.

Changes in the Deny Flight/Maritime

Guard forces patrolling former Yugoslavia from Italy included the replacement of 12 F-16C/Ds of 23rd FS/52nd FW at Aviano by a similar number of aircraft of 512nd FS/86th FW from mid-September onwards. USS *America* arrived on station in the Adriatic in late August with a slightly non-standard complement comprising just one Tomcat squadron (VF-102, but with 14 aircraft) and two of F/A-18Cs (VFA-82 and 86), plus VA-85 with A-6E Intruders, VAW-123 (E-2C Hawkeye), HS-11 (SH-3H), VAQ-137 (EA-6B), VS-32 (S-3B) and four CH-46Es of HMM-162. At about the same time, the Turkish F-16C Deny Flight element at Ghedi was rotated when 161 Filo replaced No. 141, the RAF Jaguar GR.Mk 1A detachment passing from No. 6 to No. 41 Squadron in mid-September.

Also contributing forces is Canada, which has two CP-140 Auroras from VP-405 (part of No. 14 Wing at Greenwood) based at Sigonella. These arrived on 13 September and during the first month of operations flew 19 missions, for a total of 270 hours. At sea, Canada had HMCS *Algonquin* with two Sikorsky CH-124 Sea Kings.

In addition to mounting fighter CAPs, NATO countries have been undertaking intensive reconnaissance of Bosnia. Photographic surveillance is provided by US Navy Grumman F-14A Tomcats equipped with the TARPS system, USAF U-2Rs operating out of Alconbury, and RAF Canberra PR.Mk 9s of No. 39 (1 PRU) Squadron from Wyton. The Canberras are equipped with an underfuselage bulge containing the U-2's optional horizon-to-horizon camera fit, known as System 3.

Providing electronic intelligence are USAF RC-135s, USAF EP-3E-II Aries of VQ-2 at Rota, RAF Nimrod R.Mk 1s of No. 51 Squadron from Wyton, French C.160 Gabriels of EE 11/54 at Metz and the DC-8 SARIGUE of EE 51 at Evreux, and USN S-3B Vikings from VS-32 aboard USS *America*. The last-mentioned aircraft carry 'Aladdin' art-work inspired by the codename of modifications they have received to improve overland electronic detection capability.

Although Serbian units in Bosnia have not taken direct action against UN aircraft enforcing the 'No-Fly Zone', they have regularly adopted the intimidating tactic of using SAM radars to illuminate aircraft taking part in Operation Deny Flight. The action has been recorded on several occasions by Grumman EA-6B Prowler electronic warfare aircraft of VAQ-137 during flights from USS *America*. Main offenders are the Straight Flush radars of the SA-6.

The flying ban does not apply to Serbian aircraft outside Bosnia, i.e. in Serbia itself, which is essentially the same thing as today's Yugoslavia. F-14s flying close to Yugoslavia (Serbia) are regularly shadowed by fighters of the RViPVO, or Yugoslav Air Force and Air Defence. The re-organised Yugoslav air arm has dropped the red star marking for a blue, white and red horizontally-divided tricolour on the fin, plus fuselage and wing roundels in the same pattern. Bosnian Serbs have their own air force, including J-22/IJ-22 Orao, G-2 Galeb and G-4 Super Galeb attack/armed training aircraft, plus UTVA-75 lightplanes, Gazelle helicopters and other equipment. The EEC granted recognition to the Republic of Macedonia on 21 October. Macedonia is an uneasy partner of Serbia in what remains of Yugoslavia, but is making hesitant moves towards independence.

Middle East

ABU DHABI:

Apaches arrive

Six McDonnell Douglas AH-64A Apache combat helicopters delivered to the UAE air force on 3 October were the first of at least 20 offered by the US in 1990. As with earlier exports to Israel and Saudi Arabia, the aircraft were taken from new production for the US Army, which will be repaid later. The contract for Apaches for Saudi Arabia, the UAE and Greece stands at 56 pay-back aircraft, although these customers have only publicly ordered 12, 20 and 12, respectively.

IRAQ:

Clash in 'No-Fly Zone'

For the fifth time in 1993, coalition aircraft attacked Iraqi targets after offensive action by Iraq. On 19 August, two USAF aircraft – an F-4G Phantom and F-16C Fighting Falcon – were unsuccessfully fired on by two SA-3 SAMs 10 miles (16 km) west of Mosul in the northern air exclusion zone. Four fighter-bombers were immediately called in to retaliate: two F-16Cs to drop cluster bombs and a pair of F-15E Eagles that attacked and destroyed the site with LGBs.

ISRAEL:

Apache deliveries

The promised second batch of McDonnell Douglas AH-64A Apaches began arriving in Israel during early September, ferried from Ramstein, Germany, in C-5 Galaxies. Carried in the company of two Sikorsky UH-60A Black Hawks, the 18 helicopters were second-hand, drawn from US Army units in Germany. Further deliveries are expected of six more Apaches and eight Black Hawks, to complete the equipment promised to Israel for its co-operation during the Gulf War. The IDF/AF already has 18 Apaches delivered new in 1990.

KUWAIT:

Hornet force complete

Delivery of 32 McDonnell Douglas KAF-18C and eight tandem-seat KAF-18D Hornets was completed on 21 August when the final three aircraft arrived at Kuwait IAP, from where the force is temporarily operating. Flown by Nos 9 and 25 Squadrons, both former A-4KU Skyhawk units, Hornets have already participated in Operation Southern Watch over Iraq, as well as in exercises with US and allied

Sporting a temporary civil registration, this is one of three Beech T400s (T-1A) purchased by the JASDF for pilot training.

PC-9 performance with underwing armament provided by FN of Belgium almost sank the prospective order, but the Swiss government decided early in October that it could proceed. No sooner had that decision been received than Korea again raised the question of weaponry.

TAIWAN:

Hawkeye order

Having previously planned to buy four surplus Grumman E-2B Hawkeye AEW aircraft for upgrading to E-2T standard, Taiwan changed track in August when an order was announced for four apparently new E-2Cs. The aircraft, which will be to the US Navy's current 'Group II' standard (AN/APS-145 radar and other avionics improvements), are due for delivery in 1994. Grumman, meanwhile, faces a bleak future with little work in prospect from its traditional customer, the US Navy, and announced plans in October to abandon all aircraft design activities.

Upgraded Fighting Falcons

Although Taiwan's order for 150 Lockheed Fighting Falcons in the Peace Fenhuang programme covers the ostensibly older F-16A (120) and F-16B (30) versions, it has emerged that these will be to the hitherto-unknown Block 20 standard. The highest F-16A avionics configuration previously attained was Block 15OCU, in which state most of the recent exports have been made to countries not eligible for F-16C/Ds. In any event, late production F-16As incorporate much of the systems fitted to the F-16C, which began at Block 25 and has now attained Block 50 standard. It may be conjectured that Taiwan's F-16As will not fall far short of Block 50 F-16Cs, except that they will not have the option of mounting General Electric F110 engines as an alternative to the Pratt & Whitney F100. The F110 option was only brought in at Block 30.

Talon lease

To maintain fast-jet pilot experience until the F-16 is available, Taiwan concluded an agreement in October to lease 40 USAF Northrop T-38 Talons for three years, beginning in 1994. This will be the second use of the Talon by Taiwan, 28 having been loaned during the early 1970s as surrogates for Northrop F-5E Tiger IIs diverted to South Vietnam and replaced from later production.

THAILAND:

Bell 212 order

Rejecting offers from Sikorsky and Mil, Thailand opted in August to satisfy the army's latest helicopter requirement with 20 Bell 212s, complementing 25 received in 1991 and the survivors of earlier purchases. Sikorsky's bid had been with the S-70 Black Hawk while Mil, eager for orders, had offered 33 Mi-17V 'Hips', a simulator, spare parts and a free VIP Mi-17 for marginally more than the price of 20 Bells. The Thai parliament was deeply split

---

Far East

INDONESIA:

Uprated Surveiller

Redelivery was achieved of a Boeing 737-2X9 Surveiller following upgrading by the manufacturer with nose radar, IR detection system, GPS, IFF and improved data processing and display. The main sensor remains the Motorola SLAMMR (Side-Looking Airborne Modular Multi-mission Radar). IPTN at Bandung is working on the remaining two aircraft.

JAPAN:

Last F-4EJs

Based at Naha, Okinawa, 302 Squadron became the last operator of the unmodified Mitsubishi/McDonnell Douglas F-4EJ Phantom following conversion of 305 Squadron to F-15J Eagles built by the same manufacturer. At Hyakuri, No. 305's final aircraft, 87-8409, made its final sortie on 20 July, sporting art-work to mark both this event and a 15-year association with the Phantom.

Huey upgraded

Fuji redelivered the first HU-1J upgraded version of Fuji/Bell HU-1H Hiyodori to the ASDF early in September and is working on the 24 additional conversions authorised up to and including the FY 5 (1993) budget. Refurbishment includes addition of the engine, transmission and tail rotor of the AH-1S Cobra, plus the UH-1N's main rotor. In addition, the cockpit is wider, the nose lengthened, armour has been added and self-protection been improved by an IR-suppressor and wire cutter. It is planned to include 27 more rebuilds in the FY 6-7 budgets.

SOUTH KOREA:

PC-9 plans stalled

A prospective order for 20 Pilatus PC-9s remained in the balance during October as South Korea sought to equip the aircraft for optional carriage of weapons. Earlier requests by the RoKAF for guarantees of

---

The Royal Moroccan air force has bought seven CN-235Ms for light transport duties.

forces. The KAF plans to buy more Hornets in small batches.

OMAN:

First single-seat Hawk

Destined for Oman, the initial production single-seat BAe Hawk made its first flight at Warton on 11 September, carrying the provisional UK serial number ZH669. One of 12 radar-equipped Hawk 203s, the aircraft will be delivered early in 1994 in the company of four tandem-seat Hawk 103s. BAe has also sold 18 Hawk 208s to Malaysia, while an Indonesian order for 24 Hawks is believed to include 12 of the Series 200. A long-promised Saudi Arabian contract for up to 60 Mk 205s (and 48 more Tornado IDSs) has yet to materialise. More positively, in August, the Indian government cleared the IAF to proceed with its purchase of new jet trainers – either Hawks or Alpha Jets – although the quantity has been further reduced to 80, from 94 and, originally, 150.

Southern Asia

PAKISTAN:

F-16 production halted

Differences between the US and Pakistan over the latter's alleged nuclear weapons programme reached a head on 7 September when a 'stop work' order was placed on Lockheed F-16 Fighting Falcons under construction at Fort Worth for the PAF. Pakistan received its first order for 28 F-16As and 12 F-16Bs, placing further orders in December 1988 for six As and five Bs and in September 1989 for 48 As and 12 Bs. Only then did the US Congress invoke the Pressler Amendment, a law that prevents arms exports to nations with secret nuclear programmes. Of the 71 outstanding F-16s, 11 are stored at AMARC, Davis-Monthan AFB (with three Pakistan navy Lockheed P-3C-II.75s), 17 are in various stages of completion and 43 have

yet to be started. Realising that there was little prospect of receiving the aircraft, Pakistan allowed a 25 August deadline for its next progress payment to pass, so provoking the 'stop work' order. The US will allow Pakistan to sell the aircraft to a third party, but only if it can be certain that there are no buy-back or lease-back clauses in the agreement. Meanwhile, Pakistan has begun a three-year programme to increase self-sufficiency in armaments manufacture.

Lynx requirement

Westland Helicopters was expecting an order from Pakistan to complement the navy's recent purchase of six surplus Type 21 frigates from the Royal Navy. Each is intended to have a Lynx operating from its stern platform.

on the issue, so much so that two MPs arranged to settle their differences with a boxing match.

Seahawk for RTN carrier

A decision in principle to order six Sikorsky S-70B Seahawk maritime and SAR helicopters was announced by the Royal Thai navy in October with the intention of taking delivery in 1997. The Seahawks will operate from a 12,500-tonne helicopter-carrier currently under construction in Spain and resembling that navy's *Principe de Asturias*. The vessel will also be capable of carrying Harrier IIs or Sea Harriers, although the currently favoured option is purchase of Spain's first-generation AV-8As when they are replaced.

Transport force modernisation

Presumably as replacements for its elderly Fairchild C-123B/K Provider transports, the RTAF received government permission in October to order six Alenia G222 rear-loading turboprop twins. The aircraft thus returns to production following a short break after delivery of the last of 10 C-27s for the USAF.

Australasia

AUSTRALIA:
F-111Gs for stock

Two ex-USAF F-111Gs delivered to RAAFB Amberley on 13 September were the vanguard of 15 purchased for storage and attrition replacement. An unkind stroke of fate chose to underline the new aircraft's purpose, as the RAAF's seventh F-111C loss occurred on the same day.

Chinook upgrade

Although 11 Australian CH-47C Chinooks (including one in damaged condition) are to be upgraded to CH-47D standard by Boeing, details of the contract revealed that only four are to be returned for army use. The remainder are assigned to the US Army, apparently augmenting 472 rebuilds covered by existing orders. Sale of the seven to the US has funded the conversion work on the four which Australia is retaining.

Africa

ERITREA:
Air arm building

Closely following the gift from China of two HAMC Y-12 turboprop-twin transports to mark its independence from Ethiopia in May, Eritrea received an IAI 1125 Astra twin-jet VIP transport. Operators of the Y-12 are not yet known, but the Astra has a military serial, ARJ901.

KENYA:
Air force sins forgiven

'The Kenya Air Force' was reborn in August after 11 years under the curious title of 'The 82 Air Force'. The original leadership of the KAF was purged after an unsuccessful coup attempt in 1982 and loyal army officers were drafted in to take over control, resulting in the change of name.

NIGERIA:
PC-7s imminent

Swiss government permission was given to Pilatus for the export of seven PC-7 Turbo Trainers to Nigeria. They will, presumably, be used as preliminary trainers to the Aero L-39ZAs Albatros light jets now serving in the NAF.

SOUTH AFRICA:
Rooivalks for evaluation

Fortunes of the indigenous Atlas Rooivalk combat helicopter took a sharp turn for the better on 22 October when Defence Minister H. J. Coetsee announced an order for four evaluation machines. The Rooivalk was developed for bush warfare in what is now Namibia and was understood to have been deleted from SAAF requirements when that conflict ended. It was kept alive by private funding until the South African army took an interest and reportedly allocated cash for further work.

Central America

CUBA:
MiGs defect

In spite of recent attempts to introduce a more liberal political regime to combat public dissatisfaction with financial disintegration resulting from termination of Soviet aid, Cuba has not prevented defections. The pilot of MiG-21bis 672 defected to Key West, Florida, on 15 June, followed on 17 September by Captain Enio Ravelo Rodriguez, in another 'Fishbed', at Key West. Press reports claimed the latter flight was not detected which, if true, would suggest a remarkable lapse by air defence and anti-drug surveillance systems in the Gulf of Mexico. The second aircraft was returned to Cuba on 23 September, on which day a MiG-23 landed at Guantanamo Bay, the US Navy enclave on the island itself.

A recently-noted addition to the Revolutionary Air Force is an Antonov An-30 'Clank'.

South America

ARGENTINA:
Hurons replace Guaranis

Imminent retirement of the aged IAI IA.50 Guarani is foreshadowed in the purchase of 15 surplus Beech C-12 Hurons from the USAF and army. They will replace an approximately equal number of liaison and communications Guaranis, although the intentions regarding four of the latter used for photo-survey are not known.

Trackers back on track

Following its exhibition at the Paris air show, the first naval Grumman S-2UP Turbo-Tracker conversion was returned to Argentina from Israel on 20 October. The aircraft, 0702 '2-AS-23', currently serves with the Escuadrilla Aeronaval Antisubmarina at Comandante Espora. Five more conversions are being undertaken in Argentina, equipping the aircraft with Garrett TPE331-15 turboprops, modernised avionics and a structural upgrade to permit continued operations from the aircraft-carrier ARA *25 de Mayo*.

CHILE:
Helicopter trial

Naval aviation took delivery on 8 October of a special-mission Bell 230 with quick-change kits for SAR, patrol and communications. Fitted with Bendix-King RDR 1500 radar, Trimble TNL 7880 GPS/Omega/VLF, a HUD, thermal-imaging system and rescue hoist, the helicopter is on six months' free lease in the hope of persuading the navy to purchase nine.

North America

CANADA:
EH.101 faces axe

EHI suffered a major reduction in EH.101 orders late in October after the Liberal Party won Canada's general election. Despite an August reduction in the number on order from 50 to 43 by outgoing Conservative Prime Minister Kim Campbell in an attempt to save the programme, her successor Jean Chrétien made a campaign promise to cancel the whole project.

Below left: Further to the 'Comfy Levi' article in **WAPJ 15**, *this active-duty (463rd AW) C-130H was seen recently with the Senior Scout antenna fit.*

Below: One of the aerial reconnaissance assets recently assigned to the newly-created DARO is this Beech RC-12K of the 1st MIB at Wiesbaden.

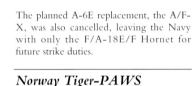

The F/A-18C Hornet has recently been cleared to fire the AIM-120 AMRAAM. Here a VFA-136 aircraft launches a missile during an exercise at NAS Roosevelt Roads, Puerto Rico.

This he did at his first Prime Ministerial press conference, on 4 November. The requirement previously stood at 28 (cut from 35) CH-148 Petrels and 15 CH-149 Chimos, the latter now possibly to be replaced by a second upgrade of the CAF's 13 SAR-tasked CH-113 Labradors and Voyageurs. For shipboard operations, the options include yet another CH-124 Sea King retrofit or smaller helicopters such as the SH-60 Seahawk or Aérospatiale Cougar. Ironically, an EH.101 was scheduled to undertake cold weather trials at CFB Shearwater in November.

Canadians return to Europe

Continued Canadian commitment to the defence of Europe following withdrawal of the last of three CF-18 Hornet squadrons in January 1993 was demonstrated during September. NATO Exercise Cold Fire included eight CF-18s of Nos 433 and 441 Squadrons deployed to Twenthe in the Netherlands, together with a CC-130T Hercules tanker and two jamming-equipped EC-144 Challengers.

UNITED STATES:

US Navy cancels BQM-145

The US Navy has cancelled procurement of the Teledyne Ryan BQM-145 UAV (unmanned aerial vehicle) which was to have performed a variety of tasks but was ordered primarily to carry the now-defunct ATARS (Advanced Tactical Airborne Reconnaissance System). The BQM-145 was tested extensively as a payload for the F/A-18 Hornet strike fighter.

Boeing B-52H conversions

Installation work on the first B-52H Stratofortress for conventional warfare missions was completed by Boeing in Wichita, Kansas, in September 1993. The modification to B-52H models includes accommodation of AGM-142 Have Nap and AGM-84 Harpoon air-to-surface missiles and the Universal Bomb Bay Adapter, as well as the Integrated Conventional Stores Management System and Global Positioning System.

The AGM-142 Have Nap missile, built by Marietta, performed well in two Sep-

tember 1993 tests. During a 3 September 1993 test at White Sands Missile Range, New Mexico, a Have Nap launched from low altitude flew a high-profile track to score a direct hit. On 8 September 1993, Air Force Materiel Command demonstrated that it can use one B-52 as a launching platform and a second remotely located B-52 as a control aircraft. On the latter occasion, the missile accurately identified and hit its target after being 'passed off' from one Stratofortress to another.

US Navy cancels A-6 rewinging

The US Navy on 17 September cancelled $900 million in contracts for the A-6E Intruder rewinging programme, due to the Pentagon's new plan to phase out the type. The cancellation halts work on the rewinging and follows the decision to eliminate the A-6E type by 1999, a part of the Pentagon's Bottom Up Review of US defence needs. The cancellation hit hardest on Boeing Wichita, which loses work on the composite wings. Also affected are Grumman and the Norfolk Naval Aviation Depot, which was to perform some of the wing installation.

The BUR steering committee accepted Navy arguments that the A-6E has become unaffordable and unsurvivable.

C-21A detachments, formerly from the 375th AW, are now assigned directly to the base wing. This aircraft serves with the 332nd ALF, 12th FTW at Randolph AFB.

The planned A-6E replacement, the A/F-X, was also cancelled, leaving the Navy with only the F/A-18E/F Hornet for future strike duties.

Norway Tiger-PAWS F-5A/Bs delivered

Norway's first three F-5A/B Freedom Fighters upgraded under Sierra Research's Tiger-PAWS (Program for Avionics and Weapon System upgrades) modification were delivered to the RNAF in September 1993. The Norwegian F-5A/B upgrade includes 1553 standard data bus, a modified GEC Marconi Avionics F-16C/D Block 40 HUDWAC (head-up display weapon aiming computer). Other major components include the GEC Miniature Standard Central Air Data Computer, Litton AN-93 ring laser gyro inertial navigation system, new angle-of-attack sensors, colour video camera/recorder, and a new multi-function throttle grip. Sierra (a division of LTV until September 1992) claims that this fit gives the aircraft a more precise air-to-ground bombing system and more flexible, off-boresight AIM-9 Sidewinder missile capability.

Norway is the launch customer for Sierra, one of several companies offering upgrades for the 2,500 Northrop F-5s of all variants in service around the world. Under the original 1991 Tiger-PAWS agreement, Norway was to receive its first upgraded F-5 in May 1992. The project grew in scope, however – adding the hands-on throttle design, building an all-new instrument panel and significantly expanding the flight test programme – so that the conversion process took longer than expected. "Our original plan was to do a couple of flight tests and turn the planes over to Norway," said Sierra's Anthony B. Gill. "As our effort expanded, we ended up doing hundreds." The contract covers seven F-5A and eight F-5B aircraft, which will constitute the entire Norwegian F-5 fleet once the programme is completed in 1994.

Two of the first three aircraft (F-5A 67-14896 and F-5B 67-14908) were temporarily deployed to Eglin AFB, Florida, in November 1993 for weapons tests, including dropping bombs.

Norway's package constitutes what

Sierra calls its 'digital core' of potential avionics and radar upgrades for F-5s in service in Brazil, Canada, Chile, Jordan, Singapore, Spain, Thailand, and Venezuela.

Bell TH-67 Creek delivered

Bell delivered the first TH-67 Creek, the US Army's new training helicopter based on the civil 206B-3, in ceremonies at Fort Rucker, Alabama, on 15 October.

US Navy squadron changes

Fleet composite squadron VC-10 'Challengers' was disestablished at NAS Guantanamo Bay, Cuba, on 14 August 1993. The squadron had operated TA-4J Skyhawk attack aircraft modified to carry conventional ordnance and AIM-9 Sidewinder missiles. In recent years, the 'Challengers' had performed target towing and dissimilar air combat training. VC-10 shared its nickname with the Oceana, Virginia-based 'Challengers' of VF-43.

Fighter squadron VF-1 'Wolfpack' was disestablished on 1 October 1993 at NAS Miramar, California. The squadron, together with VF-2, made the first operational deployment of the F-14A Tomcat on a 1975 cruise that included the evacuation of Saigon. VF-1 had been scheduled to receive the F-14D before recent drawdowns dictated its disestablishment.

VF-33 'Starfighters', formerly the 'Tarsiers', was disestablished on 1 October at NAS Oceana, Virginia. The squadron operated F-14A Tomcats.

VP-30 'Pros' at NAS Jacksonville, Florida, acquired the assets of VP-31 'Black Lightnings', NAS Moffett Field, California, on 9 September. The latter squadron was disestablished, leaving VP-30 as the Navy's sole fleet replenishment squadron used to provide type training to P-3 Orion crews.

VX-4 at Point Mugu and VX-5 at China Lake, both in California, are to be disestablished on 29 April 1994 and to be merged on the following day into a new operational test and evaluation squadron, VX-9, headquartered at China Lake.

AMRAAM cleared for F/A-18

In October 1993, the US Navy cleared the AIM-120 Advanced Medium-Range Air-

USAF Phantoms are increasingly rare. The Idaho ANG's 190th FS began its conversion to F-4Gs in June 1991. Both aircraft carry AGM-88 HARM.

to-Air Missile for use by fleet F/A-18 Hornets. This marks initial operating capability for the AMRAAM on the Hornet. One month earlier, Hornet squadrons fired 29 AMRAAMs during exercises on the East and West Coasts of the United States. The West Coast fleet missile exercise took place 7-8 September and 27 September at the Point Mugu, California, ranges of the Naval Air Warfare Center, Weapons Division, and involved 14 launches by Hornets of NAS Lemoore-based squadrons VFA-25 'Fist of the Fleet', VFA-113 'Stingers', VFA-137 'Kestrels', and VFA-151 'Vigilantes'. The East Coast AMRAAM exercise took place 25-26 September at NAS Roosevelt Roads, Puerto Rico, and involved 15 launches by Hornets of VFA-81 'Sunliners', VFA-83 'Rampagers', VFA-131 'Wildcats', and VFA-136 'Knighthawks', all stationed at NAS Cecil Field, Florida.

AMRAAM is now operational aboard USS *Abraham Lincoln* (CVN-72) participating in Operation Southern Watch over Iraq.

EC-130V Hercules retired

The US Coast Guard has withdrawn the sole EC-130V Hercules (1721) from service due to budgetary constraints. The former HC-130H was modified in 1991 by General Dynamics with a rotodome-mounted APS-145 early warning radar and was evaluated in several roles over 18 months, including fisheries patrols from Alaska and Cape Cod, SAR and drug interdiction missions off Florida and in the Caribbean. The one-off EC-130V based at CGAS Clearwater, Florida, also provided support for the space shuttle programme. Possible uses for the EC-130V by other military service branches are being considered.

US Air Force to modify 20 KC-10 Extender tankers

In a scaled-down version of a programme it once anticipated, the US Air Force is modifying 20 Douglas KC-10A dual-role tanker/transport aircraft with wing-mounted drogue pods. Under the new programme, Air Mobility Command plans to put eight of the modified KC-10As at Seymour Johnson AFB, North Carolina, eight at March AFB, California, and four at Barksdale AFB, Louisiana.

In 1991, the USAF announced earlier plans to equip its entire KC-10A fleet (59 aircraft) with refuelling units on each wing to permit refuelling of three aircraft at a time. The 60th and final KC-10A (87-0124; one aircraft has been lost in a mishap) was tested extensively with a British Mk 32B hose-drum pod beneath each wingtip to convert it into a three-point tanker. Under the 1991 plan, the modification work would have been performed by Douglas (since renamed McDonnell Douglas Transport). The new plan takes into account experience gained during Operation Desert Storm when air refuelling assets were at a premium, but is also consistent with reduced funding. In late 1993, the USAF began flying a second KC-10A (79-1951), stationed at March AFB, California, with a new refuelling kit installed by the Air Force at Oklahoma City. The additional airframes to be modified, beginning in May 1994, have not yet been identified.

The US Navy has made known a strong interest in having some land-based, long-range tankers of its own, and the KC-10A modification programme is, in part, intended by the USAF's Air Staff to defuse any such proposal.

6,000th ACES II ejection seat delivered

The 6,000th ACES II (Advanced Concept Ejection Seat) was delivered by McDonnell Douglas on 15 September 1993 for installation in an Israeli F-15C Eagle. The number of pilots whose lives have been saved by this ejection seat exceeded 300 that same month. The manufacturer says the seat has a perfect record for emergency bailouts which take place within the seat's envelope. ACES II permits ejection from 0 to 600 kt (688 mph; 1108 km/h) and from 0 to 50,000 ft (15240 m). At low speed, ACES II produces a parachute 1.8 seconds after initiation, faster than the Russian K-36 'super seat.'

US Air Force changes

On 12 November, the US Air Force decided on force-structure changes that go beyond the service's reorganisation of 1991-92. Involving 350 aircraft in 47 locations, the changes reflect a continuing draw-down of the USAF's size. Included in the changes are a reduction in air defence alert forces, a shift of most C-130E Hercules transports from active to reserve components, and transfer of KC-10 Extender tanker/transport aircraft from Air Combat Command to Air Mobility Command. The USAF is abandoning use of the Beech C-12F as an operational support airlift transport, reassigning numerous C-12Fs to mobility bases in AMC's new KC-10/KC-135 Companion Trainer Program. A new composite wing is to stand up at Moody AFB, Georgia.

The shifts comply with recommendations of the Pentagon's Bottom-Up Review and the 1993 Base Closure and Realignment Commission. Among other recommendations, the Bottom-Up Review announced 1 September calls for reducing fighter force structure, thereby freeing late-model F-16C/D aircraft for Air National Guard and Air Force Reserve units now equipped with the F-16A/B. This will postpone, if not cancel, conversion of A-10A 'Warthog' units to the F-16C/D.

The USAF is scheduled to announce further, less sweeping force changes in late January 1994.

In alphabetical order by state, the changes include:

ALASKA

Eielson AFB: The 210th Rescue Squadron at Kulis Air National Guard Station is to establish a rescue detachment with one Sikorsky HH-60G in early 1994.

Elmendorf AFB: The 3rd Wing lost one C-12F in mid-1993.

King Salmon Airport: Detachment 5, 3rd Wing, is to transfer alert operations at King Salmon Airport (two F-15C/D interceptors) to Elmendorf. The detachment will then inactivate. A contract caretaker force will preserve the airport as a weather/emergency divert airfield which will be used during exercises.

Kulis Air National Guard Station: The 210th Rescue Squadron is to establish a detachment with one HH-60G in early 1994.

ARIZONA

Luke AFB: The 58th Fighter Wing is to gain an additional 25 F-16C/D Fighting Falcons beginning in mid-1994. This resulted from a 'Year of Training' initiative which consolidated all F-16 training, including that for the ANG and AFRes, at Luke. The change means that Luke will eventually have eight F-16C/D squadrons in its single wing. The 58th FW is to lose the F-15E Strike Eagle initial qualification training mission, which is to be transferred to Seymour Johnson AFB, North Carolina, in late 1994. As a temporary measure, the 58th FW is to gain five F-15Es (three in late 1993 and two in early 1994) to meet increased training requirements. Once the training surge ends, the five aircraft will be transferred elsewhere while the remaining 33 F-15Es and the training mission will go to Seymour Johnson.

Tucson International Airport: In early 1993, the 162nd Fighter Group, Arizona Air National Guard, established the F-16A/B International Military Training School to train overseas F-16 pilots. Three F-16A/Bs will be replaced by three F-16C/Ds in early 1994, reflecting the use of the latter variant by some foreign air arms. Training of ANG and AFRes F-16 pilots has been shifted to Luke AFB.

ARKANSAS

Little Rock AFB: In mid-1993, the USAF began modernising its active-duty C-130 fleet, replacing eight of the 314th Airlift Wing's C-130Es with C-130Hs.

CALIFORNIA

Beale AFB: The 350th Air Refueling Squadron is to inactivate. Two KC-135Q Stratotankers will be shifted elsewhere in mid-1994. The 9th Wing's other tanker squadron, the 349th, is unaffected.

March AFB: The 22nd Air Refueling Wing will replace its four T-38A Talons with four C-12Fs in late 1993 as part of AMC's KC-10/KC-135 Companion Trainer Program. In January 1994, the wing is to be replaced by the 722nd ARW which will then inactivate when March-based KC-10A Extenders are transferred, apparently to Travis AFB. The 22nd ARW will transfer to McConnell AFB, Kansas.

McClellan AFB: The four WC-135B Stratotankers at McClellan will depart and the 55th Weather Reconnaissance Squadron will inactive in late 1993.

Travis AFB: Travis will receive 10 KC-10 Extenders in late 1994. The USAF plans to station 24 at Travis but arrival date of the remaining 14 has not been finalised. Travis will receive four C-12Fs in late 1994.

CONNECTICUT

Bradley International Airport: The 103rd FG, Connecticut ANG, which gave up a C-12F on 27 May, will receive a C-26B in late 1993. The group's conversion from A/OA-10A 'Warthog' to F-16C/D aircraft is postponed indefinitely.

FLORIDA

Eglin AFB: The 9th Special Operations Squadron's receipt of six HC-130M/P Hercules in late 1993 is being delayed. The aircraft will remain overseas until replacements are ready, possibly in two years. The 9th SOS received one HC-130N/P in mid-1993, raising its current fleet to 11.

Homestead AFB: The 301st Rescue Squadron with five HC-130N/Ps and eight HH-60Gs, and the 482nd FW with 18 F-16A/Bs (which was to have moved to MacDill AFB), will move to Homestead, and the latter wing's conversion to KC-135Rs is cancelled. There is no

Special schemes are rare on US Army aircraft. This OV-1D Mohawk is marked for 30 years of the type's service with the 504th MI Brigade, 15th MI Battalion.

change in the planned inactivation of the 31st FW.

Hurlburt Field: The 16th Special Operations Wing will receive three additional MC-130H Combat Talon II aircraft beginning in mid-1994.

MacDill AFB: The 56th FW is to be replaced by the 6th Air Base Wing in January 1994, reflecting the loss of a flying mission.

Patrick AFB: The 301st Rescue Squadron with HC-130N/Ps and HH-60Gs will temporarily move to Patrick from Homestead until facilities at Homestead are ready.

GEORGIA

Moody AFB: In late 1993, the 347th FW was to reduce its F-16C/D fleet by six aircraft, leaving the wing with 36. Two squadrons temporarily moved to Moody from Homestead will inactivate. The next step in formation of a composite wing at Moody will be the receipt of 12 A-10As and six OA-10As in mid-1994, followed by eight C-130Es.

Robins AFB: The 19th ARW is to replace its T-37Bs with two C-12Fs in late 1993. The USAF is considering assigning KC-10s to Robins, where KC-135s are now stationed.

ILLINOIS

Scott AFB: Beginning in late 1993, the 375th Airlift Wing was to receive four additional C-12Fs to meet the training surge caused by AMC's KC-10/KC-135 Companion Trainer Program.

KANSAS

McConnell AFB: The 384th ARS was to replace its T-38As with four C-12Fs in late 1993. The 22nd ARW is to stand up at McConnell in January 1994, replacing the 384th Bomb Wing as the base host. The 384th Bomb Wing was to become the 384th Bomb Group and remain until its B-1B bombers depart in May 1994. McConnell was to gain 11 KC-135Rs, the first three in early 1994. McConnell is to transfer from ACC to AMC. The 184th FG, Kansas ANG, will not lose its C-12J as announced earlier.

LOUISIANA

Barksdale AFB: On 1 October 1993, the 2nd Wing was redesignated the 2nd Bomb Wing as a result of the transfer of its KC-135s from ACC to AMC. The 14 KC-135Qs assigned to the 71st ARS are to begin departing in early 1994 and the squadron will inactivate in mid-1994.

Barksdale will lose 10 KC-10As in late 1994. The 46th Fighter Training Squadron, AFRes, formerly equipped with A-10s, will be equipped with eight B-52H Stratofortresses.

MARYLAND

Andrews AFB: The USAF is eliminating its C-12F operational support airlift fleet so the aircraft can be used in AMC's KC-10/KC-135 Companion Trainer Program. The 458th Airlift Squadron will lose its six C-12Fs in late 1993.

MASSACHUSETTS

Barnes Municipal Airport: The conversion of the 104th FG, Massachusetts ANG, from the A/OA-10As to F-16C/D, once slated for early 1994, is postponed indefinitely.

MICHIGAN

K. I. Sawyer AFB: The 410th Bomb Wing will draw down by five B-52Hs in early 1994, rather than in 1993 as once announced.

MISSISSIPPI

Columbus AFB: Because of the USAF decision to transfer basic fighter training to undergraduate pilot training wings, Columbus began receiving 14 AT-38B Talons in mid-1993.

MONTANA

Malmstrom AFB: The 43rd ARW is to replace its four T-38As with two C-12Fs.

NEBRASKA

Offutt AFB: The 55th Wing will receive three OC-135Bs to perform the Open Skies mission. The first OC-135B arrived in late 1993.

NEW JERSEY

McGuire AFB: Previously announced changes have been altered. The 438th Air-

During 1993 the 480th FS, 52nd FW upgraded to the F-16C Block 50. The squadron renumbers as the 22nd FS in 1994.

lift Wing and its C-141B StarLifters will remain at McGuire, as will 21st Air Force headquarters. The 514th Airlift Wing, AFRes, will remain as an associate unit rather than receiving its own aircraft. The 913th Airlift Group, AFRes, with C-130Es, will not transfer here from Willow Grove, Pennsylvania. Nineteen KC-10s will move here from Barksdale, with the first 10 arriving in late 1994. The USAF plans eventually to base 24 KC-10s here but timing for the remaining 14 has not been finalised. McGuire will receive five C-12Fs in late 1994.

NEW MEXICO

Holloman AFB: Due to the transfer of BFT to undergraduate pilot training wings, Holloman began transferring its 30 AT-38Bs in mid-1993.

NEW YORK

Plattsburgh AFB: This base will close. While plans for the closure were being finalised, the 380th ARW was to replace its three T-37Bs with two C-12Fs and to replace its remaining six KC-135Qs with six KC-135Ts, both changes taking place in late 1993.

NORTH CAROLINA

Pope AFB: The 23rd Wing will give up eight C-130Es in mid-1994, leaving the wing with 28 C-130Es equipped with Adverse Weather Aerial Delivery System.

Seymour Johnson AFB: The 4th Wing was to lose six F-15Es in late 1993, reducing its strength to 60. Beginning in late 1994, the USAF was to transfer its F-15E initial qualification training here from Luke. This will result in a gain of 28

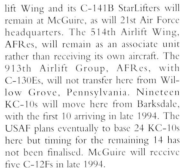

Complete with jamming pod, this Rockwell NT-39B serves with AFMC's 453rd Test Squadron, 412th TW at Edwards AFB.

F-15Es. The decision to assign the majority of KC-10s to two large air mobility bases will result in the transfer of Seymour Johnson's KC-10 force. Ten will depart in late 1994, while timing of the departure of the remaining nine has not been finalised. Because of the loss of the KC-10s, the 918th Air Refueling Group, AFRes, will receive 10 KC-135Rs and become unit equipped, ending its status as an associate group.

NORTH DAKOTA

Grand Forks AFB: The 319th ARW is to replace its T-38As with six C-12Fs and to begin receiving 14 of 27 scheduled KC-135Rs in early 1994.

Minot AFB: The 14 KC-135Rs assigned to the 906th ARS are to begin departing in early 1994 and the squadron is to inactivate in mid-1994.

OHIO

Wright-Patterson AFB: The 645th Air Base Wing was to lose six C-12Fs.

OKLAHOMA

Altus AFB: Because of the 1993 base closure and realignment decision to move KC-135 combat crew training from Fairchild AFB, Washington, to Altus, the 457th Operations Group's 22 KC-135Rs were to begin departing in late 1993. In late 1994, Air Education and Training Command is to begin replacing the 457th's operational aircraft with 24 KC-135R training aircraft.

Tinker AFB: The 507th FG, AFRes, is to become the 507th ARG upon converting from 24 F-16A/Bs to 10 KC-135Rs in mid-1994.

Military Aviation Review

PENNSYLVANIA
Willow Grove Air Reserve Station:
The 913th Airlift Group and its C-130Es will not transfer to McGuire as previously announced.

SOUTH CAROLINA
Shaw AFB: As part of an effort to preserve the names of certain establishments, the 363rd FW is to be replaced by the 20th FW in January 1994.

SOUTH DAKOTA
Ellsworth AFB: The 11 KC-135Rs assigned to the 28th ARS are to begin departing in mid-1994 and the squadron is to inactive in late 1994.

TEXAS
Bergstrom AFB: Some decisions announced in early 1993 have changed. The 924th FG, AFRes, with its F-16A/B aircraft, were to remain until at least until the end of 1996. Conversion to F-16C/Ds was postponed indefinitely. The 10th Air Force, AFRes, is to remain at Bergstrom.
Carswell AFB: The 924th FG will not be reassigned to Carswell as had been previously announced.
Randolph AFB: Because of the decision to transfer BFT to undergraduate pilot training wings, Randolph was to receive eight AT-38Bs in late 1993.
Sheppard AFB: Because of the BFT decision, Sheppard was to receive eight AT-38Bs in late 1993.

WASHINGTON
Fairchild AFB: The 453rd Operations Group is to replace its T-37Bs with six C-12Fs. and 17 of its 26 KC-135Rs with 20 KC-135Ts in early 1994. The 92nd Bomb Group was to lose four B-52Hs beginning in late 1993. On 1 July 1994, the base is to transfer from ACC to AMC, changing its mission from long-range bombing to air refuelling. The 141st ARW, AFRes, C-12J was to be replaced by a C-26B in late 1993.

C-141 StarLifter flying restrictions

The C-141 StarLifter fleet has encountered additional structural problems necessitating the imposition of flying restrictions. On 9 August the Air Force imposed a grounding order to enable extensive inspections to be carried out on 45 aircraft that had exceeded 45,000 flying hours. In addition, a further 116 whose flight hours had exceeded 35,000 were banned from being inflight refuelled. To help fill the vacuum left by the grounding order, eight reserve C-141Bs were temporarily reassigned to active-duty units, with five Air Force Reserve C-141Bs joining the 62nd Airlift Wing at McChord AFB, Washington, while three Air National Guard examples were loaned to the 437th Airlift Wing at Charleston AFB, South Carolina. During mid October the Air Force began using civilian contractors to fulfil some of its routine European flights, including Southern Air Transport with a Lockheed L.100-30 Hercules and American Transair employing a Boeing 727.

Nine C-141Bs had been withdrawn from service and placed in storage with the Aerospace Maintenance and Regeneration Center at Davis-Monthan AFB, Arizona, by late August 1993. Seven of the aircraft were formerly with wings located on the west coast of the USA, while the remaining two were from the 97th Air Mobility Wing at Altus AFB, Oklahoma, which is the training unit. A further seven were in short-term store at Travis AFB, California, during October 1993, no doubt awaiting inspection before being declared fit to resume flying duties. Among these was 63-8075, one of a small number of early production StarLifters which were identified as 'lead-the-force' airframes early in their careers. These aircraft were intended to accumulate a high number of flight hours ahead of the remainder of the fleet, with regular inspections taking place to identify structural problems. A further two C-141Bs had been relegated to ground instruction usage by the 80th Training Wing at Sheppard AFB, Texas.

It is likely that the high utilisation of airlift generally, and the StarLifter in particular, during Desert Shield/Desert Storm had a major contributory effect on the problems associated with the C-141. The Air Force is still considering a Service Life Extension Program (SLEP) involving the replacement of structural areas which have suffered from excessive flight conditions. If funds are approved for the SLEP the opportunity would be taken to upgrade various systems, including a state-of-the-art autopilot, enhanced flight display instrumentation and an improved all-weather landing system. The Air Force is in dire need for the C-17 to enter service in substantial numbers to relieve the C-141 and enable these repairs and modifications to be carried out, making it inconceivable that the Globemaster III programme will cut be back from the 120 examples planned to just 40 aircraft as has been suggested.

USAFE unit news

Two of the three airlift squadrons in Germany have recently been involved in changing their base or equipment. At the beginning of 1993 the 58th Airlift Squadron at Ramstein was assigned six C-12Fs, three C-20As, three C-21As, five UH-1Ns, and a CT-43A. These perform a variety of VIP and communications roles throughout Europe and the Middle East. In addition, the 58th ALS had three C-21As stationed at Stuttgart to support Headquarters US European Command. The squadron lost its C-12Fs, which were ferried back to the USA, and their UH-1N Twin Hueys which were airfreighted to the USA inside C-5 Galaxies. The C-12Fs departed during September, while the UH-1Ns left during September and October. At least one of the UH-1Ns had subsequently been transferred to Edwards AFB, California, with the 412th Test Wing by mid-October 1993.

The three C-21As at Ramstein had increased to eight by late September with the arrival of all five Learjets formerly assigned to the 45th Airlift Flight at Barksdale AFB, Louisiana. Having completed its change of equipment, the 58th ALS inactivated on 1 October and was replaced by the 76th ALS, which was transferred from Charleston AFB, South Carolina.

The aeromedical evacuation role moved from Rhein Main AB to Ramstein on 1 July, together with the four C-9As of the 55th Airlift Squadron. The latter squadron was also inactivated on 1 October and replaced by the 75th ALS, formerly at Travis AFB, California.

The two Ramstein-based F-16C/D squadrons, the 512th and 526th FS, are to be transferred to Aviano AB, Italy, during the early part of 1994. The base is at present administered by the 401st FW, although this unit is to inactivate when replaced by the 31st FW on 1 April 1994. The latter was formerly the host wing at Homestead AFB, Florida, before Hurricane Andrew destroyed the base in August 1992. Aviano has no aircraft directly assigned, although USAFE and stateside-based units have been rotated to conduct Deny Flight sorties over Bosnia. The transfer of the F-16s from Ramstein to Aviano will enable the 31st FW to concentrate on Deny Flight and free other USAFE squadrons from this mission. It will also provide the 16th Air Force with a combat capability in its own right, something it has lacked since the F-16s were withdrawn from Torrejon AB, Spain, a couple of years ago.

Once the F-16s have vacated Ramstein, the 37th Airlift Squadron at Rhein Main AB will move to Ramstein, thereby consolidating all USAFE airlift resources within a single operator. The 86th Wing will change designation to become an airlift wing.

The 36th FW at Bitburg AB, Germany, began transferring its F-15C/Ds to other units prior to the unit inactivating during 1994 and the base closing. Aircraft of the 22nd FS began returning to the USA on 13 October to join the 59th FS, 33rd FW at Eglin AFB, Florida, enabling the late production Eagles of the latter squadron to join the 493rd FS, 48th FW at Lakenheath. Prior to the Bitburg aircraft being ferried home, the base undertook a 10-day transfer inspection to return the Eagles to 'factory condition'. These inspections began on 1 September and were followed by two test flights before repainting. The 53rd FS, together with its aircraft, will be transferred to the 52nd FW at Spangdahlem during late 1993/early 1994.

The 22nd FS number plate will move without personnel or equipment to Spangdahlem, where it will acquire the F-16C/Ds of the 480th FS, which will inactivate. The 81st FS, which at present operates the F-16C/D together with a handful of F-4Gs, will re-equip with the A-10As of the 510th FS, enabling the latter squadron to inactivate. The fourth squadron assigned to the 52nd FW is the 23rd FS, which will continue to fly the F-16C/D as before. Once completed, the 52nd FW will then consist of the 22nd and 23rd FS operating the F-16C/D, the 53rd FS flying the F-15C/D and the 81st FS

The 48th FW at Lakenheath received its first F-15Cs, which are reviving the 493rd FS.

with the A-10A.

Although the 36th FW at Bitburg is due to inactivate, the unit will not remain dormant for long, as it is scheduled to be reactivated at Andersen AFB, Guam, as the 36th Wing under Pacific Air Forces control, replacing the 633rd ABW. The unit has no aircraft assigned, as it is purely responsible for the administration of the mid-Pacific air base.

B-52s scrapped under SALT agreement

The US Air Force began the destruction of surplus B-52 bombers under the terms of the Strategic Arms Limitation Treaty (SALT). The first examples were broken up on 17 August, with the wings removed and the fuselage cut into three sections to enable Russian reconnaissance satellites to observe the Stratofortresses being rendered irreparable. Following removal of all reusable parts and engines by technicians of the Aerospace Maintenance and Regeneration Center at Davis-Monthan AFB, Arizona, the remains were towed to a specific area where a huge guillotine was employed to slice the aircraft into pieces. Three hundred and fifty aircraft are due to suffer a similar fate during the coming years.

By January 1992 AMARC contained 29 B-52Cs, 92 B-52Ds, 49 B-52Es, 58 B-52Fs and 65 B-52Gs. The latter number gradually increased to more than 100 as additional SAC wings retired their complements. The latest unit to send its aircraft for storage was the 42nd BW at Loring AFB, Maine, which despatched two each week to Arizona throughout the autumn and early winter of 1993.

The Air Force purchased 193 B-52Gs between 1957 and 1959, followed by 102 B-52Hs during 1960 and 1961. By 1986 the number of Stratofortresses in service was 167 B-52Gs and 96 B-52Hs, with two B-52Gs and one B-52H lost through accidents subsequently. The SALT agreement permits an eventual strength of 130 Stratofortresses, which will enable the Air Force to retain all of its B-52Hs and a nominal strength of 35 B-52Gs. In reality, the latter type will be operated only by the 366th Wing at Mountain Home AFB, Idaho.

New role for Cobra Ball?

The Air Force is giving consideration to a revised role for the two RC-135S Cobra

Ball ballistic missile intelligence gathering platforms. The Air Force has given serious consideration to modifying both RC-135Ss for a tactical mission that could include the detection of clandestine tests of ballistic and cruise missiles by nations other than those signatories of the Strategic Arms Limitation Treaty. In addition, the modifications could be extended to enable sensors to identify low-observables aircraft. The US has the lead in the development of stealth technology at present, although it is likely the Russians will catch up in due course as they have with previous defence initiatives.

Consideration was given to employing Cobra Ball as a 'Scud' missile hunter during Operation Desert Storm, although in the event it was not needed. Now the Air Force, Navy and Army would like the RC-135S programme switched to the search for the launch of theatre ballistic missiles and low-flying cruise missiles.

Above: The McDonnell Douglas C-17A Globemaster III has entered US Air Force service, the first squadron being the aptly numbered 17th Airlift Squadron, part of the Charleston-based 437th Airlift Wing.

And new role for Looking Glass?

The Air Force is also considering modifying a small number of its EC-135C Looking Glass airborne command posts to perform the role of Airborne Battlefield Command and Control Centre (ABCCC). At present the mission is conducted by seven EC-130Es that are operated by the 7th ACCS at Keesler AFB, Mississippi. The primary duty is to provide an airborne command post for the battlefield commander orbiting close to the edge of a combat theatre.

AMC organisation

The intercontinental airlift structure of AMC was as follows at 1 October 1993:

15th Air Force: HQ Travis AFB

60th Airlift Wing Travis AFB, CA		
60th OG	19th ALS	C-141B
	20th ALS	C-141B
	21st ALS	C-5A/B
	22nd ALS	C-5A/B

62nd Airlift Wing McChord AFB, WA		
62nd OG	4th ALS	C-141B
	7th ALS	C-141B
	8th ALS	C-141B

21st Air Force: HQ McGuire AFB

436th Airlift Wing Dover AFB, DE		
436th OG	3rd ALS	C-5A/B
	9th ALS	C-5A/B
	31st ALS	C-5A/B

437th Airlift Wing Charleston AFB, SC		
437th OG	14th ALS	C-141B
	15th ALS	C-141B
	16th ALS	C-141B
	17th ALS	C-17A

438th Airlift Wing McGuire AFB, NJ		
438th OG	6th ALS	C-141B
	13th ALS	C-141B
	18th ALS	C-141B

DARO formed to oversee reconnaissance assets

The Pentagon has established the Defense Airborne Reconnaissance Office (DARO) to oversee all relevant intelligence-gathering aircraft operated by the Air Force, Navy and Army. The new organisation, which mirrors the National Reconnaissance Office that is responsible for overseeing all spy satellite programmes, will control strategic and tactical reconnaissance operations along with unmanned air vehicles (UAVs). Among the surveillance aircraft types which will be managed by DARO are the RC-135S Cobra Ball, RC-135U Combat Sent, RC-135V and W Rivet Joint all operated by the 55th Wing at Offutt AFB, plus the U-2Rs of the 9th RW at Beale AFB, California. DARO will also control the Navy EP-3E 'Aries' flown by VQ-1 and VQ-2 at NAS Agana, Guam, and NAS Rota, Spain, plus the RC-12D, K and N Guard Rail aircraft operated by the Army in the United States, Europe and the South West Pacific.

DARO will assume responsibility for the research and development of UAVs, including both unclassified and black projects. The 545th Test Group at Hill AFB, Utah, is tasked with the development of UAVs and employs a small number of specially modified C-130s and CH-53s for launch and recovery. The unit is part of the Air Force Flight Test Center at Edwards AFB, California.

Special ops redesignation

The 1st SOW at Hurlburt Field, Florida, was redesignated the 16th SOW on 1 October as the primary unit within Air Force Special Operations Command. The change was brought about to avoid two wing level designations with the same identity, the 1st FW at Langley AFB having a more illustrious history. The Air Force has formed a ranking system based on the seniority of all major wings, which will ensure that those with a lengthy history remain active.

New tailcodes

The transfer of theatre airlift units from AMC to ACC has resulted in Air National Guard and Air Force Reserve C-130 airlift units adopting tactical-style markings and tailcodes. No tailcode details have been received for the ANG, although the Reserve has allocated the following:

'DB'	700th ALS/94th AW Dobbins AFB, GA	'PI'	758th ALS/911th AG Greater Pittsburgh IAP, PA
'KT'	815th ALS/403rd AW Keesler AFB, MS	'PP'	731st ALS/302nd AW Peterson AFB, CO
'MK'	95th ALS/440th AW Milwaukee, WI	'VO'	64th ALS/928th AG Chicago/O'Hare IAP, IL
'MS'	96th ALS/934th AG Minneapolis/St Paul IAP, MN	'WG'	327th ALS/913th AG NAS Willow Grove, PA
'MX'	357th ALS/908th AW Maxwell AFB, AL	'YO'	757th ALS/910th AG Youngstown, OH
'NF'	328th ALS/914th AG Niagara Falls, NY		

Tailcode details for the Air National Guard will follow when announced.

Above: VMA-231 has adopted these new markings for its AV-8B Harrier IIs.

Below: Using an NAWC Hornet at Patuxent River, Loral have demonstrated a radar frequency targeting system which is housed in the empty space within the weapons pylons. This provides 'Wild Weasel'-like capabilities without the need for major modifications and at much-reduced cost, while leaving all ordnance stations free for weapons carriage.

Strike Force over Bosnia

With Operation Deny Flight aircraft effectively ruling the skies over Bosnia, NATO forces extended the air support to cover United Nations troops on the ground. Attack aircraft from four nations were moved into the theatre, where they undertook constant armed patrols to answer any request for close air support. The use of these aircraft has made the hazardous tasks facing UN troops that much easier.

"When our aircraft are overhead there is no doubt the warring parties take note – things calm down when we fill the sky with aeroplanes," said a senior NATO commander.

On 22 July 1993 NATO declared it was ready to provide close air support for UN Protection Force (UNPROFOR) troops escorting humanitarian relief convoys in Bosnia. Some 100 attack aircraft from four NATO nations, supported by reconnaissance, tanker, radar, electronic warfare, command and control aircraft were deployed at Italian air bases or on aircraft-carriers in the Adriatic Sea. Every day since then, fully bombed-up NATO attack aircraft have been flying round-the-clock patrols over Bosnia, ready to respond to the call.

The strike force grew out of the NATO air power involved in Operation Deny Flight, as the enforcement of the UN 'No-Fly Zone' over Bosnia was codenamed. After the failure of the Vance-Owen peace plan in May 1993, the UN and NATO developed plans to provide close air support for UNPROFOR troops bringing aid to Bosnia. NATO's ambassadors gave approval for the plans at a meeting on Brussels on 7 July and within the week American, British, Dutch and French strike aircraft were en route to Italian bases.

America provided the bulk of the assets for this new force. The 52nd Fighter Wing at Spangdahlem in Germany sent 12 A/OA-10 'Warthogs' of the 510th Fighter Squadron to Aviano in northern Italy on 9 July. They joined 12 F-16C Fighting Falcons from Spangdahlem's 23rd FS, which had already been carrying out combat air patrols over Bosnia in support of Operation Deny Flight since 2 July. Further US fire power was on hand at Aviano in the shape of the eight US Marine Corps F/A-18C Hornets, of Marine All Weather Attack Squadron 553 (VMFA(AW)-533), equipped for night laser-guided bombs attacks thanks to the installation of AN/AAS-38A FLIR and laser target designator systems. They deployed to Italy from MCAS Beaufort on 20 July. At Brindisi, four AC-130H Spectre gunships of the 16th Special Operations Wing were deployed to provide more night attack capability. The 23rd FS served three months at Aviano before handing over to the 512th FS of the 86th FW from Ramstein. The Marine Hornets however were slated to stay in Italy until April 1994.

Jaguars answer the call

Britain sent 12 Jaguar GR.Mk 1s to Gioia del Colle, in southern Italy, from RAF Coltishall from 15 July. On the same day, France sent eight Jaguars, of EC 11 at Toul, to Rivolto, in northern Italy. The land-based strike element was completed by the reroling of six F-16As deployed for Deny Flight at Verona-Villafranca. Ground-attack trained pilots from Volkel went to Italy to fly any attack missions requested by NATO.

Out in the Adriatic, the USS *Theodore Roosevelt* returned from Middle East duty and put its complement of 10 F-14A 'Bombcats' (VF-84), 14 A-6E Intruders (VA-36) and 30 F/A-18Cs (VFA-15, VFA-87, VFMA-312) at the disposal of NATO strike planners. Six British Fleet Air Arm Sea Harrier FRS.Mk 1s on HMS *Invincible* and six Super Etendards on the French carrier FS *Foch* were also assigned to the operation for attack and recce missions.

Communications links

Command and control for the strike force was provided by NATO, RAF and French E-3A/D/F Sentry AWACS aircraft, augmented by five USAF EC-130E of the 7th Airborne Command and Control Squadron, from Keesler AFB. The EC-130E ABCCC III aircraft had special communications equipment, including the new Joint Tactical Information Distribution System (JTIDS) secure datalink to pass real-time information between NATO AWACS, ships and strike aircraft. Some 23 secure radios in EC-130Es allowed communications with UN troops on the ground. The close air support operation was controlled by the NATO Combined Air Operation Centre at the 5th Allied Tactical Air Force (5 ATAF) Headquarters at Del Molina Air Base near Vicenza.

The USAF also had to increase the size of its tanker assets in-theatre during July, establishing a new 100th Air Refueling Wing detachment of KC-135Rs at Milan/Malpensa, alongside the RAF two-strong detachment of Tristar K.Mk 1 tankers. Other KC-135Rs remained at Sigonella in Sicily to support US Navy air operations. A total of 10 aircraft operated from the two locations and plans were being made in October to set up another tanker detachment at Pisa.

Throughout the final days of July and into

Left: Providing night attack capability are the eight F/A-18Ds of VMFA(AW)-533 deployed to Aviano in Italy. The intake-mounted sensor pods also allow the launch of laser-guided bombs.

Right: Aircraft from the Aviano strike wing – a 510th FS A-10A leads a night-attack Hornet and an AMRAAM-toting F-16C from the 23rd FS. The latter aircraft have since been replaced by 86th FW F-16Cs from the 512th FS.

August the strike force began preparations for air operations over Bosnia. The *Roosevelt*'s US F-14As with TARPS pods, French photo-reconnaissance Jaguars and Mirage F1CRs from Istrana plus British Sea Harriers flew scores of missions to photograph Serbian positions around Sarajevo. American U-2Rs from the 9th Wing, based at RAF Alconbury, and deployed U-2Rs from Cyprus were also reported to be flying surveillance missions over the former Yugoslavia using Senior Span datalink pods. Electronic reconnaissance flights were made over and around Bosnia by USAF RC-135s, US Navy EP-3E-II Aries II from VQ-2 at Rota, RAF Nimrod R.Mk 1s, French C.160 Gabriels from EET 11/54 at Orléans/Bricy and a DC-8 SARIGUE from EE 51 at Evreux.

By 22 July NATO declared the strike force operational, although it took until early August for the UN 100-strong forward air control contingent to be fully trained and deployed at UN bases in Bosnia. France provided six FAC teams, the UK sent four teams and the Netherlands deployed an unknown number of teams. Britain provided an air operations co-ordination centre at the UN Bosnia-Herzegovina Command headquarters at Kiseljak, near Sarajevo. UN troops from non-NATO countries, such as Egypt and the Ukraine, were not able to deploy FACs.

Daylight protection

NATO established a constant flow of close air support jets over Bosnia during daylight hours to provide continuous protection for UN troops. Pairs of attack aircraft generally spent an hour on patrol over Bosnia, before heading out to a waiting tanker over the Adriatic. After refuelling they would fly inland again for another hour. When over the beach pilots would first establish communications with the EC-130E, before starting to work with the FACs. The FACs would then practise the procedures for talking CAS aircraft onto their targets.

This enabled NATO pilots to became familiar with the terrain in possible target areas and build confidence in their communications with the FACs. Even though NATO chiefs dubbed these missions 'training sorties', the aircraft were generally fully armed and ready to go into action if they received the call. During these in-country training sorties, all aspects of the CAS sortie were practised except 'ordnance release'.

A wide range of ordnance was carried by the NATO aircraft. US A-6E Intruders and F/A-18 Hornets normally carried 500-lb (226-kg) GBU-12 Paveway II laser-guided bombs, Maverick AGM-65F infra-red or AGM-65E laser-guided missiles. 'Warthogs' from Aviano took to the skies over Bosnia with Mavericks and LAU-97 rocket pods for target marking. The British and

Spangdahlem increased its contribution to the Deny Flight force by sending 12 'Warthogs' from the 510th FS. These included attack-dedicated A-10As and FAC-orientated OA-10As.

French Jaguars, as well as the US and Dutch F-16s, tended to fly loaded with iron or cluster bombs.

At any one time up to three CAS patrols were over Bosnia. Other attack aircraft and tankers were held on strip alert in Italy or on carriers to respond to calls for action. NATO commanders developed and practised plans to surge the operation (a 'push CAS' system) so that any UN troops under attack could count on aircraft being constantly overhead. At night the AC-130H gunships took over the CAS role with their devastating night attack and surveillance capability. The CAS missions were co-ordinated with Operation Deny Flight fighter patrols to ensure the attack aircraft were protected from Serbian or Croatian MiGs.

Refuelling orbits

The provision of tanker support was vital for the operation, with a boom-equipped KC-135 being airborne over the Adriatic 24 hours a day. Drogue-equipped British, American and French tankers were airborne whenever probe-equipped aircraft needed to be refuelled. Deny Flight fighters, AC-130s and EC-130Es were also served by these tanker orbits.

The need for CAS became apparent on 25 July when French troops in a Sarajevo base came under Serbian tank fire and a number of UN armoured vehicles were destroyed. Five days later a Spanish peacekeeper was killed after Croat troops fired artillery at the UN base in Jablanica. During a visit to Washington, DC, on 26 July the French Defence Minister, François Leotard, asked the Americans to provide CAS if his troops came under direct attack again.

A major Serb offensive aimed at capturing the strategically important Mounts Igman and Bjelsnica pushed Western leaders to the edge at the beginning of August. In addition to causing widespread civilian casualties in nearby Sarajevo, the Serbs were reported to have flaunted the UN 'No-Fly Zone' by using helicopters in the offensive to carry troops into battle and attack Muslim positions on 1 August.

Strike planning

The following day NATO ambassadors ordered alliance planners to prepare for air strikes to relieve the siege of Sarajevo. These were approved on 9 August and NATO then issued an ultimatum to the Serbs demanding they lift the siege of Sarajevo. US Secretary of State Warren Christopher visited the strike force at Aviano to add to the war of words with the Serbs.

Strike Force over Bosnia

The most potent deterrence to opposing UN forces at night comes from the four AC-130H Pave Spectre gunships deployed to Brindisi. The gunships can rapidly bring their guns to bear with great accuracy.

Lockheed EC-130E ABCCC III airborne command posts are used to control the CAS sorties, and to liaise between air and ground forces. The aircraft are equipped to use the JTIDS network.

Inside the ABCCC III module over Bosnia: the communications equipment and operator stations are housed in a large capsule which slides into the cabin of the EC-130E.

Details of the plans had been worked by US Admiral Mike Boorda, commander of NATO's Allied Forces Southern Europe, and the UNPROFOR commander in the former Yugoslavia, French Lieutenant General Jean Cot, and Belgian Lieutenant General Francis Briquemont of the BHC. Under the agreed rules of engagement UN commanders could call in CAS if they came under direct attack. As tension rose when the Serbs refused to leave the two peaks over looking Sarajevo on 11 August, Briquemont travelled to Italy to meet with Boorda, to make the final preparations for the first air strikes.

NATO increased the tempo of its operations, with attack aircraft making repeated passes over the disputed mountains in a show of force, which seemed to have the desired effect. The Royal Navy Sea Harriers were alone flying 12 sorties a day over Sarajevo. Within days, the Serbs had withdrawn their troops and a French UN force occupied their positions. A deceptive calm descended on Sarajevo after the battles for Mount Ingman. Amid this crisis an F-16C of the 23rd FS, piloted by Colonel Donald Merton, Director of Operations of the USAF 16th Air Force, crashed in the Adriatic off Split on 11 August. A Royal Navy Sea King HC.Mk 4 rescued him after two UN C-130s, two Dutch F-16s and other NATO aircraft launched a search operation. An EC-130E then picked up the unlucky pilot from Split airport and flew him back to Aviano. US Army CH-47s, of Company E, 502nd Aviation Regiment, were then used in a follow-up operation to recover the wreckage. During July another 23rd FS F-16 had to spend the night at Split after diverting with hydraulic problems during a fighter patrol over Bosnia.

CAS over Mostar

At the end of August the focus of attention shifted to Mostar in the south. When a Spanish UN convoy became trapped in the town, USAF A-10As were seen flying patrols over the town on 27 August, supported by US Navy Tomcats and Hornets. Humanitarian efforts to save the town's starving residents were stepped up, including nightly food drops by Rhein Main-based C-130s from 24 August. On that day, two C-130s made drops over Mostar and five others over Maglaj and Tesanji in central Bosnia. The following day six US Hercules made drops over Mostar to deliver 41 tons of supplies. A French C.160 joined the American airlift effort to Mostar on 25 August and the Germans sent a C.160 over the city on the next day. A mission by six US C-130s plus French and German C.160s was aborted on 29 August because of communications equipment malfunctions. Three French Pumas flew five seriously injured Muslim children from the city to the US Army field hospital at Zagreb.

In early September the USS *America* took over Adriatic duty from the USS *Theodore Roosevelt* and its air wing began immediate operations over Bosnia. In line with the US Navy's 'adapted force package' policy, Carrier Air Wing One on the USS *America* boasted a significantly different mix of aircraft to that of the departing *Roosevelt*. VF-102 had 14 F-14A Tomcats, VFA-82 and VFA-

Above: RAF Jaguars were deployed from Coltishall to Gioia del Colle to support the Deny Flight CAS effort. Similarly the French deployed Jaguars to Rivolto.

Below: Air Wing One on board USS America is providing many of the CAS patrol missions. The 14 A-6Es of VA-85 have been active on these duties, and on maritime blockade sorties.

USS **America** *boasts two squadrons of F/A-18C Hornets, this being an example from VFA-86 (with an aircraft from VFA-82 in the background). The Hornet has been used mostly on daytime missions, both on CAS and CAP duties.*

86 fielded 22 F/A-18C Hornets, VA-85 boasted 14 A-6E (SWIP) Intruders, VAQ-137 had four EA-6B Prowlers, VAW-123 deployed with four E-2C Hawkeyes (Group 1), VS-32 sailed with six S-3B Vikings and HS-11 with six SH-3H Sea Kings completed CVW-1. The carrier also deployed with four US Marine Corps CH-46Es of HMM-162 and a 300-strong detachment of combat Marines. When the Somalia crisis escalated in early October they transferred from the carrier to the USS *Guadalcanal* and sailed for the Horn of Africa.

Combat rescue

With the redeployment of the US Mediterranean-based Marine Expeditionary Unit (Special Operations Capable) to Somalia, the USAF had to move a detachment of Special Forces MH-53J helicopters and HC-130P tankers to Italy to provide long-range combat search and rescue support over the former Yugoslavia. The 352nd Special Operations Group's 21st and 67th Special Operations Squadrons set up base at Brindisi for this mission.

The USS *America*'s flight operations were fully integrated with NATO's daily missions over Bosnia, with 30-40 sorties a day being tasked by 5 ATAF. The carrier's Tomcats initially concentrated on Deny Flight fighter and photo-recce missions. Tomcat pilots reported they were often shadowed by Serbian MiGs as they flew TARPS

The original air supremacy Deny Flight mission is very much alive, and even more important given the need to protect NATO CAS aircraft. **America** *provides the Tomcats of VF-102, which have also been employed on tactical reconnaissance missions with the TARPS pod.*

missions along the Bosnia-Serbian border, while the ship's Hornets teamed with the F-14s for fighter missions or flew CAS missions. The A-6Es concentrated on strike warfare, both over land and over sea in support of the UN naval blockade of Serbia

VAQ-137 Prowlers reported that Serbian SA-6 'Gainful' surface-to-air missile radars often tracked the NATO flights over Bosnia. Very unusual missions were flown by the carrier's S-3Bs, which had been optimised for overland surveillance at Cecil Field under the codename Project Aladdin. VS-32's crew were very active, using their electronic support measures to detect Serbian radar sites. Det 3 of VR-40 took a pair of C-2A Greyhounds to Sigonella to support the *America*.

From early September CVW-1 aircraft were over the beach daily, apart from during a number

of brief port visits. When the British base at Vitez came under Croat fire on 7 September, A-6Es flying from the *America* were overhead in case CAS was needed to silence the guns.

In the second week of September UN air operations from Zagreb airport came under threat when Croat-Serb fighting broke out near the Croat capital. A Croat MiG-21 was reported shot down over Krijina by Serbian anti-aircraft fire during an early morning bombing run on 14 September. This incident did not escalate and no attempt was made by either side to interfere with NATO air operations.

Three months into the close air support operation NATO attack aircraft had flown some 2,000 missions, but have yet to drop any bomb in anger on Bosnia, although the lack of a lasting peace deal means that threat of air strikes remained in place as winter approached.

BRIEFING

IAI S-2UP

Turbine Tracker for the 1990s

One area in modern military aviation that has seen proliferation in recent years is the maritime patrol aircraft, particularly of smaller airframes tailored to nations of limited resources. These have almost exclusively been conversions of existing airliner/feederliner/executive transport types. Although these can make adequate platforms, they are not as ideal as a purpose-built patrol aircraft, constructed from the outset to cater for the rigours of operating in a maritime environment. Also none is carrier-capable, should such a requirement exist. However, to purchase a new purpose-built aircraft is prohibitively expensive for all but the wealthiest nations.

One answer is to take an old airframe, available cheaply, with many airframe hours left, and fit modern systems to enable it to perform the allotted tasks with state-of-the-art capabilities. IAI's Shaham Division has produced a range of maritime patrol options which can be fitted to many aircraft platforms, for which its first and most important application is the Grumman S-2 Tracker. The Tracker upgrade is available to existing operators, such as launch customer Argentina, or to new nations. Trackers are available from surplus US stocks for around $250,000. Design life is 80,000 hours, and the average age of the fleet is only 10,000 hours. Those airframes examined by IAI have shown no trace of corrosion.

Trackers were fitted with Wright R-1820 radials, and these were the main problem with keeping the Tracker alive as a viable warplane. Difficulties with maintainability, spares support and fuel supply meant that for any serious attempt to remarket the aircraft, an engine change was imperative.

IAI looked at the various re-engining kits offered for the Tracker, and chose that offered by Marsh Aviation of Mesa, Arizona, as the best, the US company becoming a sub-contractor to IAI. Indeed Israeli technicians were instrumental in fine-tuning the engine fitment.

Marsh uses the Garrett TPE331-15 turboprop, rated at 1,645 shp (1227 kW) and driving a five-blade Hartzell propeller, with reversible pitch capability. There are no airframe changes aft of the engine firewalls, but the nacelle is lengthened at the front to cater for the lighter engine, causing a centre-of-gravity change. New fuel, lubrication and fire extinguishing systems are fitted, and new electrics. Marsh produces the new kits, with IAI overseeing the programme and controlling quality.

Fitting the Garrett turboprops radically alters the aircraft's performance. A water injection system provides extra power for five minutes at full power, allowing full performance in hot weather (up to ISA+25°C). The booster mix is held in a separate tank in each engine nacelle. The stall speed remains the same as an unmodified aircraft, yet the installed power is greater and far more responsive. During a carrier landing, the pilot can land with normal approach power, slamming open the throttles

The Garrett TPE331 turboprop requires a longer nacelle to maintain the centre of gravity. There are no airframe modifications aft of the engine firewall.

should the need arise with instant results. Reverse pitch is a much appreciated feature.

From a mission standpoint, the S-2UP can climb at a much greater rate than the standard Tracker, which allows its sensors to be operative much earlier. This is of great importance when reacting to sudden threats, or when relieving another aircraft on patrol station. Endurance is about 7 hours at 5,000

The S-2UP ground runs at Ben Gurion during trials with Shaham. Only this first aircraft was tested in Israel: the remaining five conversions will be accomplished in Argentina.

ft (1524 m) when fitted with an auxiliary 150-US gal (568-litre) tank in the weapons bay. However, a typical mission would be flown at much higher altitude, the profile starting at about 17,000 ft (5180 m) and rising slowly as fuel is burned off up to 25,000 ft (7620 m). As this operational height is greater than previously attainable, new oxygen and environmental control systems are fitted. The standard crew consists of four, and the co-pilot's station can be reconfigured for additional equipment in some roles.

Unlike its rivals, IAI has opted for a more comprehensive upgrade package for the Tracker, involving many of the aircraft's systems. A new, more powerful searchlight is fitted, with joystick control, and the aircraft features a highly capable autopilot. This allows the pilot to orbit a precise point, or undertake a precise pattern, automatically.

As one would expect, IAI offers a comprehensive range of options for the S-2UP (or any other maritime platform). Due to the shrinkage in modern electronics, large-aircraft capability can now be fitted in a medium-sized airframe. A complete range of new equipment is offered, the full-specification package comprising: a central integrated mission management tactical control and display system with central computer and interchangeable operator stations; a coherent, multi-mode search radar with 'zoom' facility; electro-optical system with FLIR, TV and laser; electronic warfare suite with excellent long-range detection and classification capability and employing differential time-of-arrival (DTOA) technology; threat-adaptable self-defences with chaff, flares and jammers; ASW suite with integral MAD and light-weight acoustic processing system; modern jam-resistant communications and datalink; advanced navigation suite with mission program-

Most Tracker upgrade programmes have been aimed at firefighting. The Conair Turbo Firecat uses the PT6A turboprop.

ming; extended range of weapons. The latter can even include air-to-air missiles for self-defence – a concept employed by RAF Nimrods during the Falklands War.

Naturally IAI works closely with its customers to provide exactly what they require, and costs vary enormously according to the nature of equipment to be included. Pessach Rubin, programme manager, quotes a rough price of $6 million for the basic engine/aircraft systems conversion, and a similar amount further for a surface patrol fit including ESM and day/night reconnaissance system. Yet a similar amount again will buy a full ASW kit on top, all functions fully integrated.

Marsh flew its first Garrett-engined Tracker (for the fire-fighting role) on 24 November 1986. Argentina became the first customer for the S-2UP, and an aircraft was supplied for conversion. Marsh per-

formed the re-engining and the aircraft was sent to Israel for systems fitment, first flying in S-2UP configuration in late 1992. Earlier, another re-engined Marsh aircraft undertook FCLP (Field Carrier Landing Practice) certification. The first S-2UP (0702/2-AS-23) appeared at the 1993 Paris Salon at Le Bourget, marking the type's first long flight. The test flights were completed in the autumn of 1993, Koren Hagai being programme pilot, after which the aircraft was redelivered on 20 October to the Comando Aviacion Naval Argentina.

Five further Argentine navy S-2Es are due for rework, with kits supplied by IAI/Marsh. The work is to be undertaken at the Taller Aeronaval Central facility, the navy's main overhaul centre at BAN Comandante Espora, Bahia Blanca. When back in squadron service with the Escuadrilla Anti-submarina, part of 2 Escuadra

Flight tests showed a dramatic improvement in performance, resulting in far greater mission versatility.

Aeronaval, the Trackers will operate from the shore-base at Bahia Blanca and from the carrier *25 de Mayo*. Mission equipment is believed to be unchanged, although Argentina may later adopt some of IAI's equipment options.

So far Argentina is the only announced customer for the Tracker upgrade, but others are likely to follow. Looking beyond the MPA/ASW mission, IAI is studying an electronic warfare platform version of the S-2, and also an AEW version, which would mount its radar in a dorsal fairing similar to that employed years ago by the E-1 Tracer derivative.

Marsh's previous Tracker work has re-engined fire-bombers for the California Department of Forestry.

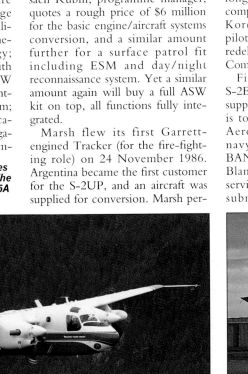

Ilyushin Il-102

Aborted jet *shturmovik*

Indisputably one of the most unusual sights to confront the visitor to the 1992 Moscow Aerospace trade show at Zhukhovskii (MosAeroshow '92) was the Il-102. Before its Zhukhovskii appearance, the Il-102 was unknown to analysts in the West, although the intelligence community knew of the aircraft and had reportedly allocated a provisional 'Ram-' series reporting name. To the casual show attendee, however, the aircraft was a complete enigma. Freshly painted in a gaudy brown and green camouflage and surrounded by the latest weapons, the aircraft had an indefinably ancient appearance, emphasised by its rearward-facing gunners cockpit high on the rear fuselage decking. Those familiar with Soviet aviation history noticed a resemblance to the Il-40, a little-known prototype of the 1950s, better known by its NATO 'Brawny' reporting name. The similarity between the new exhibit and the old Il-40 was extremely strong and, since nothing was known about the new aircraft, the Western aviation press cautiously expressed the belief that the new aircraft might be some kind of derivative; some went as far as to surmise that it might have been a low-risk alternative contender for the requirement won by the Su-25 and now being desperately offered to export customers.

In April 1993, G. Novozhilov, general designer at Ilyushin, wrote a long letter to *Flight International* complaining that this august journal had described his Il-102 as differing only slightly from the Il-40 of the 1950s. He went on to outline the differences, explaining Ilyushin's concept and quoting erstwhile Russian vice president, Alexander Rutskoi (himself a former Su-25 pilot), as having given the aircraft a high appraisal. From Novozhilov's remarks, and from the aircraft's surprise appearance at the 1992 Moscow Aeroshow, one might have thought that it was a current project, being seriously offered for export. In fact, the truth is rather different.

Despite Mr Novozhilov's protestations to the contrary, the Il-102 does indeed have its roots in the Il-40, the company's first jet *shturmovik*, and was originally designated Il-42. The Ilyushin Design Bureau popularised the *shturmovik* concept with its wartime Il-2 and Il-10 family, which proved that heavily armoured, rugged, dedicated tank-killing close-support aircraft could survive over the battlefield and make a significant contribution to winning the battle. The concept went out of fashion after the war, with the dawn of the jet age, especially after Korea, when Il-2s and Il-10s proved easy meat to UN Sabre pilots.

The limitations of using the last generation of jet fighters (MiG-15s when the MiG-17 entered service,

Above: The angular lines of the Il-102, its small cockpit canopy and unusual intake configuration mark it out as the derivative of a much older design.

MiG-17s when the MiG-19 came in, etc.) quickly became apparent, however. Just as fighters and bombers were switching from piston engines to jet power, it was reasoned that a jet-engined *shturmovik* might regain sufficient survivability to be viable. Accordingly, Ilyushin was encouraged to step up work on its first jet *shturmovik*, which had been formally ordered during 1948. The Soviet air force's requirement was for a jet-engined ground attack aircraft, heavily armoured to give maximum resistance to battle damage, and with transonic performance.

Ilyushin's response was to design an aircraft powered by two RD-9F turbojets (as used in the MiG-19 and, interestingly, by then long obsolete, in the prototype Su-25), with a wing with 30° sweep on the leading edge. A fence was added to reduce induced drag (by preventing

spanwise migration of the boundary layer) and to add strength. The twin-engined configuration was chosen to maximise thrust-to-weight ratio. Heavy armour plate protected the cockpits, fuel tanks and fuel system. The aircraft was able to carry a bombload of up to 1000 kg (2,205 lb), on six external hardpoints, and in a real throwback to the Great Patriotic War, in four internal bomb bays in the wings themselves. Bombs were to be augmented by a quadruple NR-23 23-

Below: For its appearance in the static display at MosAeroshow '92, the Il-102 received a shiny new paint job and was fitted with a plethora of modern weapons. More of these were arranged before it.

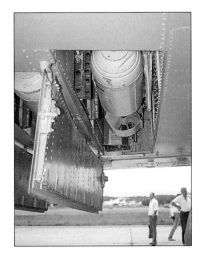

Above left and above right: One of the most unusual, and most archaic, features of the Il-102 was its use of three weapons bays in each inner wing. These allowed the low-drag carriage of tiny 250-kg bombs, with more viable stores carried further outboard on conventional pylons. Few observers at Zhukhovskii realised that the Il-102 had not flown for eight years.

mm cannon, able to fire horizontally and to be traversed to a nearly vertical position for strafing ground targets. From the start, Ilyushin proposed that the new aircraft should be a two-seater, with a rear-facing gunner controlling a power-operated remotely controlled Il-K10 gun turret in the tail. The company had suggested this layout for the original Il-2 of wartime fame, but the concept had been rejected, a tail gunner's cockpit subsequently being added as a result of operational experience.

The first Il-40 finally made its maiden flight on 7 March 1953, but flight tests soon began to reveal unexpected problems. The most serious of these included gun gas ingestion that caused engine flameouts. A variety of deflectors were fitted to the gun muzzles but none were really satisafctory and, as a result, the engine intakes were extended forward along the fuselage sides to the nose, where they met as two side-by-side circles. This unusual and ungainly looking solution worked perfectly, and in January 1955 the type passed its state acceptance tests. It was decided to begin production immediately, at the Rostov on Don plant which now manufactures a variety of Mil helicopter designs. At this late stage, politics began to intervene, and the Il-40 fell victim to Kruschchev's policy of cutting back spending on military aviation in favour of mis-

siles (a mistake repeated in Britain in the infamous Sandys White Paper of 1957) in the belief that strategic missiles rendered the manned bomber obsolete, and that surface-to-air missiles would make tactical aircraft similarly useless. A visit to the factory by Kruschchev sealed the fate of the Il-40 project. He ordered immediate termination and the destruction of the five complete aircraft (it is not known whether this number included the OKB-built prototype).

The Il-40 began its resurrection in the aftermath of the Six Day War of 1967, in which Israeli fighter bombers armed with heavy 30-mm cannon proved devastatingly effective as tank killers. This led directly to the drawing up of a requirement for an armoured jet *shturmovik* for Frontal Aviation, and while Sukhoi concentrated on a single-seat configuration, following the US

approach exemplified by the A-4, A-7 and A-10, Ilyushin dusted off the Il-40 drawings (and perhaps a surviving prototype) and decided that it would still be most suitable for the role, with only a minor redesign. Under the designation Il-42, the new design was presented to the air force, which rejected it on the very grounds that it was a two-seater, and would therefore require a new generation of tactical gunners to be trained, while offering, in their opinion, little worthwhile increase in survivability. Ilyushin were not deterred, however, and after refining some elements of the design and allocating a new Il-102 designation in order to dissassociate it with the original 'Brawny', they

Below: The gunner's rearward-facing cockpit is separated from his turret by the rear fuselage and tail unit, which would have made aiming awkward.

decided to press on with construction of a prototype using company funds, in order to test their ideas.

Thoroughly dead to all intents and purposes, the Il-102 lingered on as a private venture, albeit in the face of disapproval by the powerful Defence Minister, D. F. Ustinov, who was quoted as stating that "Novozhilov must stop his dilettante activities!" He ordered that work on the aircraft should cease, and that the incomplete prototype be scrapped. The Ilyushin OKB had other ideas, however, and the flight test programme was therefore car-

Ilyushin Il-102

1 Nosecone, provision for electro-optical sighting systems equipment
2 Radar warning receiver
3 Aft-retracting nosewheel with low-pressure tyre
4 Hydraulic retraction jack
5 Upper IFF antenna
6 Nosewheel bay
7 Forward avionics equipment bay
8 Dynamic pressure sensors
9 Front pressure bulkhead
10 Windscreen wiper
11 Armoured glass windscreen panels
12 Head-up display
13 Pilot's cockpit enclosure
14 Rear view mirror
15 K-36L zero-zero ejection seat
16 Engine throttle levers
17 Control column
18 Rudder pedals
19 Armoured cockpit enclosure
20 Engine air intake, thermally de-iced
21 Underfloor avionics equipment bay
22 Honeycomb intake ducting
23 Incidence transmitter
24 Ventral weapons bay, gun pack installed – interchangable with bombs
25 Wing spar attachment main frame
26 RD-331 non-afterburning engine
27 Engine accessory equipment
28 Self-sealing bag-type fuel tanks, polyurethane foam filled: total internal capacity 5370 litres (1,181 Imp gal)

29 Hydraulic reservoirs
30 Canopy hinge and jettison mechanism
31 Inertial unit
32 Upper equipment bay
33 Fuel filler
34 UHF aerial
35 Starboard wing weapons bays
36 S-25 OFM, 240-mm heavy rocket
37 Starboard wing pylons
38 Pitot head
39 Retractable landing light

40 EW antenna
41 Wingtip Automat-P chaff/flare dispenser
42 Starboard aileron
43 Aileron tabs
44 Double-slotted flap
45 Spoiler panels
46 Rear gunner's cockpit enclosure

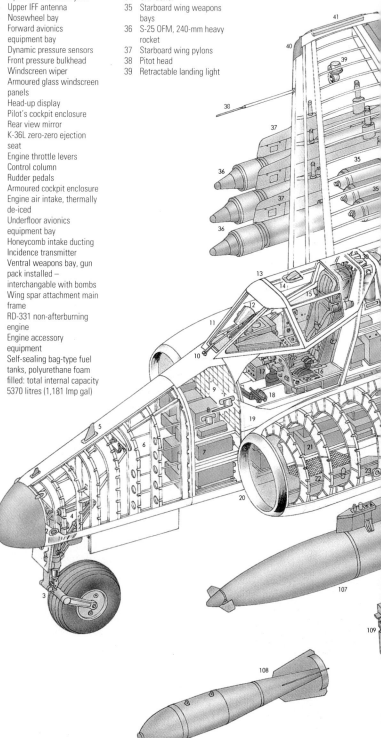

Above: The cockpit of the Il-102 contains few surprises, apart from its rocket-powered 'zero-zero' Severin K-36L ejection seat. This forms part of a command ejection system which can be initiated by the pilot and which allows him to eject his crewman even if the latter is injured, and if the intercom is knocked out. The seats fire in a synchronised order and direction which removes the possibility of seat collision while minimising the ejection interval.

Above: The rear gunner's cockpit is heavily framed, and rather cramped. The gunner also acts as a radio operator, navigator, systems operator and lookout, dramatically reducing pilot workload.

Left: The GSh-23L twin-barrelled gun is fed from a magazine in the centre fuselage, with rounds being passed along a continuous electrically driven belt to the gun, some 3 m further aft.

Modernised MiG-29s

The basic MiG-29 is an excellent close-in dogfighter, with a useful BVR capability, and has won itself an enviable reputation that is tarnished only by its lack of range and the lack of onboard radar processing capacity, which limits simultaneous engagement capability. To remedy these shortcomings Mikoyan set out to produce an improved MiG-29 derivative, with longer range, better radar and improved versatility. In the MiG-29M they have succeeded beyond their wildest dreams but, incredibly, have still received no launch order for this, Russia's best-ever lightweight multi-role tactical fighter aircraft.

The MiG-29M is probably the best all-round fighter ever produced by the Russian aviation industry: versatile, with unsurpassed handling characteristics, superb performance and a wide range of highly effective weapons. While the basic, original MiG-29 was broadly equivalent to the A-model F-16, with marginally better agility and BVR capability, and marginally worse air-to-ground capability and handicapped by lack of range, the MiG-29M is a very much more capable machine. The new MiG-29M has improved handling characteristics and even better manoeuvrability, and its much greater fuel capacity makes it far more versatile. The new radar radically improves BVR multiple target capability and the aircraft is compatible with anti-radar, TV- and laser-guided and fire-and-forget missiles. Effectively, the aircraft has been transformed into the equivalent of a HARM- and AMRAAM-compatible F/A-18C Hornet. Perhaps most importantly, in the post-Cold War world of shrinking defence budgets and amid a plethora of low-level conflicts, the MiG-29M is relatively cheap and very maintainable. At first glance it thus seems extremely surprising that the aircraft, having passed its State Acceptance Tests, has received no production funding or orders, while what many judge to be an inferior (and certainly less ubiquitous) aircraft, Sukhoi's rival Su-35, which costs twice as much,

is already in series production. The reasons for such an extraordinary state of affairs are many and complex, one such reason being the radical restructuring and realignment of Russian defence posture, with an increasing reliance on longer-range aircraft for greater power projection and to allow concentration at more centralised bases. This is an extraordinary state of affairs, and once the remaining Su-17Ms and MiG-27s have been retired, the Russians will almost certainly miss the MiG-29M, especially since they will have no cheap, lightweight strike attack aircraft (apart from the inflexible Su-25) with which to conduct local operations or even to participate in UN peacekeeping operations. The MiG-29M, with its formidable multi-role capability, would be particularly well suited for such operations. Another root cause of Mikoyan's misfortune seems to be the Sukhoi OKB's recent rise to political pre-eminence.

Belyakov's genius

Whereas the Mikoyan OKB's senior management have acquired a seemingly unjustified reputation for being slightly 'unreconstructed', Sukhoi, under the leadership of the charismatic but controversial Mikhail Simonov, have a more liberal reputation. In reality such political labels mean little, since Mikoyan, from designer general Rostislav Belyakov down, have shown con-

siderably more aptitude than their rivals at putting their message across to the press, potential overseas customers and Western aerospace companies. This relative flair for marketing and media management (and the bureau's expertise in such areas is impressive by Russian standards) unfortunately has had no impact on winning the crucial home orders which must underpin any successful aircraft programme.

Rostislav Belyakov is one of Russia's aerospace giants and has been at the helm of Mikoyan, the nation's most famous and prestigious fighter design bureau, since the death of Artyom Mikoyan. Before that he was a senior deputy of the great man, directly responsible for many of the OKB's most successful aircraft. His popularity, position and standing were enhanced recently when he won a massive majority in a worker's ballot confirming him in his post, despite one of his most talented younger deputies, Anatoly Belosvet, standing against him.

Mikoyan's present troubles began with the

Below: The sixth MiG-29M taxis out for a long ferry flight, carrying standard underwing drop tanks. Deeper, larger-capacity tanks are reportedly under consideration for the type. A head-on view emphasises the sharper leading edge root extensions of the M, and the broad-chord dogtooth tailplanes and bulged wingtips can also be seen.

Transport
The aircraft can be quickly disassembled for transport by rail (on two standard pallets) or in the hold of an Il-76. This is just as well, since the aircraft's limited range would make self-ferrying a tedious business.

Wing
The Il-102 inherited its wing virtually unchanged from the original Il-40. Modestly swept and slightly tapering, the wing is built around two enormous spars, and this construction allows the provision of three internal weapons bays in each inboard section. These each contain a BDZ-UMK2 bomb rack, capable of carrying a 250-kg bomb. Outboard are three underwing hardpoints, with two more hardpoints under the fuselage bringing the total to 16 and allowing the carriage of up to 7200 kg (15,875 lb) of ordnance. The wingtips curve downwards and the tips have provision for Beryoza-L ECM equipment and Automat-F chaff/flare dispensers. The single-section double slotted flaps occupy the inboard trailing edge, with conventional ailerons outboard. Twin section spoilers are fitted on the upper surface of each wing.

Internal bomb bays
The use of the internal bays alone improves handling characteristics and, say Ilyushin, cashing in on the 'stealth' boom, reduces radar cross-section. This is a cheeky bit of marketing since, even clean, the Il-102's radar cross-section must exceed that of the largest Mack truck.

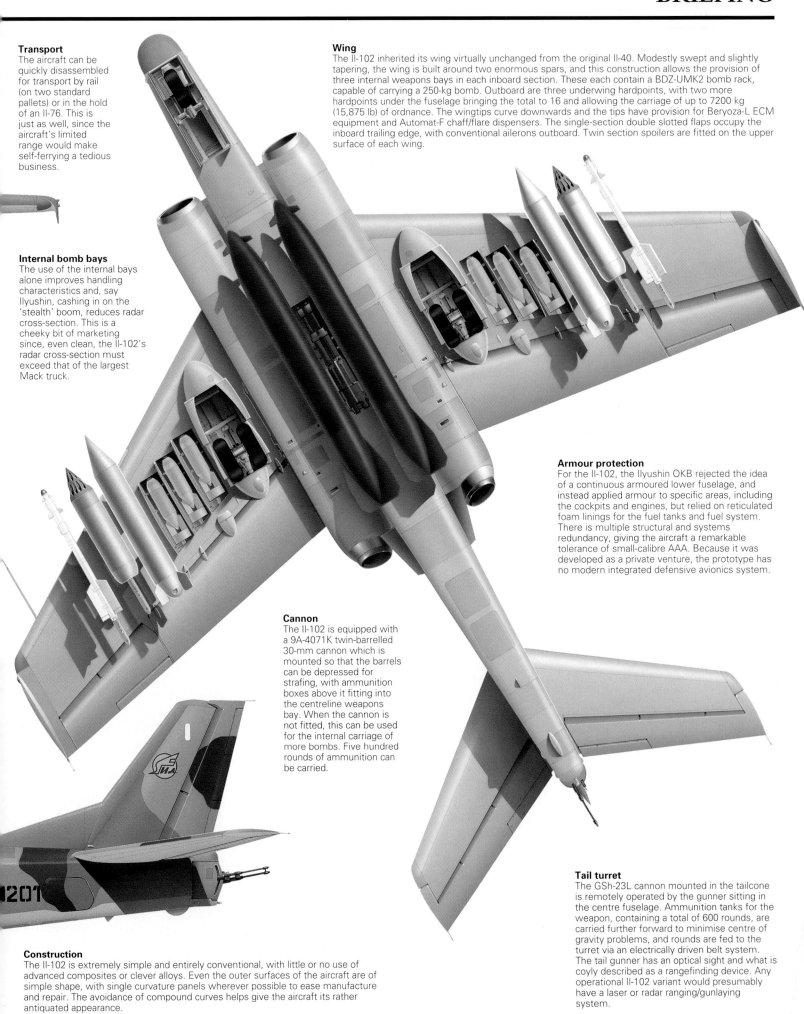

Armour protection
For the Il-102, the Ilyushin OKB rejected the idea of a continuous armoured lower fuselage, and instead applied armour to specific areas, including the cockpits and engines, but relied on reticulated foam linings for the fuel tanks and fuel system. There is multiple structural and systems redundancy, giving the aircraft a remarkable tolerance of small-calibre AAA. Because it was developed as a private venture, the prototype has no modern integrated defensive avionics system.

Cannon
The Il-102 is equipped with a 9A-4071K twin-barrelled 30-mm cannon which is mounted so that the barrels can be depressed for strafing, with ammunition boxes above it fitting into the centreline weapons bay. When the cannon is not fitted, this can be used for the internal carriage of more bombs. Five hundred rounds of ammunition can be carried.

Construction
The Il-102 is extremely simple and entirely conventional, with little or no use of advanced composites or clever alloys. Even the outer surfaces of the aircraft are of simple shape, with single curvature panels wherever possible to ease manufacture and repair. The avoidance of compound curves helps give the aircraft its rather antiquated appearance.

Tail turret
The GSh-23L cannon mounted in the tailcone is remotely operated by the gunner sitting in the centre fuselage. Ammunition tanks for the weapon, containing a total of 600 rounds, are carried further forward to minimise centre of gravity problems, and rounds are fed to the turret via an electrically driven belt system. The tail gunner has an optical sight and what is coyly described as a rangefinding device. Any operational Il-102 variant would presumably have a laser or radar ranging/gunlaying system.

Ilyushin Il-102

Armament
The Il-102 prototype is seen here carrying a variety of modern stores externally. Outboard underwing are R-73 (AA-11 'Archer') IR-homing AAMs for self-defence, with an S-8 80-mm rocket pod inboard of those, and then a KMGU dispenser weapon. It is not clear how many weapons were actually cleared for use by the Il-102 during its 250-hour flight test programme, if any, but the aircraft is claimed to be an exceptionally stable delivery platform.

Undercarriage
The Il-102's tricycle undercarriage is optimised for operation from semi-prepared strips, with an exceptionally low 'footprint' by virtue of its massive, relatively low-pressure tyres and twin wheels on the main units. These actually allow the Il-102 to operate from softer surfaces than the Su-25, its great rival. The main gear retracts aft into semi-conformal fairings, while the nose gear retracts forward into the long, largely empty nose. Tyre pressures have been quoted as 5 kg/cm².

Crew
The Il-102 is operated by a crew of two. The pilot sits forward of the massive dorsal hump, his cockpit armour protecting him from head on, while the gunner faces aft behind him. Use of the simple term 'gunner' is probably something of a misnomer, since the Il-102 backseater is systems operator, navigator, radio operator and lookout as well as defensive gunner, and a well co-ordinated crew can increase the efficiency of the aircraft immeasurably.

Shturmovik
The *shturmovik* concept originated before the Great Patriotic War, when a number of marginally successful armoured ground attack aircraft were constructed. The concept was proved during the war, however, when Ilyushin's Il-2 and Il-10 were devastatingly effective against Hitler's Panzers. Ever since, Russia has sought a modern equivalent, the so-called jet *shturmovik*.

war, to the OKB's delight, ancient Il-28 medium bombers were sent to participate in the conflict, proving extraordinarily successful chiefly by virtue of their tail gun turret, which had a marked effect on Mujahideen anti-aircraft gunners, whose normal tactic was to wait for an Su-25 or MiG-27 to fly past before opening fire on their unprotected rear. This combat experience had no effect though, and the Il-102 project was terminated even within the bureau. Equipment bailed to Ilyushin, including ejection seats and weapons, was returned, and the Il-102 did not emerge again until 1992, although things looked promising for a while in 1986, when discussions were held about the need for an Su-25 replacement. This requirement was eventually filled by the Su-25T.

Why then did Ilyushin display the Il-102 at the 1992 MosAeroshow? The clue may lie in the final sentence of Novozhilov's letter to *Flight*, referred to earlier, which declared: "Finally, I would like to state that Ilyushin has not had the last word yet and is still working to create the best ground attack aircraft in the world." Perhaps the sudden emergence of the Il-102 into the spotlight was one way of reminding the world of Ilyushin's long history of producing combat aircraft, particularly those dedicated close support flying tanks known to the Russians as *shturmovikii*, and simultaneously demonstrating the company's often radical approach to design problems. All may become clear when Ilyushin's next jet *shturmovik* is revealed.

Ilyushin Il-102

The sole flying Il-102 prototype (a second was built for static testing) is shown as it appeared at the 1992 Moscow air show at Zhukhovskii. The camouflage paint scheme is believed to have been applied especially for the show, Ilyushin's sales brochure showing the aircraft in natural metal finish. No NATO reporting name has been allocated, but a provisional name in the 'Ram-' series allocated to aircraft first seen at Zhukhovskii (long known to Western intelligence agencies as Ramenskoye, after the nearby town) was given. Like most Russian design organisations, Ilyushin has extensive facilities at Zhukhovskii, as well as workshops and an airfield in Moscow itself. Flight testing of the Il-102 was exported to a Byelorussian airfield, such was the political sensitivity of the project.

Powerplant
The Ilyushin Il-102 is powered by a pair of Klimov Corporation (Isotov) RD-33I turbofans, non-afterburning versions of the engine fitted to the MiG-29. These are rated at 51 kN (11,465 lb st). The engines are fed by simple pitot intakes which project forward from each wingroot, reaching forward to a point just level with the base of the windscreen, and exhaust through plain circular jet pipes in the wingroots. Because they are widely separated, each engine has its own independent starter, generator, hydraulic pump and accessories gearbox. The design bureau reportedly considered fitting thrust-vectoring nozzles for short take-off performance, and later examined the possibility of reverse thrust. No exhaust diffuser/cooler is fitted, nor are any chaff or IR flare dispensers, although such equipment could be fitted to a production version.

Operational equipment
The Il-102 is not fitted with an attack radar, nor does it have a laser rangefinder, marked target seeker or designator, or any other electro-optical targeting devices. Such equipment would obviously be fitted to any production version of the aircraft, however.

Prospects
The Il-102 is theoretically available for export, but the Ilyushin OKB's prime motive for showing the aircraft is understood to be as a means of raising the company's profile as a military aircraft design organisation. At the moment, all of the bureau's products are airliners or transport aircraft, but the company retains a wealth of experience of military aircraft, and wants to re-enter the field with a new attack aircraft. Given the political connections of Sukhoi's leadership, this may be a forlorn hope.

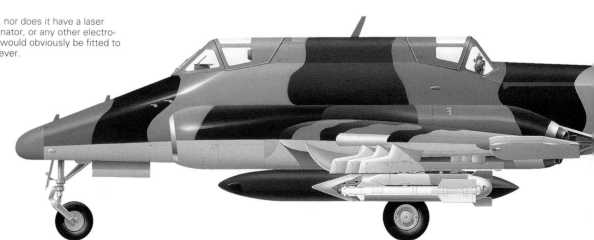

ried out under false pretences. The prototype was moved to Byelorussia to avoid the prying eyes of hostile Air Marshals, and its designation was changed to Experimental Aircraft No. 1 to bolster the pretence that the flight test programme would be pure research. These

political moves succeeded and Minister of the Aviation Industry, I. S. Silaev, authorised what he thought was an aeronautical research programme by a pure research aircraft. Accordingly, Ilyushin OKB chief test pilot S. G. Blisnyuk nursed the aircraft into the air for the first time

on 25 September 1982. Between 1982 and 1984 the prototype made some 250 flights (a second prototype was used for static testing), being grounded when the engine life expired (there was no money available for an overhaul). The aircraft was returned to Zhukovskii

and buried in the back of one of the hangars allocated to Ilyushin. Ironically, by this time the war in Afghanistan was raging and combat experience was already demonstrating that Sukhoi's relatively lightweight single-seat Su-25 concept had some serious flaws. Later in the

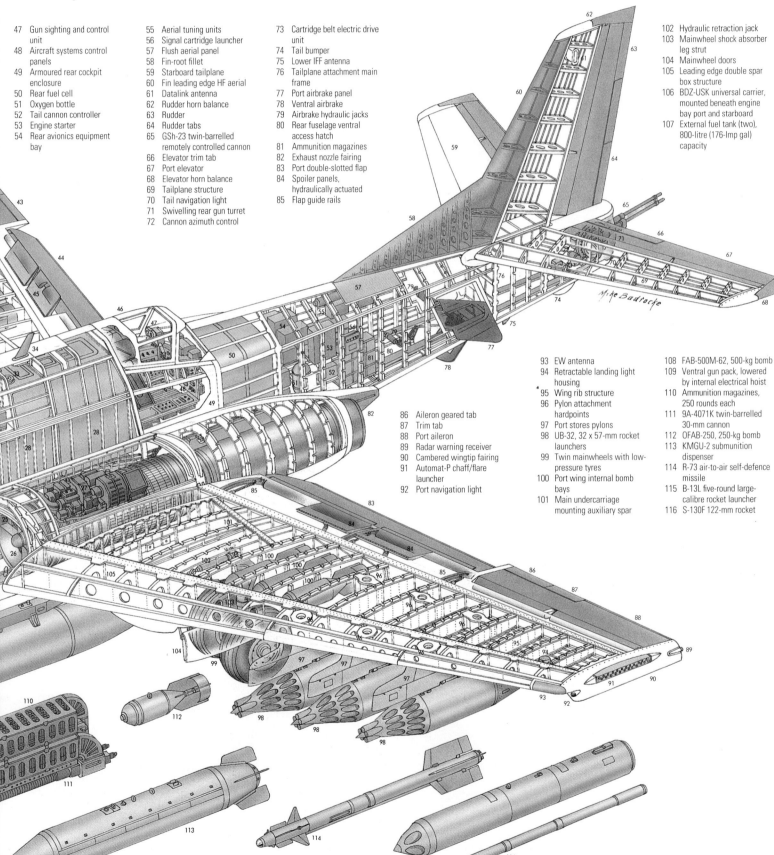

47 Gun sighting and control unit
48 Aircraft systems control panels
49 Armoured rear cockpit enclosure
50 Rear fuel cell
51 Oxygen bottle
52 Tail cannon controller
53 Engine starter
54 Rear avionics equipment bay

55 Aerial tuning units
56 Signal cartridge launcher
57 Flush aerial panel
58 Fin-root fillet
59 Starboard tailplane
60 Fin leading edge HF aerial
61 Datalink antenna
62 Rudder horn balance
63 Rudder
64 Rudder tabs
65 GSh-23 twin-barrelled remotely controlled cannon
66 Elevator trim tab
67 Port elevator
68 Elevator horn balance
69 Tailplane structure
70 Tail navigation light
71 Swivelling rear gun turret
72 Cannon azimuth control

73 Cartridge belt electric drive unit
74 Tail bumper
75 Lower IFF antenna
76 Tailplane attachment main frame
77 Port airbrake panel
78 Ventral airbrake
79 Airbrake hydraulic jacks
80 Rear fuselage ventral access hatch
81 Ammunition magazines
82 Exhaust nozzle fairing
83 Port double-slotted flap
84 Spoiler panels, hydraulically actuated
85 Flap guide rails

86 Aileron geared tab
87 Trim tab
88 Port aileron
89 Radar warning receiver
90 Cambered wingtip fairing
91 Automat-P chaff/flare launcher
92 Port navigation light

93 EW antenna
94 Retractable landing light housing
95 Wing rib structure
96 Pylon attachment hardpoints
97 Port stores pylons
98 UB-32, 32 x 57-mm rocket launchers
99 Twin mainwheels with low-pressure tyres
100 Port wing internal bomb bays
101 Main undercarriage mounting auxiliary spar

102 Hydraulic retraction jack
103 Mainwheel shock absorber leg strut
104 Mainwheel doors
105 Leading edge double spar box structure
106 BDZ-USK universal carrier, mounted beneath engine bay port and starboard
107 External fuel tank (two), 800-litre (176-Imp gal) capacity

108 FAB-500M-62, 500-kg bomb
109 Ventral gun pack, lowered by internal electrical hoist
110 Ammunition magazines, 250 rounds each
111 9A-4071K twin-barrelled 30-mm cannon
112 OFAB-250, 250-kg bomb
113 KMGU-2 submunition dispenser
114 R-73 air-to-air self-defence missile
115 B-13L five-round large-calibre rocket launcher
116 S-130F 122-mm rocket

end of the old order, when the country's political institutions began to gain real power and influence. Even as the new political infrastructure began to take shape, Mikhail Simonov found himself elected to the new Congress of People's Deputies and thence to the Supreme Soviet. From there it was a small step to become head of the committee which oversees the 'military-industrial complex', from which position he has been able to gain what some see as an unfair advantage over his competitors. There is no public row between the Sukhoi and Mikoyan OKBs, and senior people from both organisations have openly praised their competitors – stating that the existence of a competitor serves to improve the excellence of their own aircraft. This is public relations whitewash, though, and insiders report a bitter ongoing feud which has only been exacerbated by the blatantly 'political' aircraft procurement policy presently being followed by the Russian government.

Mikoyan's problems have had little effect on their products, however, and it may be that an almost warlike atmosphere has enhanced the cohesiveness and resolve of the team. The end of the Cold War has had the effect of destroying the privileged status of the defence industry, with salaries and working conditions declining dramatically. This has obviously had an effect on the retention and recruitment of skilled workers at all levels, particularly since Mikoyan now has to compete with hard currency-earning industries for its staff. The best graduates from the various technical institutes and universities are no longer directed to the top military OKBs, but may themselves choose to work in the increasingly important civil sector, or even to leave the aeronautical industry altogether. Among those who have left the bureau in recent years (some having reached their planned retirement age, others having felt the pull of 'market forces') have been some of its best-known names.

Deputy chief test pilot Anatoly Kvotchur, of Farnborough and Paris fame, went to the LII Gromov Flight Research Institute at Zhukhovskii, where his duties now include leading the Su-30-equipped 'Test Pilots' demonstration team. His former mentor, the famously ebullient and good-humoured Valery Menitsky, has left to pursue a career in banking – a sad loss to the flight test team, and to Mikoyan's marketing, press and public relations effort. Deputy general designer (and Belyakov's erstwhile heir apparent), Mikhail Waldenburg, widely described as the 'father of the MiG-29', has also

Above: The MiG-29M blasts into the air at the beginning of a Farnborough display routine. The gridded intake debris guards have already swung away, and the variable area intake lips have closed. Greater excess power, bigger aerodynamic control surfaces and a new fly-by-wire control system have made the MiG-29M an even more agile aircraft than its precursor.

retired, although his services will continue to be used since he remains a consultant. Mikoyan insiders stress the vital importance of his work over the years, yet pay the surprising tribute that he will be missed as much for his sense of humour as for his immense design expertise and leadership.

While some old faces have disappeared, Mikoyan retains a pool of considerable talent. Roman Taskaev, familiar to Western air show audiences as a demonstration and display pilot

Left: The first MiG-29M prototype pulls up into a steep climb. The aircraft has false overwing air intakes painted onto the tops of the LERXes. The first MiG-29M made its maiden flight in the hands of Valery Menitsky.

Right: The retirements of chief test pilot Menitsky and his deputy, Anatoly Kvotchur, have left Roman Taskaev, familiar to Western air show audiences as a demonstration pilot, with the job of chief test pilot.

Left and above: The N-010 (RLPK-29UM) radar fitted to the MiG-29M and MiG-29K is reportedly a close member of the same family as the Fazatron Zhuk seen here. This uses a conventional slotted plate antenna.

without peers, but also renowned as a test pilot of the first order, has stepped into Menitsky's flying boots, while younger test pilots such as Pavel Vlasov and Marat Alykov have already shown that Mikoyan's reputation for astonishing air show demonstrations will continue. Waldenburg has been replaced by Valery Novikov as deputy designer general responsible for the MiG-29, while Anatoly Belosvet becomes the bureau's number two as first deputy designer general. Novikov brings considerable experience to the job, and even if he lacks Waldenburg's easygoing, bantering style, he is no less impressive a figure. His previous post was as a deputy designer general responsible for flight testing. This

Inside the MiG-29M

1 Pitot head
2 Vortex generator
3 Reprofiled glass-fibre radome
4 Slotted, flat-plate scanning antenna
5 N-010 ('Zhuk') multi-mode pulse-Doppler radar equipment
6 Yaw and pitch vanes
7 Dynamic pressure probe
8 Infra-red/laser/TV seeker head
9 Infra-red, laser and TV equipment module
10 Command guidance antenna
11 Temperature sensor
12 Cannon muzzle aperture and gun gas vent
13 Rudder pedals
14 Monochrome CRT head-down multi-function displays (two); input by HOTAS controls

24 ECM aerials
25 Cartridge case collector box
26 Ammunition magazine, 100 rounds
27 Nosewheel mounting and starboard side retraction jack
28 Canopy hydraulic actuator and jettison strut
29 Canopy hinge positioning unit
30 Kh-35 ('Harpoonski') air-to-surface anti-shipping missile
31 Leading edge extension welded aluminium/lithium integral fuel tank
32 Dorsal avionics equipment bay
33 Cockpit air conditioning unit

42 Single-point pressure-refuelling receptacle
43 Centre fuselage integral fuel tanks, total internal fuel capacity 5700 litres
44 Upward/outward-firing chaff/flare launchers, port and starboard; 60 cartridges each side
45 Stand-by mechanical linkage (half range of movement) for reversionary rudder and aileron control
46 Mainwheel leg strut

51 KAB-500L, laser-guided 500-kg bomb
52 Wingtip L-150 Petal radar warning antennas
53 Starboard navigation light
54 Starboard aileron
55 Plain flap
56 Artificial feel system control valves
57 Engine accessory equipment
58 APU intake
59 GTDE-117 turboshaft auxiliary power unit

65 Afterburner nozzle control jacks
66 Tailplane pivot mountings
67 Tailplane hydraulic actuators
68 Rudder hydraulic actuators
69 Rudder panel
70 Fin-tip communications antenna fairing
71 Tail navigation light
72 ILS aerial

76 EW antenna
77 Twin brake parachute stowage
78 Hinged parachute door
79 Port all-moving tailplane
80 Inboard wing pylon-mounted external fuel tank, 1220 litres
81 Centreline external fuel tank, 1540 litres

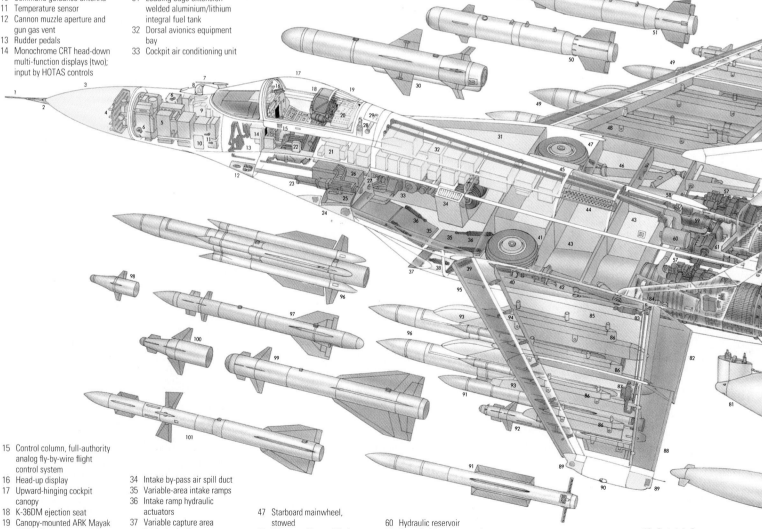

15 Control column, full-authority analog fly-by-wire flight control system
16 Head-up display
17 Upward-hinging cockpit canopy
18 K-36DM ejection seat
19 Canopy-mounted ARK Mayak ADF/radio compass aerial
20 Circuit breaker control box
21 Avionics equipment bay
22 Slide-mounted engine throttles
23 GSh-301 cannon

34 Intake by-pass air spill duct
35 Variable-area intake ramps
36 Intake ramp hydraulic actuators
37 Variable capture area intake lower lip
38 Lip actuator hydraulic jack
39 Hinged FOD screen
40 Ground power receptacle
41 Port mainwheel, stowed position

47 Starboard mainwheel, stowed
48 Wing panel integral fuel tank
49 Starboard wing weapons carriage
50 KAB-500KR, television-guided 500-kg bomb

60 Hydraulic reservoir
61 Central airframe-mounted accessory gearbox
62 Single dorsal airbrake
63 Airbrake hydraulic jacks
64 RD-33K afterburning turbofan engines

73 Starboard all-moving tailplane
74 Radar warning antenna
75 Variable-area afterburner nozzles

82 Port plain flap
83 Flap hydraulic jack
84 Main undercarriage hydraulic jack
85 Port wing integral fuel tank
86 Wing stores pylons

brought him a deep knowledge of all aspects of every current OKB programme, especially the MiG-29M, whose highly successful flight test programme was completed under his leadership.

The MiG-29M is believed to have originated as a Mikoyan private venture, developed in anticipation of a Soviet requirement to replace the first-generation MiG-29, and to produce a more versatile multi-role aircraft for the Soviet air forces and for export. The general aerodynamic shape and basic structure of the MiG-29 were retained, since they had proved so successful from the point of view of handling characteristics and strength. For the multi-role mission a minimum-change version of the MiG-29 could

87 Aileron hydraulic actuator	95 Port leading edge
88 Port aileron	manoeuvre flap
89 Wingtip radar warning	96 Kh-31P air-to-surface
antennas	missiles
90 Port navigation light	97 Kh-25MP (AS-12 'Kegler')
91 AAM-AE ('AMRAAMski')	radar-guided air-to-surface
air-to-air missile	missile
92 R-73 (AA-11 'Archer') air-to-air	98 Kh-251 laser-guided
missile	missile, alternative nose
93 Missile pylons/launch rails	section
94 Leading edge flap hydraulic	99 Kh-29T (AS-14 'Kedge')
actuators	television-guided air-to-surface missile
	100 Kh-29L (AS-14 'Kedge')
	semi-active laser guided
	air-to-surface missile
	101 R-27 (AA-10 'Alamo') air-to-air missile; all variants can be carried

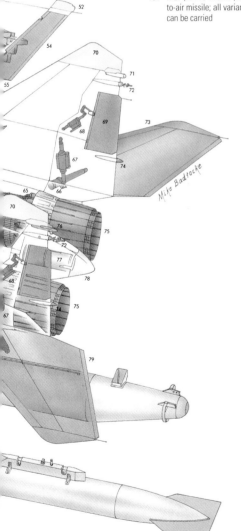

Right: The tailcone fairing of the MiG-29M has been recontoured to reduce transonic drag and to accommodate twin braking parachutes. It no longer mounts ventral and dorsal airbrakes, since these have been replaced by a single dorsal unit further forward.

have been designed, but the need for increased fuel and increased internal volume for avionics would have added considerably to the weight of the basic aircraft and detrimentally affected performance and handling. The alternative was a more extensive redesign which was given the internal OKB designation 9-15 (the basic MiG-29 was the 9-12, and the fat-backed 'Fulcrum-C' is the 9-13).

In fact, the MiG-29M is so different to its predecessors that some in the bureau wanted to allocate a new service designation as well, MiG-33 being the hot favourite and actually being used in public at the first Berlin air show. Belyakov would have none of this, and publicly contradicted the champion of the new designation, Anatoly Belosvet, reaffirming that the MiG-33 designation had no basis in fact. Rejection of the MiG-33 designation confirmed Belyakov's pride in his original creation, and marked a significant difference in approach by comparison with the Sukhoi Design Bureau, who have tended to use at least one new designation for every new sub-variant of the Su-27, apparently in the belief that a 'new' aircraft will attract funding more easily than a new sub-type of an existing type. One cynical analyst commented that, "The allocation of new designations is already outstripping the production of new airframes, so it's best to ignore them and wait until you see what actually rolls out of the factory with wings on." Despite retaining the MiG-29 designation and the same basic configuration, the MiG-29M is virtually a new aircraft, with extensive structural and aerodynamic changes, as well as new systems and avionics.

Although the MiG-29M still looks like the basic 'Fulcrum' externally, it has been subjected to a major redesign. The airframe has been strengthened, yet the extensive use of welded aluminium/lithium alloy components and sub-assemblies (without conventional fasteners, sealants and rivets) actually saves weight and provides extra internal volume for fuel and avionics. Twenty-nine per cent of the MiG-29M by

Above: The port intake of a MiG-29M, with the gridded FOD protection screen in place. This swings upward to lie flat in the roof of the intake when not in use. The lower intake lip is articulated to open up at low air speeds and high power settings, thereby increasing mass flow.

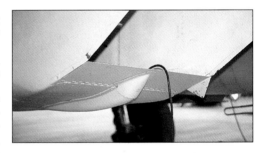

Above: The lower lip of the intake is fitted with an external actuator, housed in a streamlined fairing on the underside.

Above: The one-piece composite engine cover has been removed to show the installation of the RD-33K turbofan.

Below: The installation of the RD-33K engine allows extremely fast replacement, using only the most basic tools. The engine is also installationally interchangeable with the less-powerful standard RD-33 fitted to earlier MiG-29 variants.

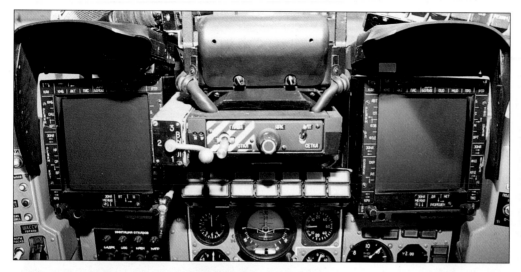

Above: One of the MiG-29M's monochrome CRT multi-function display screens. These are virtually unique in that they are not surrounded by input buttons, meaning that the pilot does not have to lean forward and push buttons to change his displays, using instead HOTAS controls on the stick and throttle.

Above left: On at least one MiG-29M prototype (155), the CRT multi-function displays have been raised closer to the pilot's eye level.

Left: Apart from its two CRT MFDs, the MiG-29M cockpit is similar to that of its predecessor. It should be remembered that the MiG-29M prototypes are development aircraft, and some lack items not directly associated with their particular segments of the trials programme, which might be expected to appear in an operational cockpit. They may also have non-standard equipment associated with foreign navigation, telemetry and recording.

weight is aluminium/lithium 1420 alloy, with 35 per cent steel, 27 per cent aluminium alloys, 3 per cent titanium and 6 per cent composites. This is a comparatively high proportion of composites, and saves further weight. The airbrake, air intake ducts, engine access panels and vertical fins are now of composite construction, with honeycomb cores providing exceptional rigidity. Airframe life is increased to 2,500 flying hours, with an extension to 4,000 hours being possible. The heavy intake door system of the original MiG-29 has been removed to save weight and has been replaced by lighter meshed grilles like those fitted to the Su-27. These are reportedly protected against icing (a known Su-27 problem) and were 'proved' against birdstrikes when an unfortunate duck was ingested on take-off. It reportedly dented the grille, but the integrity of the mesh was not compromised.

The overwing auxiliary intakes have also gone, the space they used to occupy being taken by a large aluminium/lithium fuel tank of about 2550-litre (561-Imp gal) capacity. In an effort to deceive US spy satellites and casual observers as to the extent of the changes made to the MiG-29M, the prototypes initially had false overwing intakes 'painted on'. The second fuselage fuel tank is of similar construction, and aluminium/lithium is also used in the forward fuselage. Like the 'Fulcrum-C', the MiG-29M has a bulged

Above: The MiG-29M can get airborne after only a very short take-off run, and like its predecessor can operate from primitive, semi-prepared strips. The extra power of the RD-33K is necessary to compensate for the greater payload of the new variant.

fuselage spine, although it differs in cross-section and side elevation, sloping smoothly away from the cockpit back to the tailcone, giving a less hunchbacked appearance. The new spine contains extra fuel and new avionics systems. It also contains a pair of flush-mounted upward/outward-firing chaff/flare dispensers, of unknown designation. These contain a total of 120 cartridges, twice as many as could be carried by the basic MiG-29.

Total internal fuel capacity is increased by about 1500 kg (3,300 lb) by comparison with the 'Fulcrum-C', bringing the total to between 6000 and 6250 litres (1,320-1,375 Imp gal). This is equivalent to the maximum internal fuel load carried by the F/A-18, and is greater than the fuel capacity of the Dassault Rafale. This is impressive, since although the F/A-18 has been criticised for its lack of range in the US Navy context, the RAAF and Canadian Forces have found it more than adequate for very-long-range intercept duties and for interdiction. The long-standing lack of range problem suffered by the original MiG-29, once dismissed as 'a fighter to gain air superiority over the airfield boundary', has finally been addressed. Further increases in range are possible, since Mikoyan engineers have already discussed work being carried out on the development of new 2500-litre (550-Imp gal)

underwing fuel tanks, the same length as the standard 1150-litre (250-Imp gal) tank but with greater depth. These will have a round-topped and round-bottomed, slab-sided rectangular cross-section. The pylons of these tanks may be fitted with Tornado F.Mk 3-style 'stub-pylons' to allow AAMs to be carried as well as the tanks.

Aerodynamically, the MiG-29M has sharper leading edges on its distinctive wingroot leading-edge extensions, these improving vortex generation at high angles of attack. The tailplanes have been considerably increased in area, with increased chord and a dogtooth leading edge. This provides greater pitch authority, improving instantaneous turn performance, while the dogtooth 'notches' improve airflow at high deflection angles by generating powerful vortices which keep the airflow attached. The ailerons are of extended span, leaving a smaller gap between their outer edge and the wingtip itself, and improving roll control at low speed and

general handling at high angles-of-attack.

The fuselage spine (which incorporates an enlarged airbrake mounted well forward on the upper surface only) now terminates in a revised beaver tail, this incorporating a stowage for twin 13-m² (140-sq ft) braking parachutes in place of the single 17-m² (182-sq ft) braking chute fitted to previous 'Fulcrum' variants. The use of twin chutes (traditional on Soviet heavy fighters) gives greater area without the disadvantages of using a single larger chute, which could scrape along the runway. The increased weight of the MiG-29M demands the use of more powerful high-energy wheel brakes. The new MiG-29 version also has slightly revised tailfins. Fitted with the extended-chord rudders of later 'Fulcrum-As', the MiG-29M's rudder trailing edge drops vertically down to line up with the trailing edge of the lower fin, which has been extended aft and has lost its slope. The lower corner of the rudder is still slightly cropped, but

Right: The sixth MiG-29M prototype has often been used as the demonstrator for the new variant, and has carried a wide variety of weapon loads for publicity photos and displays. Here the aircraft carries four Vympel R-77 AAM-AE medium-range air-to-air missiles. Integration of this missile with the MiG-29M was reportedly one of the unsolved problems at the time of cancellation.

To provide greater stopping power, the heavier MiG-29M needs more brake chute area. A single chute large enough would scrape on the runway, so instead the aircraft has two side-by-side cruciform chutes.

the fin trailing edge/rudder junction has been modified so that there is no cut-out. This gives a neater trailing edge profile and fractionally increases keel area; it may also add to the rigidity of the lower part of the fin.

These aerodynamic improvements were augmented by the provision of an entirely new flight control system. Having eschewed fly-by-wire on the original MiG-29, the designers of the 9-15 have incorporated a new analog fly-by-wire system. This is heavier than a digital system, but is claimed to be more reliable (an increasingly valid argument as experience with the YF-22, Rafale,

EFA and Saab Gripen is showing) and is more resistant to electromagnetic interference. The new system has four channels for pitch control and three for roll and yaw, with a mechanical back-up.

The new flight control system imposes 'hard' g and Alpha limits which cannot be overridden simply by 'pulling through' stick stops by using greater control forces. Instead, if the MiG-29M pilot wants to make a brief excursion into those 'tatty bits of the envelope' where departure becomes progressively more likely, he now has to switch the limiters off. This is, however, a freedom not enjoyed by Western fighter pilots, whose flight control system 'hard' limits cannot be switched off on a whim. The Alpha limits of the MiG-29M are increased by comparison with the standard MiG-29, from 28° (24° service

limit) to 35° (30° service limit), and Waldenberg has predicted that the final Alpha limit of a production MiG-29M will be considerably higher. The new fly-by-wire control system also allows increased instability in pitch, improving agility, and in cruising flight this reduces drag generated by the horizontal tailplanes and noticeably increases range.

The MiG-29M's greater fuel and weapons load made the provision of extra engine thrust extremely desirable, and this was achieved by using the new RD-33K engine developed for the MiG-29K (K in both designations standing for Korabelniy, or naval/shipborne). This 86-kN engine has a new fan giving a mass flow of 82 kg/second (up from 77 kg/second) with a variable stator before the first stage of the compressor and featuring a full-authority digital engine control unit, which also controls the variable intake ramps. Afterburning thrust is increased from 8300 kg (18,298 lb) to 8800 kg (19,400 lb), and some sources suggest that the increase in maximum dry thrust is significantly greater. The new engine may use modern materials and single crystal technology turbine blades, but this cannot be confirmed. Specific fuel consumption figures for the RD-33K have not been released, but are likely to be in the same ballpark as the original engine's 2.1 kg/kgf hr.

Some reports suggest that the new engine was not available for the first flight of the MiG-29M, and that the first 9-15 prototypes initially flew with the basic RD-33 engine. Articulated lower lips on the intakes can open to increase intake area on take-off or at high angles of attack, helping 'feed' the greater mass flow of the new

Mikoyan MiG-29M

The sixth and final MiG-29M prototype was built in the Mikoyan OKB's own Moscow workshops. Contrary to many published reports, none of the MiG-29M prototypes were converted from standard aircraft: all were newly built. The three-digit code '156' confirms that this was the sixth Type 9-15 constructed. Wearing standard camouflage, with Soviet-style red stars and a red, white and blue Russian tricolour fin flash, the aircraft has often been used as a demonstrator, in addition to its primary role as the air-to-ground weapons integration aircraft. It is seen here carrying a mixed load of air-to-air and air-to-surface weapons, with R-73 (AA-11 'Archer') and R-77 (AAM-AE) AAMs outboard and Kh-31 anti-radiation missiles inboard. It was, for example, the aircraft which visited the 1992 Farnborough and 1993 Paris air shows. Since

termination of the MiG-29M as an active programme, the six aircraft have had no formal role to play, and unless an export customer is found they seem likely to become development hacks for other programmes, testing avionics systems, displays and weapons destined for new combat aircraft. The six aircraft are nominally based at the LII Gromov Flight Research Institute at Zhukhovskii, but are often deployed to other experimental bases, including the test centre at Akhtubinsk. The Russian tricolour carried by 156 is by no means a definitive national insignia; front-line Russian aircraft have retained their red stars, while a variety of styles of Russian flag have been applied to some (mainly OKB-owned) aircraft. Several of the MiG-29M prototypes originally had false overwing intake louevres painted on, to fool US satellites into thinking that they were ordinary MiG-29s. These markings have since been removed.

Air-to-ground radar
Whereas the basic MiG-29 had a dedicated air-to-air radar in the shape of its N-019 (RLPK-29) 'Slot Back', the MiG-29M has a more versatile, more modern multi-mode radar with multiple air-to-air and air-to-ground modes. The latter include terrain following and terrain avoidance, real-beam or synthetic aperture mapping, target designation for ASMs, and a range of navigation options.

Canopy
One of the least obvious changes to the MiG-29M is its reprofiled canopy. As well as having an ARK radio compass antenna embedded in the rear section, the whole canopy has been both lengthened and raised, allowing a raised seat position and thereby giving the pilot a better all-round view, particularly over the nose.

Tailfin profile
The trailing edge of the MiG-29M is slightly changed by comparison with the standard aircraft. Below the extended chord rudder the trailing edge follows the rudder trailing edge, dropping vertically and presenting an unbroken silhouette, whereas on the basic version the trailing edge is cut back further forward than the rudder trailing edge, similar to the trailing edge profile at the top of the rudder.

Spine
The MiG-29M has an increased-volume fuselage spine, containing extra fuel and avionics displaced by other internal changes. This is of less obvious profile than the big spine fitted to the 'Gorbatov' (Hunchback) 'Fulcrum-C', although it is of greater volume.

Radome
The new flat plate antenna of the N-010 has allowed the radome shape to be refined, omitting the prominent bulge which was previously necessary to accommodate the bulky front element of the N-019's twist cassegrain antenna.

Antenna
The tiny loop antenna below the intake serves telemetry equipment.

Engine covers
Among the many structural changes to the MiG-29M is the provision of single-piece composite engine covers. Engine access is exceptionally quick and easy.

Origins

The MiG-29M was conceived as a private venture in response to an anticipated Soviet air forces' requirement for a new tactical air superiority and counter-air fighter to replace the standard MiG-29, but with improved air-to-ground capability to increase operational flexibility and better suit the aircraft to the export market. Increased volume for extra fuel and avionics were clearly two major factors, and the opportunity was also taken to refine handling characteristics, increase performance and improve maintainability, operability and life cycle cost. While retaining the basic aerodynamic configuration of the MiG-29, its designers gave the aircraft a complete structural redesign, and made provision for many new systems, including radar, a modernised and improved IRSTS, and new defensive aids. The changes accompanying the end of the Cold War should have ensured the MiG-29M's future. As a lightweight, cost-effective multi-role strike fighter it was just what the Russian air force needed, but politics intervened and they received instead a larger, more expensive fighter primarily intended for long-range intercept missions.

Defensive systems

The MiG-29M has an all-new defensive avionics suite, with a Gardeniya active jammer, a new IFF system and an L-150 Pastel radar warning receiver, which can automatically cue ARMs and chaff/flare launchers.

Ailerons

The MiG-29M introduced extended-span ailerons, extending out closer to the wingtips. Their greater area gives improved control authority in roll. Unlike the MiG-29K, overall wingspan is unchanged.

Powerplant

The MiG-29M, and its nautical cousin the MiG-29K, are powered by a pair of increased-thrust Leningrad/Klimov (Isotov) RD-33K afterburning turbofans. These are externally indistinguishable, and installationally interchangeable, with the basic 'Fulcrum-A' powerplant, the RD-33, and some recent export customers have been offered RD-33K-engined MiG-29 'Fulcrum-As'. It is believed that the new engine was developed specifically for the heavier, carrierborne MiG-29K, and was then applied to the MiG-29M, since extra thrust was felt to be no bad thing, especially in view of the aircraft's greater maximum take-off weight. Thus the first MiG-29M originally flew with standard RD-33s fitted, and the new engine was installed later. The new engine has a redesigned fan, giving a mass flow of 82 kg/second (compared with 77 kg/second), with full-authority digital engine controls, and probably with increased use of single-crystal blade technology and advanced materials to allow higher operating temperatures. All of these improvements add up to an increase in afterburning thrust from 81.42 kN (18,298 lb st) to 86.33 kN (19,400 lb st). Articulated lower intake lips allow greater mass flow at low speeds, for example on take-off. Engine life is low by Western standards, claimed at around 1,400 hours with a 350-hour TBO, although Rostislav Belyakov has stated an intention to guarantee a 2,000-hour TBO, a figure now being used by Malaysia as a requirement. Originally wrongly credited to Tumanskii, the RD-33 was designed by the Isotov engine OKB, later renamed as the Leningrad Industrial Association, and most recently as the Klimov Corporation. The actual designer of the engine was general designer Alexander A. Sarkisov.

Fly-by-wire

Whereas Mikoyan eschewed the use of fly-by-wire controls in the original MiG-29, the new technology has been adopted for the MiG-29M. The aircraft uses an analog system, with four channels for pitch and three for roll/yaw, and has a mechanical back-up. Using analog signalling is claimed to improve reliability, and to reduce vulnerability to interference at the cost of slightly higher weight. With advanced digital FBW prototypes (EFA, Gripen and YF-22) suffering control system problems in the West, perhaps Mikoyan's choice has been proved to be a wise one.

Fuel

The MiG-29 has traditionally been handicapped by its very short range, imposed mainly by its limited internal fuel capacity. The use of space-saving welded aluminium lithium alloys and deletion of auxiliary intakes has provided much extra internal volume for fuel in the MiG-29M, which has risen by about 1500 kg (3,300 lb).

Prospects

The MiG-29M project was effectively cancelled just as it had passed its acceptance tests and gained certification. It should therefore be available for export. Unfortunately, however, some loose ends remain, and a small amount of development work still needs to be done, most notably surrounding integration of the Vympel R-77 missile. With no Russian air force order in prospect any export customer for the MiG-29M would have to pay to complete the necessary development and, having done that, would have to place a large enough order to justify tooling up for production of the new variant. The unsold stock of MiG-29s at the factory is a further complication, since the factory wants to sell these aircraft before beginning production of a new variant.

LERX

The shape of the MiG-29M's wing leading-edge root extension is subtly changed in profile, with a much smaller radius on the leading edge, giving a distinctively sharper appearance. The new LERX generates more-powerful vortices than the old, blunter LERXes of the basic 'Fulcrum-A', improving handling characteristics at high angles of attack. There is no appreciable change to the aircraft's planform. Now that they do not have to accommodate the auxiliary air intakes used on take-off and landing, the LERXes can house a significant amount of fuel, contributing to the aircraft's greater internal fuel capacity.

Tailplane

The MiG-29M has an increased-area horizontal tailplane, giving greater control authority in pitch (when both tailplanes are used symmetrically) and in roll (when used differentially). An inboard dogtooth discontinuity generates a vortex which keeps flow attached at high deflection angles.

Hardpoints

The MiG-29M has an extra pair of underwing hardpoints, bringing the total to eight. All are restressed for the carriage of heavier stores, allowing an increase in warload to 4500 kg (9,920 lb), including individual weapons weighing up to 1000 kg (2,205 lb) on each of the four inboard pylons.

Above: Damp air allows vortices to be clearly seen because the moisture in the air vapourises in the low-pressure air inside the vortex. The sharp-edged LERXes of the MiG-29M generate more powerful vortices than those on the standard MiG-29. These flow back over the vertical tailfins, improving directional control at high angles of attack.

engine. Engine life remains low by Western standards, having been quoted as 1,200 or 1,400 hours, with checks every 100 hours and with an overhaul at half-life. In an effort to counter this problem, Mikoyan and engine-makers Klimov are working hard to extend engine life, and at the 1993 Paris Air Salon Rostislav Belyakov offered to guarantee an engine TBO of 2,000 hours. The RD-33K uses the same installation as the basic RD-33, and the two engines are interchangeable on the MiG-29M, though obviously with a thrust penalty.

The MiG-29M was designed from the start to be more maintainable than the basic 'Fulcrum', with lower maintenance man hours per flying hour, increased intervals between overhauls, and

Below: The MiG-29M is generously endowed with high lift devices, including full-span trailing edge flaps and massive inboard trailing edge flaps. . The rugged undercarriage is capable of absorbing high sink-rate landings, and the landing roll can be shortened by using the powerful pneumatic wheel brakes and twin brake chutes.

better access to frequently removed or inspected components. The MMH/FH figures of the basic MiG-29 were not unimpressive, but have been improved in the MiG-29M, despite its mass of sophisticated equipment and more complex systems. Rapid turnaround times have always been a feature of Soviet combat aircraft, but Mikoyan set itself ambitious targets for a host of maintenance and repair activities, including an eight-hour mean time between failures, an 11.5 MMH/FH figure, a 1.2-hour fault elimination time, a 15-25-minute turnaround time depending on weapons loadout, and an engine change in 11.6 man hours and an elapsed time of 2.2 hours. The ideal groundcrew consists of seven personnel. That these targets have been met was dramatically demonstrated at the 1992 SBAC show at Farnborough, when a small team of ground crew changed a MiG-29M engine in only 35-40 minutes, witnessed by this writer. Most remarkably, an engine change is affected using only the most basic tools.

The most agile and maintainable fighter in the world, regardless of how sweet its handling characteristics or how impressive its performance, is nothing without an effective weapons system. The MiG-29M's operational capability is enhanced by greater warload and by improved versatility. Warload capacity is increased by adding an extra pair of outboard underwing pylons (bringing the total to eight) and by re-

stressing the other pylons. The centreline pylon can carry a 1540-litre (340-Imp gal) fuel tank, or similar stores weighing up to 2000 kg (4,409 lb). The inboard pair of pylons under each wing can carry up to 1000 kg (2,205 lb), while the outboard pylons are stressed for between 400 and 500 kg (881 and 1,102 lb). The maximum external warload is increased to 4500 kg (9,920 lb). Although the baseline MiG-29 can operate successfully in the ground attack and strike role, using unguided rockets or free-fall bombs, the air-to-ground capability of the MiG-29M is considerably increased. The electro-optical complex has been replaced by a new unit which incorporates an IRST and laser rangefinder as before, but which also includes a laser designator and marked target seeker plus a TV camera, which give compatability with laser- and TV- guided missiles.

The new unit does not just improve air-to-ground capability. The laser can provide ranging information for calculating air-to-air missile launching parameters, while the TV allows visual identification of targets at extended range. The IRST has a new sensor with improved cooling, which increases range significantly and which also enhances target discrimination. Finally, the pilot's helmet-mounted sighting/designation system has reportedly been redesigned to give greater angular coverage limits, and to reduce weight and improve weight distribution on the helmet. Front-line RAF and USAF pilots still wait for any form of helmet sight.

Radar antennas

The radome of the MiG-29M is of more curved profile than that of the basic aircraft, without the slightly concave conical leading edge of the 'Fulcrum-A' radome. The new single curvature ogival shape is more aerodynamically efficient and is made possible because the forward part of the nosecone no longer needs to be bulged in order to accommodate the broad front reflector element of a twist cassegrain antenna. In appearance this resembles a slightly tapering closed 'bin', with the narrow end pointing forwards. When installed this is covered by a tight dark green fabric 'sock'. Inside the antenna is an offset feed and receive unit which transmits radar energy forward to be reflected back from the forward face of the bin, onto the moving rear face. Here its polarity changes as it is reflected forward again. The re-reflected radar energy is now able to pass through the front face of the antenna, by virtue of its changed polarity. The rear plate, which acts as the scanning mechanism, moves to deflect the beam up and down and from side-to-side, achieving a beam displacement equal to twice its own movement. This allows faster movement, using less power, than a conventional antenna. The feed unit is offset from the centre of the rear plate to minimise blanking, and to compensate for this the front plate is not parallel, sloping forward to reflect energy back evenly onto the whole of the rear plate.

The new N-010 radar (understood to be related to the Fazatron Zhuk radar shown publicly at Paris, Moscow and Farnborough) by contrast has a modern, slotted flat plate antenna, taking advantage of the recent advances in lightweight antenna design and actuator technology to replace the old twist cassegrain antenna of the basic N-019. The new radar closely resembles the

AN/APG-65 fitted to the F/A-18 in appearance and performance.

There have been frequent accusations in the past that the N-019 radar of the basic 'Fulcrum' was based on APG-65 technology gained through espionage. That such technology was acquired has not been denied, but Mikoyan always maintained that it was too late to influence the design of their fighter's radar. Such a statement seems to be confirmed by the basic MiG-29's lack of air-to-ground radar modes and use of a twist cassegrain antenna. The new N-010 radar may, however, incorporate lessons learned from the AN/APG-65, to which it is broadly comparable. It has about a 25 per cent increase in detection range by comparison with the N-019, but does have a range of air-to-ground modes. These include terrain following and terrain avoidance, uniform scale radar mapping with real beam or synthetic aperture, freeze-and-zoom mapping, Doppler speed measuring for nav system updates and weapons delivery computations, and measuring the co-ordinates of ground targets and designating them for engagement by air-to-surface missiles.

Radar modes

In the air-to-air role the radar can operate in the look-up or look-down modes, and allows the simultaneous engagement of multiple targets. Up to four targets can be engaged while 10 are being tracked. The new radar is compatible with active, semi-active and passive radar homing AAMs. There are also track-while-scan and close air combat modes, the latter optimised for gun and IR-homing missile engagements. Radar data processing capacity is reportedly increased by a staggering 400 per cent, freeing the MiG-29 pilot from his reliance on GCI stations for assigning target prioritisation, etc. Finally, Fazatron claims new standards of maintainability and reliability for their new radar.

The MiG-29M packs an impressive punch, in whatever role it is operating. Mikhail Waldenberg once boasted that he would have halved the capacity of the ammunition tank for the GSh-30-1 (9A-071K) cannon had he known how accurate it was going to prove. Even in the MiG-29M he has not managed to achieve his aim, since the ammunition tank has been reduced in capacity only from 149 to 100 rounds. Since a burst of four or five rounds is generally sufficient to destroy a target, however, this is regarded as being more than sufficient. In the air-to-air role, the MiG-29M can carry all of the missiles previously used by the basic 'Fulcrum'. It can also carry the new extended

range R-27RE variant of the AA-10 'Alamo' (with a range of 170 km/106 miles) that offers faster acceleration and higher speed, which can be crucial in head-on engagements. The number of BVR 'Alamo' missiles which can be carried has been increased from two to four.

The air-to-air arsenal will also include the new Vympel R-77 (previously known by the manufacturer's designation AAM-AE), a new active radar homing missile with a maximum range of up to 100 km (62 miles) in a high-altitude head-on engagement, or 40 km (25 miles) in more normal circumstances. With these characteristics, the AAM-AE has inevitably been dubbed 'AMRAAMski'. The missile has latticed, gridded control fins (predictably known as 'potato mashers') which give a massive total aerofoil area within a very small volume. The small chord of the fins allows them to be moved using very small actuators, and a small movement produces a huge turning force. The small actuators save weight and internal volume. The lattice wing gives excellent lift characteristics at high angles of attack, because airflow stays attached at angles of incidence of up to 50 or 60 units of Alpha. This high-Alpha capability and effective actuators confer excellent agility, and allow the AAM-AE to shoot down targets manoeuvring at up to 12 g.

Lattice wings are nothing new in Russia. In his definitive 1938 treatise 'The Theoretical Bases of Aeronautics', Zhukhovskii, the father of Soviet aeronautical science, noted that "in previous times it was hoped to obtain high lift using lattice-type lift vanes." This influenced the choice of such fins for a number of post-war surface-to-surface and surface-to-air missile projects.

In the air-to-surface role the MiG-29M can carry a greater weight of unguided rockets or free-fall dumb bombs than the basic MiG-29, but is also compatible with a new generation of precision-guided munitions (PGMs) courtesy of the new electro-optical complex. The laser can

provide guidance for the semi-active laser homing Kh-29L (AS-14 'Kedge') or the Kh-25ML (AS-12 'Kegler'), or for the free-fall KAB-500L laser-guided bomb, while the TV camera can provide automatic contrast correlated target tracking for Kh-29T ASMs or the KAB-500KR TV-guided bomb.

Defence suppression

In the defence-suppression role, the MiG-29M is a deadly performer, using up to four examples of the 320-kg (705-lb) Kh-25MP (typically against Hawk SAM sites). These can be automatically fired by the new L-150 Pastel RWR, which controls the launch sequence, and which is claimed to be accurate enough to cue anti-radiation missiles onto their targets. The high-speed passive radar homing Kh-31P can also be carried, and this is claimed to be deadly against all known SAM systems, including Raytheon's Patriot. The missile has a wide-band anti-radar seeker, weighs in at 600 kg (1,322 lb) (including a 90-kg/198-lb warhead) and a range in excess of 100 km (62 miles). This gives it an important secondary air-to-air role as an AWACS killer.

There have been changes inside the cockpit, too. The original 'Fulcrum' cockpit was often criticised for being primitive, largely because of its reliance on conventional analog instruments. The MiG-29M's cockpit has been redesigned, and is dominated by a pair of multi-function CRT display screens. These are controlled by HOTAS buttons on the throttle and stick, and not by conventional input buttons which would require the pilot to reach and look down into the cockpit to call up the information he needed. This marks a major advance over the CRT

Mikoyan MiG-29M, MiG-29K and MiG-29S

Above: The tailhook of the second MiG-29K prototype. The hook is misnamed, since it is actually a heavily grooved block, rather than a conventional 'hook'.

Above: The MiG-29K is unique among 'Fulcrum' variants in being fitted with a neat retractable refuelling probe, although this could be offered as an option on the M or S.

Above: The nose oleo of the MiG-29K is a heavier casting, and incorporates amber, green and red lights, used to signal position relative to the glide path to the LSO on the carrier deck.

screens fitted to the rival Su-35. These displays are monochrome and have usually been described as being used to give IRST, radar, TV or EO displays on the right-hand screen, with navigation, ILS and other information displays on the left. In fact, the displays are both used for weapons and tactical displays, air-to-air on the right-hand screen and air-to-ground on the left. The HUD has reportedly been redesigned, too. The seat is raised, increasing the view down and over the nose by 1.5° to 15°. The cockpit canopy is slightly bulged and is extended further aft, uncovering more of the circuit breakers behind the headrest of the Zvezda K-36 ejection seat, which is unchanged. An ARK/Mayak radio compass antenna is embedded in the rearmost part of the canopy, consisting of eight parallel fore-and-aft strips, linked by their trailing edges.

The MiG-29M has a host of new equipment that has not so far been mentioned. There are new computers, a new IFF system, a new Gardeniya-1-FUE active radar jammer, and new communications radios. Mikoyan will happily consider integrating Western equipment, if required, and at the 1993 Paris show revealed that there was provision for a podded FLIR.

The first of six MiG-29M prototypes made its maiden flight from the LII Gromov Flight Research Centre airfield at Zhukhovskii on 24 April 1986, in the hands of Valery Menitsky. The new variant's 9-15 internal OKB designation formed the basis of the codes applied to the prototypes: 151 for the first 9-15, 152 for the second, etc. The prototypes all had multiple tasks to perform in the flight test programme and evaluations, but each airframe had primary responsibilities. 151 was used for FBW control system development and proving, 152 was an aerody-

namic and engine testbed, 153 a radar workhorse, 154 an engine testbed, 155 a radar/avionics aircraft and 156 a ground-attack avionics integration aircraft. 156 has also traditionally been the MiG-29M taken abroad for air show appearances, usually with its radar removed and replaced by ballast. All six aircraft were new-build aircraft and not conversions of existing MiG-29 airframes, and all were constructed in the OKB's own experimental shop, although using a progressively larger proportion of MAPO-built components and even sub-assemblies.

The MiG-29M has passed its State Acceptance Tests after an exceptionally successful and relatively trouble-free flight test programme, although certification was at one stage reportedly withheld for a brief period because of radar problems. Other problems reportedly included integration of the R-77 missile, and these may not have been fully resolved. Military test pilots who flew the aircraft during these trials described its control characteristics as the best they had ever experienced, while Valery Menitsky said simply, "I have flown many aircraft during my career, but I can say without reservation that this is the best aeroplane I have ever flown." No production funding has been allocated, although the rival Su-35 (which began life as the Su-27) that many consider to be an inferior aircraft and which reportedly still suffers FBW control system, radar and other problems, has been ordered into production. This is a bitter blow to Mikoyan and to the Russian air forces, since while the Su-35 is potentially a great long-range interceptor, the MiG-29M is probably a better all-round multi-role tactical fighter, cheaper and more flexible, and therefore

better suited to the post-Cold War world. A launch order for the MiG-29M could still materialise, perhaps from India and/or Malaysia, and the Moscow Aircraft Production Organisation is reportedly tooled up and ready to begin series production.

On 28 January 1993 President Yeltsin reportedly signed a memorandum of understanding covering the purchase of 30 MiG-29Ms (and six two-seaters based on the MiG-29M) during his visit to New Delhi. Under the terms of the agreement India would reportedly set up a MiG-29 overhaul and support facility. India has allegedly already conducted talks with a number of Western aerospace companies with a view to modifying its MiG-29Ms after delivery. These discussions reportedly included talks with Lucas Aerospace for the supply of Full Authority Digital Engine Control units, which would improve engine performance and longevity. When Malaysia announced its intention to order 18 MiG-29s (including six two-seaters) it specified several stringent pre-conditions. These led many to believe that the MiG-29M would be selected, since it already met some of the Malaysian requirements and could be more easily adapted to meet the others than could the basic MiG-29. Such an aircraft could also be maintained and supported in conjunction with the Indian MiG-29Ms.

The availability of about 60 surplus unsold MiG-29s lying in storage at MAPO (24 of which have been purchased by Hungary, along with four two-seaters) and of MiG-29s considered surplus by the Russian air force may cause some tensions. In the short term there will be pressure to sell these aircraft, rather than to spend money

Right: The second MiG-29K prototype wore a sinister camouflage scheme, with dark grey top sides and lighter grey undersides. Because the MiG-29K was basically a standard MiG-29M with folding wings and naval equipment, only two actual prototypes were built, whereas Sukhoi built about 10 Su-27K prototypes.

The extra wingspan, changed leading edge sweep, broader wingroot chord and increased-area double-slotted flaps of the MiG-29K are clearly visible in this extremely rare air-to-air view. The aircraft has the same extended-span ailerons as the MiG-29M, with extended wingtips outboard of these.

Mikoyan MiG-29M, MiG-29K and MiG-29S

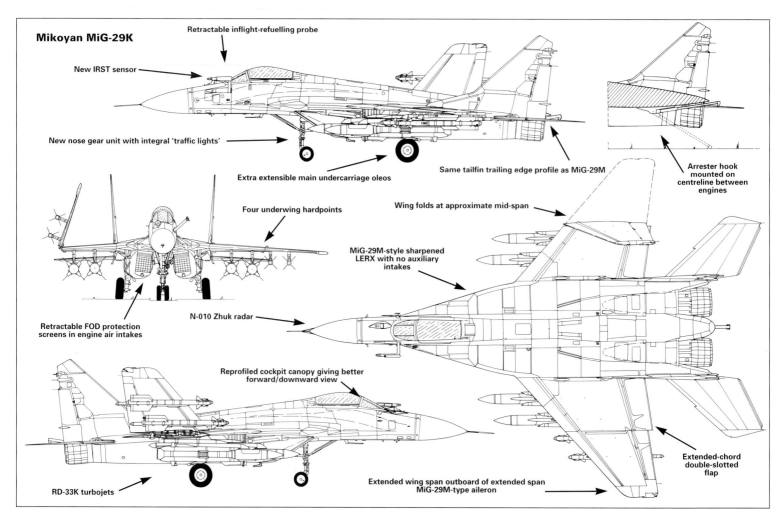

Mikoyan MiG-29K

Retractable inflight-refuelling probe

New IRST sensor

New nose gear unit with integral 'traffic lights'

Extra extensible main undercarriage oleos

Same tailfin trailing edge profile as MiG-29M

Arrester hook mounted on centreline between engines

Four underwing hardpoints

Wing folds at approximate mid-span

MiG-29M-style sharpened LERX with no auxiliary intakes

Retractable FOD protection screens in engine air intakes

N-010 Zhuk radar

Reprofiled cockpit canopy giving better forward/downward view

RD-33K turbojets

Extended wing span outboard of extended span MiG-29M-type aileron

Extended-chord double-slotted flap

putting a new variant into production. In the longer term it may well be wiser to build the MiG-29M, which has the potential to really enhance Mikoyan's reputation and to win orders from customers who simply would not consider the original basic MiG-29. The MiG-29M could quite conceivably have been selected by Finland and Switzerland had it been offered, whereas the basic 'Fulcrum' lost out to the F/A-18. Belyakov has even expressed the belief that the MiG-29M could form the basis of an alternative to the trou-

Below: The second MiG-29K had its traditional Soviet AVMF pennant (blue and white with red hammer, sickle and star) replaced with the flag of St Andrew, the traditional emblem of the Russian navy.

bled Eurofighter EFA. Upgrading basic aircraft to MiG-29S configuration can only ever be a partial solution to Mikoyan's problems.

The fly-by-wire, multi-role MiG-29M formed the basis of a dedicated carrierborne navalised derivative, the 9-31 or MiG-29K, which Mikoyan claims to have been working on for some 10 years. First flown by Takhtar Aubabikirov on 23 June 1988, the MiG-29K was designed as a multi-role strike-fighter to serve aboard the Kuznetsov (formerly *Tbilisi,* and before that *Brezhnev*) and its sister carriers: the *Varyag* (formerly *Riga*), the larger, nuclear-powered *Ulyanovsk*, which was scrapped on the slipway, and a fourth ship, which was also abandoned. The MiG-29K is said to have been

intended as a complement to the dedicated Su-27K interceptor, in just the same way that the F/A-18 Hornet complements the F-14 Tomcat on US Navy carrier decks. In fact, because the *Kuznetsov* and its sisters are so small (and because poor planning gives relatively limited hangarage area), any air wing deployed would be extremely small, and assuming that some five helicopters were carried for COD, SAR and EW duties only about 22-25 MiG-29Ks could be carried, or between 12 and 16 Su-27Ks. Such small numbers of aircraft would tend to make the carriage of two individual types impractical.

Because it shared so many features and systems with the MiG-29M, the MiG-29K development programme was completed using only two prototypes, while Sukhoi used at least seven Su-27Ks. The MiG-29K prototypes were built by the bureau, and were coded '311' and '312'. They were augmented by a handful of early 'Fulcrum-As', including some with ventral fins, which received arrester hooks and a carrier landing system for trials, and for training test and naval evaluation pilots at Saki in the Crimea. This naval airfield was equipped with both dummy carrier decks and ski-jump take-off ramps. Designated MiG-29KVP (and/or perhaps as MiG-29TVK), these aircraft lacked folding wings and did not have the MiG-29K's fully strengthened undercarriage, so could not routinely operate from a carrier, where a pitching deck can dramatically increase landing loads. One MiG-29KVP (coded '18') was involved in the early trials on *Tbilisi*, making a series of approaches (and perhaps touch-and-go landings) to familiarise test pilots with the carrier's deck.

For trials aboard the *Tbilisi* (as it then was), '311' initially made 20 launches (using the vessel's ski-jump, and running up against the unique deck restrainers since no catapults are fitted). These trials began on 21 November 1989, when examples of the Su-27K, Su-25UTG and MiG-29K flew out to the carrier. The MiG-29K landed after the first Su-27K, but did make the first fixed-wing launch from the new ship. Approaches are flown at some 130 kt (149 mph; 240 km/h) and about 14° Alpha, some 25 kt (29 mph; 46 km/h) lower and 3° higher than a normal approach. The RD-33K engine provides useful extra thrust, making the missed-approach/go-around case less critical. An emergency regime can be used to increase thrust to 92.22 kN (20,725 lb). At one stage '311' carried 50 small black anchors, each with a red star superimposed, and four of them with a white numeral '5' below the port canopy rail, indicating 66 successful arrested landings. By this time Mikoyan's Roman Taskaev (star of various Farnborough and Paris air show displays) had joined then chief test pilot Valery Menitsky and project pilot (and deputy chief test pilot) Takhtar Aubakirov, who had made the first 20 launches. The trials were extremely successful, although the jet blast deflectors on *Kuznetsov* had to be replaced with strengthened units after they were destroyed by the MiG-29s.

Airframe and weapons

Both MiG-29K prototypes have operated from the carrier, these differing in many ways from the standard MiG-29M. Like the MiG-29M, the big-spined naval aircraft lack the usual 'Fulcrum' overwing chaff/flare dispensers, and have a single large airbrake on the spine, the same modified tailfins and dogtooth tailerons and the same intake grids and LERX fuel tank. The aircraft has eight underwing hardpoints that can carry the same range of air-to-air and air-to-ground weapons as the MiG-29M, as well as the anti-ship version of Kh-31 or the new Kh-35 'Harpoonski' anti-ship missile. The MiG-29K also uses the MiG-29M's enlarged and bulged cockpit canopy, and has a similar ARK antenna embedded in the rear part. A new Uzel navigation system is also fitted. The ACLS allows the aircraft to touch down within a circle of 6 m (20 ft) radius, with vertical speed being controlled within 0.6 m (2 ft) per second and approach speed within 5 km/h (3 mph).

The MiG-29K prototypes have been 'navalised' by the substitution of an arrester hook for the braking parachute and by the provision of a strengthened undercarriage. Western naval aviators would be perplexed to find no provision for catapult launch, but the MiG-29K uses a combination of mechanical restrainers which 'pop-up' from the deck to 'run-up' against a 12° ski-jump ('trampoline' in Russian parlance). Equipment changes seem to include a new defensive ECM system (with bulged wingtips apparently housing passive receivers) and a new IRST (which may be different in detail to that fitted to the MiG-

Above and right: The basic MiG-29 'Fulcrum-A' and 'Fulcrum-C' are equipped with the older N-019 radar, which uses a twist cassegrain antenna. This is usually covered by a green fabric 'sock' (above) seen peeled away in the photograph to the right.

29M). The prototypes have a solid IRST ball with a small circular window, this probably housing a test camera to record carrier approaches.

Various intakes and antennas have been changed, and like the MiG-29M the MiG-29K lacks the small undernose sensor/equipment pod. A retractable inflight-refuelling probe is fitted below the port side of the windscreen. On the first prototype this is entirely covered by a single-piece aft-hinging door, but on the other the tip of the probe lies in an open recess, with the rear part covered by a fairing. This is similar to the arrangement on the various probe-equipped Su-27 variants. The aircraft apparently incorporates various corrosion-protection measures. Typical of the MiG-29K's clever design is the provision of a belly-mounted spotlight that illuminates the arrester hook during night carrier approaches, letting the LSO see for himself that the hook has been extended. A similar spotlight can illuminate the probe.

The MiG-29K also has an entirely new wing, with powered folding and of slightly greater chord at the root, perhaps with slightly reduced leading edge sweep. The aircraft retains the extended-span ailerons of the MiG-29M (though these now droop), and has extended wingtips, giving greater overall span. New, broader-chord double-slotted trailing-edge flaps are fitted, these projecting further aft than the ailerons even when retracted. These new flaps dramatically

increase lift on approach, thereby permitting slower landing speeds and a lower nose attitude. Initially flown in bare metal (and unpainted composite) finish, the first MiG-29K wore a standard grey/grey-green camouflage scheme, but on the second this soon gave way to an overall sea grey on the upper surfaces.

Varyag is almost complete (albeit without electronics) but its fate remains uncertain, with Ukraine and Russia squabbling over ownership. China and India have both been revealed as possible purchasers and Russia itself still wants to take the vessel into service. The sudden reduction in carrier numbers, coupled with funding problems, have reduced the requirement for carrier-based fighters, and the original plan to have a mix of multi-role MiG-29Ks and dedicated Su-27K interceptors seems to have been abandoned in favour of using a single type.

Logically, the MiG-29K was the ideal choice, by virtue of its credible ground attack capability and due to the success of its flight test programme. It is also smaller than its rival, meaning that a larger number can be fitted onto a carrier's

Right: A new aircaft and one of Mikoyan's new faces, test pilot Pavel Vlasov, whose impressive flying display routines have already gained an enviable reputation after appearances at Farnborough and Paris. One of Mikoyan's greatest assets is the enormous pool of talented engineers, designers and pilots it employs.

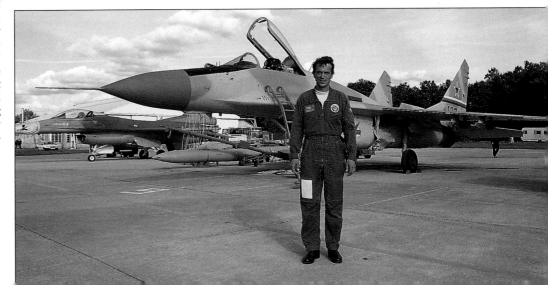

Above: This aircraft was the first MiG-29S to appear in the West. Based on a 'Fulcrum-C' airframe and said to be compatible with the R-77 AAM, it features underwing fuel tanks and other improvements. The fuel tank installation was already fitted to some 40 per cent of Soviet air force MiG-29s.

deck and hangars. Unfortunately, Sukhoi's political clout is such that the Su-33 (previously designated Su-27K) has been selected for production, even though this is a simple navalised version of the basic Su-27 with no real multi-role capability, and without any of the advanced features of the MiG-29K or Su-35. Certainly it would seem reasonable to expect power projection rather than fleet air defence to be the Russian carrier's primary role (for which a multi-role aircraft would be more valuable than a simple interceptor). If a dedicated long-range interceptor was deemed essential for some missions, then it would have made sense to buy MiG-29Ks and simply use the eight or so prototype Su-27Ks (brought up to a common standard) to augment these when necessary. Undeterred by their ill-fortune, Mikoyan has continued to promote the MiG-29K, and in a fit of over-ambitious optimism offered the aircraft to France as an alternative to the indigenous

Rafale M, loftily pointing out that the MiG-29K would be available first and would be superior to the French aircraft. At Le Bourget for the 1993 Paris Air Salon, Rostislav Belyakov displayed his renowned sense of humour to good effect by publicly feigning surprise that his offer had been rejected.

The MiG-29K would in many ways be an ideal export aircraft, even for customers without any need for a carrierborne aircraft. The aircraft's inflight-refuelling probe, folding wings, strengthened undercarriage, arrester hook and docile approach handling characteristics all have applications on land (as export customers for the F/A-18 have found), and there are persistent but unconfirmed rumours that an export 'MiG-29X' with these features may be on offer.

Since the view from the rear cockpit of the MiG-29UB was inadequate for aircraft-carrier operations (even without the increased angle of attack used on a carrier approach), Mikoyan proposed a new two-seat trainer variant for naval training. Designated MiG-29KU, the aircraft was to have incorporated the same naval modifications as the MiG-29K (folding wings, removal of the intake doors, corrosion resistance, etc.) with a new stepped cockpit, covered by a huge bubble canopy, which would have given it what Belyakov called 'a hunchbacked appearance'. Whether or not the MiG-29KU would have retained radar is unknown. The scaling down of the carrier programme killed off any chance of a

Left and below: The MiG-29SE development aircraft shown at Paris was based on a 'Fulcrum-A' airframe, and featured Western navigation equipment and some English language cockpit captions and instrumentation. The full MiG-29SE upgrade offers many more advanced features.

dedicated trainer, and the Su-25UTG is now likely to be the only carrier trainer procured.

For many years, Belyakov has argued for combining R & D, design and production under a single structure, and was reportedly furious when Sukhoi (with its political influence) organised such groupings 'experimentally' between the Sukhoi OKB and its factories, while ensuring that Mikoyan remained separated and isolated from its production plants. Fortunately, the Sukhoi groups showed such great promise that the obstacles were soon removed, and the Mikoyan OKB now works hand-in-glove with the Moscow Aircraft Production Organisation on the MiG-29, and with the Nizhny Novgorod (Gorkii) plant on the MiG-31. This teaming has had a highly beneficial effect on the OKB. Some of the advantages of a design organisation forging links with the manufacturer are obvious, but what was less predictable was the energy, drive and flair for marketing by senior MAPO officials, which complement the skills of Belyakov and his team.

This association has borne fruit with proposals for an ambitious MiG-29 upgrade, which can be retrofitted to existing MiG-29s or applied on the production line. The new variant has received the internal designation 9-13S and is more commonly known as the MiG-29S (presented as -29C in Cyrillic script) or as the MiG-29SE for export. Based on the fat-backed 9-13, known to NATO as the 'Fulcrum-C' (but with no different MiG-29 designator in Soviet or Russian service), the MiG-29S was designed as an increased-capability version of the basic MiG-29. Mikoyan claims that the MiG-29S represents 'what happened when we squeezed all we could from the basic MiG-29 airframe'.

The new variant has a modified flight control system, using small computers to improve stability and controllability, and the control surfaces may have greater deflection. Alpha and g limits are certainly increased. Like many Russian air force MiG-29s (including some early 'Fulcrum-As' with ventral fins, but no export aircraft), the MiG-29S is plumbed for the carriage of a pair of underwing fuel tanks. The gun can now also be fired even when a centreline fuel tank is fitted, which is apparently not possible on the baseline MiG-29. Operational capability has been enhanced by fitting a new sighting system, and will be further improved by making provision for the active homing R-77 'AMRAAMski' (AA-12). Provision is also made for a new active jammer, and for a new training system which generates synthetic radar or IR targets and thereby allows the pilot to simulate combat operations

even when no real targets are available. Onboard test equipment is refined, allowing more complex checks of many systems, especially the radar which would normally require the use of ground equipment during scheduled maintenance. The first MiG-29S made its maiden flight during 1984, and three prototypes were followed by production aircraft and by the conversion of existing 'Fulcrum-Cs'. Two *polk* (squadrons) were claimed to have been in service in 1992, presumably without AAM-AE compatibility.

Similar modifications are applied to the export MiG-29SE, although some confusion arose regarding this aircraft after it was represented at the 1993 Paris Air Salon by a standard 'Fulcrum-A' serving as an avionics testbed. In fact, like the MiG-29S, the MiG-29SE is based upon the 9-13 ('Fulcrum-C'), although the package of modifications could be retrofitted to extant 'Fulcrum-As'. At the moment, the full MiG-29SE modification is being offered as a staged programme, with some modifications not being available until 1995 or after. Initially the MiG-29SE will be offered with provision for a pair of underwing 1150-litre (253-Imp gal) fuel tanks, and the inboard underwing hardpoints will be uprated to allow the aircraft to carry a maximum warload of 4000 kg (8,818 lb). This is double the present limit, and represents the decision to provide bomb racks accommodating tandem side-by-side pairs of 500-kg (1,102-lb) bombs under each inboard underwing pylon.

'AMRAAMski' capability

The air-to-air capability can be enhanced by modernisation of the radar to allow use of the RVV-AE (AAM-AE) known to NATO as AA-12 (unofficially as 'AMRAAMski') and to allow simultaneous engagement of two targets. When modified, the radar is redesignated N-019ME, this representing a downgraded version of the MiG-29S's N-019M (service designation RP-29M). The flight control system can also be upgraded, giving improved handling and stability at high angles of attack, and raising the Alpha limit to 30 units. Finally, the aircraft can be supplied with Western navigation and radio equipment, and with instruments and HUD displays calibrated in knots and feet rather than km/h and metres. The new variant can be fitted with an AN/ARN-118(V) TACAN, ILS-71, and a TNL-1000 GPS. The R-800 1 radio is upgraded to include 243 MHz – the international distress frequency – and the SO-69M transponder is compatible with Western ground systems.

From 1995, the MiG-29SE will be even more capable. Options available then will include the provision of an inflight-refuelling probe, a ground mapping radar mode for the basic N-019E radar and compatibility with TV, laser and active radar homing ASMs and passive radar homing AAMs. These capabilities will transform the basic MiG-29, bringing a level of capability almost similar to that enjoyed by the MiG-29M. MAPO is keen to point out that a customer can select any or all of the different elements of the modification package to tailor the existing aircraft to precise requirements, and to minimise expenditure by ignoring modifications not considered relevant. Unfortunately, the MiG-29M's massive aluminium/lithium centre section tank cannot be retrofitted to completed aircraft, so the MiG-29S will never be able to offer the same

unrefuelled radius of action as the MiG-29M.

There have been various reports of other advanced MiG-29s. An aircraft with a new wing planform, increased span and no sweep on the inboard trailing edge, canard foreplanes on the LERXes and what appeared to be vectoring engine nozzles was illustrated by a line drawing in a brochure released at Paris in 1993, and the prestigious *Jane's All the World's Aircraft* has been reporting the existence of a 'fifth-generation' variant with multi-axis thrust-vectoring engine nozzles for several years; some credit this aircraft with having canard foreplanes. The existence of such an aircraft, except as a paper project, has been vehemently denied by Rostislav Belyakov and would seem to be a 'MiG-29 too far' in view of the bureau's continuing development of a new-generation ATF-type heavyweight fighter, the Mikoyan 1-42. The first prototype is ready to fly, but is awaiting its Lyul'ka engines (development of which has not progressed so smoothly). Confusingly, the existence of a vectored-thrust 'Fulcrum' (perhaps only a testbed, and apparently with two-axis nozzles) was confirmed by Magomed Talboev, a senior test pilot. This aircraft may simply be a development hack for the 1-42, however. A leading Russian glass

Above: This MiG-29SE development aircraft displayed at Zhukhovskii wore a colourful multi-tone air superiority colour scheme, perhaps associated with the marketing effort for the Malaysian deal.

company also confirmed the existence of a fly-by-light MiG-29 with fibre-optic flight control system.

With the MiG-29M, MiG-29K and MiG-29S all ready for production, Mikoyan and its manufacturing partner, the Moscow Aircraft Production Organisation, have an unbeatable trio of aircraft available for export. Political rather than operational considerations seem to have removed any possibility of a domestic launch order for any of the aircraft, although the types which have been selected in their stead are widely regarded as being less versatile and flexible, if not actually inferior. The MiG-29SE may find customers, if not as a new-build aeroplane then as a retrofit package and, with a generous slice of luck, the MiG-29M may one day enter production. If it does not, it will go down in history of one of those great 'might have beens', and may also serve as Mikoyan's epitaph if the highly advanced 1-42 falls by the wayside.

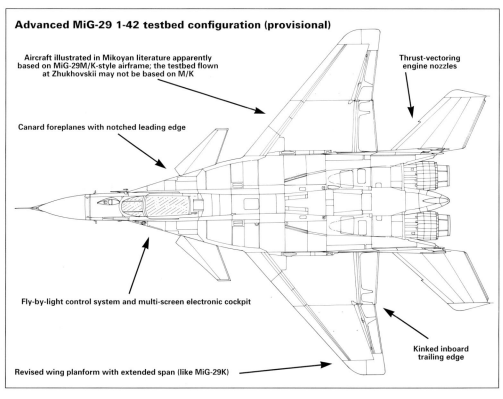

Advanced MiG-29 1-42 testbed configuration (provisional)

Aircraft illustrated in Mikoyan literature apparently based on MiG-29M/K-style airframe; the testbed flown at Zhukhovskii may not be based on M/K

Thrust-vectoring engine nozzles

Canard foreplanes with notched leading edge

Fly-by-light control system and multi-screen electronic cockpit

Kinked inboard trailing edge

Revised wing planform with extended span (like MiG-29K)

Dassault Mirage F1
Gallic Guardian

Intended as a successor to the phenomenally successful Mirage III/5/50 family, the Mirage F1 – Dassault's 'non-delta' – has in many ways repeated the achievements of the earlier type, though it was neither built in such large numbers nor exported to so many overseas customers, nor has its service life been so long. Nevertheless, the aircraft provided the backbone of French air defences for a vital decade, then lingered on in front-line CAFDA service in declining numbers for another 10 years. When they were eventually freed from air defence responsibilities, Armée de l'Air Mirage F1s were switched to the air-to-ground role to begin a second career. Overseas, Mirage F1s remain in widespread use, often in the world's more troubled areas. Fast and deadly, the Mirage F1 remains a force with which to be reckoned.

A South African Air Force Mirage F1CZ pops an IR decoy flare high over the veldt. The aircraft carries indigenous Armscor V3B Kukri IR-homing missiles on its wingtip launch rails. These distinctive weapons have fixed twin canards ahead of the four cruciform control fins and, like the Magic, four free-moving tailfins.

Dassault Mirage F1

Right: The two Mirage IIIG-8 prototypes are seen in flight, wings swept fully forward. The Mirage G family, like the F, was an enlarged design derived from the original Mirage III to meet an Armée de l'Air requirement for a new tactical fighter/ interceptor. Four basic designs reached prototype stage, including the VTOL Mirage IIIV and the incredibly powerful delta-winged IIIT. The swing-wing Mirage IIIG was felt to show huge promise, and several sub-types were planned, including single- and twin-engined designs with one and two seats, and even including a carrierborne fighter for the Aéronavale. The Mirage G8s were simplified, cheap versions, each powered by a pair of SNECMA Atar 09K-50 engines instead of the SNECMA M53s or single TF306 once planned. The first of these made its maiden flight on 8 May 1971, the second following on 13 July 1972.

If operational experience can be used as a yardstick for judging a combat aircraft's potential, then Dassault's Mirage F1 must rate as one of the world's most effective warplanes. Should Jordan and (less likely) Spain become embroiled in separate conflicts during the next decade, an unusual and probably unbeatable aviation record will have been established: operational use by all 11 of the Mirage F1's customer air forces. Even allowing that aircraft of the Greek and Qatari air arms have not had cause to fire at their opposition, the Mirage F1 has been involved in shooting conflicts with 64 per cent of its operators. The war record varies considerably: with Iraq alone, billions of dollars' worth of damage has been caused to world shipping; in contrast, Ecuador's 1980 skirmish with Peru saw a single, ineffective missile being launched from a Mirage F1. Whatever the outcome of these aerial conflicts, it cannot be denied that the second-generation Mirage has had an uncanny knack of being in the right place at the right time to see action.

It would be wrong to attribute this quality entirely to chance. France's aggressive arms sales policy has meant that the Mirage could be sold to pariah countries whose requests for armaments the United States inevitably turned down on

Right: First of the Mirage F family into the air was the Mirage IIIF2, which was based on the big tandem-seat fuselage and tail surfaces of the Mirage G, with a new shoulder-mounted cropped delta wing. First flown on 12 June 1966 under JTF10 power, the Mirage IIIF2 demonstrated a convincing mix of high performance, good short-field figures and docile approach characteristics. The uncompleted Mirage IIIF3 was slightly smaller, and the definitive Mirage IIIF1 – the only one of the trio developed as a private venture – was smaller still. Like many Dassault prototypes, the IIIF2 wore escadrille badges representing the previous units of its test pilots.

political grounds. At the time of purchase, no less than 70 per cent of the F1's export customers were hostile to the US or subject to a temporary embargo (all-embracing, or just denying top-line aircraft) imposed by Washington. As a result, the aircraft was predisposed to conflict as soon as contracts were signed, although that is far from saying that the Mirage F1 is a second-best aircraft. In short, it inherited the Mirage III's qualities of being a versatile fighter at an affordable price, possessed of an airframe, engine and avionics which tend more to reliability than to adventurism. This rugged simplicity, too, is no accident.

When the Armée de l'Air (AA) was seeking to define a new combat aircraft during the early 1960s, the potential of VTOL and variable geometry had yet to be fully explored. Unsure of the best direction in which to proceed, the AA issued basic guidelines to the French aircraft industry so that it might be progressing roughly in the right directions when the next fighter requirement emerged. Groupement Avions Marcel Dassault effectively was the French combat aircraft industry, a position it secured completely when the Louis Breguet firm was taken over to form Avions Marcel Dassault-Breguet Aviation. Two decades later, in April 1990, Dassault Aviation was created and even the Breguet name vanished.

The thrust of AA thinking in the early 1960s was towards a dual role aircraft which, as an interceptor, could perform a Mach 2.5 dash, sustain Mach 2.2 at 15240 m (50,000 ft), manoeuvre at 3 g at Mach 2, and carry armament of two internal 30-mm cannon and one or two collision-course AAMs. In tactical fighter guise, requirements included carriage of a tactical nuclear bomb or conventional ordnance over a lo-lo radius of 300 nm (556 km/345 miles) (the last 80 nm/150 km/93 miles at Mach 0.9 dash speed), a Mach 0.7 cruising speed, operability from an 800-m (2,625-ft) runway, and 3 g manoeuvrability at 300 kt (553 km/h; 343 mph).

All shapes

Four potential answers to this outline specification were built and flown in the commendably short period of four years, some more as proof-of-concept testbeds than as mature designs seriously expecting to enter production. Using designations in the Mirage III series, although mostly having only a tenuous link with the IIIE fighter-bomber then in production, these were:

Mirage IIIT: Closely related to the Mirage IIIE, the IIIT was a single-seat tailless delta with increased power provided by a SNECMA-built variant of the Pratt & Whitney JTF10,

designated TF306. Prototype IIIT No. 01 first flew on 4 June 1964 (powered by an interim TF104B engine of 46 kN/10,417 lb st thrust). It was re-engined (with an 88.3-kN/19,842-lb st TF106 afterburning turbofan) and reflown on 25 January 1965.

Mirage IIIF: The IIIF had a conventional high-mounted wing, plus horizontal tail surfaces. Three were built, two of these as officially-funded prototypes and one as a private venture.

Mirage IIIG and IIIG8: A variable-geometry Mirage III derivative, only one example of the basic Mirage IIIG was built. The two-seat No. 001 flew on 18 November 1967 with one 88.3-kN (19,842-lb st) SNECMA TF306. It was only ever intended as an interim prototype, with a carrier-borne single-engined Mirage IIIG2 and a scaled-up twin-Atar 9K-50 (and later twin 83.3-kN/18,740-lb st SNECMA M53) engined production G4 planned. These variants were too costly and were cancelled, and the basic G8 prototype was followed by two prototype Mirage G8s, Nos 01 and 02, which flew on 8 May 1971 and 13 July 1972 with two 71-kN (15,870-lb st) SNECMA Atar 9K-50s each.

Mirage IIIV: The vertical take-off Mirage IIIV No. 01 first flew on 12 February 1965, powered by one TF104B and eight 20.0-kN (4,409-lb st) Rolls-Royce RB.162 lifting engines; No. 02 flew 22 June 1966 with P&W JTF10 forward power.

The VTOL aircraft was impractical with its dead-weight lifting engines and the Mirage IIIT suffered the tailless delta's undesirable characteristics of high gust response, long take-off run and high approach speed. The Mirage G8 showed more promise for long-term development, becoming the basis of the G8A, or Avion de Combat Futur (ACF), until high costs killed the programme in December 1975, forcing

Left: The first Mirage F1 prototype retained a short, blunt, Mirage IIIE-style radome, and bore the legend Mirage F1C on the nose. Based on the configuration and wing of the bigger Armée de l'Air-commissioned F2 and F3, the private venture F1 was based on the Mirage IIIE airframe and avionics (rather than those of one of the enlarged derivatives) and was powered by an Atar 09K engine. Designed with exports in mind, the Mirage F1 was intended to be a cheap multi-role warplane, unlike the Armée de l'Air Mirage F3 dedicated interceptor. The first prototype was lost on 18 May 1967, when it broke up due to severe airframe flutter, killing its pilot.

Left: The second prototype Mirage F1 was labelled 'Super Mirage F1' on the nose. It had a longer Cyrano IV/Mirage 50-style nose radome, but was otherwise externally identical to the ill-fated first prototype. This aircraft made its maiden flight on 20 March 1967, and was powered by an Atar 9K-31, pending availability of the intended 9K-50. As originally flown, the aircraft lacked ventral fins and had a straight horizontal fin top. By the time 02 made its maiden flight, the private venture F1 had seen off its competitors, the Mirage F3 having been scrapped, and the bigger two-seat F2 having clearly been relegated to also-ran status.

Dassault Mirage F1

Right: The second Mirage F1 prototype in its later production-style configuration featured cropped fin-top and (added after the fin modification) twin ventral fins. The aircraft went to the CEV for armament testing, and then to the CEAM for interception and air-to-ground firing trials, where it joined the No. 4 prototype. Carriage trials with a captive MATRA R530 on the centreline pylon began during early 1970. By comparison with later Mirage F1s, the second prototype lacked leading-edge slats.

substitution of the Mirage 2000. (The VG Mirage programme had deviated on 17 May 1965 when the UK and French governments agreed to joint development of an AFVG [Anglo-French VG] aircraft, from which France unilaterally withdrew on 5 July 1967. Second-time lucky, the RAF went on to be a founder member of the Panavia Tornado consortium.)

While development of the Mirage G proceeded, the Mirage IIIF was left to meet near-term requirements. Of the two officially sponsored aircraft, the IIIF2 had a fuselage and tail surfaces nearly identical to the IIIG. As its intended TF306 engine was not ready because of protracted development difficulties, prototype No. 01 was first flown on JTF10 power by Jean Coureau at Istres on 12 June 1966. Designed by a team under the leadership of Jean-Jacques Samin, the IIIF2 was intended to meet an AA requirement calling for an all-weather interdictor and secondary interceptor capable of

low-level attack. A key stipulation in this was for an approach speed less than 140 kt (260 km/h; 160 mph), eliminating the tailless delta configuration. Two days after its maiden sortie, IIIF2-01 exceeded Mach 1.2. On 29 December 1966 a flight at Mach 2.0 was followed by a landing run of only 480 m (1,575 ft), convincingly demonstrating the short-field performance of what was then known as the Mirage F2. That was to no avail, for six days previously another version of the same aircraft, destined for greater success, had first taken to the air. This was a smaller, private-venture machine which Dassault called the Super Mirage F1.

All sizes

To produce the highly-successful Mirage III, Dassault had scaled up the officially-approved Mirage I. Now, a decade later, the firm was again telling the AA its business when the Mirage F2 was shrunk to Mirage III size and fitted with

Wearing the black triangle badge of CEAM, the fourth Mirage F1 climbs away after take-off. The aircraft has a red fuselage stripe reminiscent of that applied to some Mirage IIIs. One of the work horses of the early test and development effort, No. 4 was flown by pilots from the Armée de l'Air, the Aéronavale and some seven foreign nations, several of which later bought F1s of their own. The way in which the twin wheel main undercarriage units fold forwards and inwards as they retract is clearly apparent. The leading-edge slats applied from the third prototype can also be discerned.

Mirage IIIE avionics and a tried-and-tested Atar 09K afterburning turbojet from the Mirage IVA bomber. The resultant Mirage F1 was launched late in 1965 under the temporary name of IIIE2 and proceeded through the design stage at remarkable speed, under the joint leadership of François Cordié and Pierre Atlan.

Two stages of size reduction had been proposed for the Mirage F2, the first of which was the F3, a prototype of which was under construction as the second officially-funded IIIF. Placed between the F2 and F1 in terms of size, the F3 was optimised for interception and, accordingly, had a high thrust:weight ratio of 1:1.3. In contrast, the F1 was seen as more of a multi-role aircraft, having a higher maximum weight than the F3 in spite of a less-powerful engine. Its corresponding thrust to weight ratio was 1:2.1. All three Mirage Fs had two internal cannon and provision for bombs, rockets and guided missiles. Salient details were:

	Mirage F2	Mirage F3	Mirage F1
Powerplant	TF30	TF306E	Atar 9K
Thrust kN	84.3	101.5	70.6
Thrust lb st	18,960	22,818	15,873
Span m (ft)	10.5 (34.45)	9.04 (29.66)	8.4 (27.56)
Length m (ft)	17.5 (57.42)	16.00 (52.49)	15.0 (49.21)
Empty wt kg (lb)	9800 (21,605)	9300 (20,503)	7400 (16,314)
Max wt kg (lb)	18300 (40,345)	13525 (29,817)	14900 (32,849)
Max speed km/h (mph)	808 (1,300)	1450 (901)	1300 (808)

Marked 'Mirage F1C' on the nose, and powered by an Atar 9K, prototype No. 01 lifted off at Melun/Villaroche on 23 December 1966 with chief test pilot René Bigand at the controls. On only the fourth sortie, on 7 January, Bigand and No. 01 achieved Mach 2.0 and then landed at 120 kt (222 km/h; 138 mph). However, Mach 2.0 was as nothing compared to the rapid movement then under way within the corridors of power in Paris. A few days later, Armed Forces Minister Pierre Messmer announced that the AA had sufficient attack aircraft for its immediate requirements and needed more interceptors. Consideration was being given to ordering 100 Mirage F1s, said Messmer, the decision to be made in February. The programme was formally launched in March but an announcement was delayed until 26 May 1967 (for dramatic effect at the Paris air show), the official contract for three prototypes following in September.

Sadly, Bigand and the first F1 were unable to display at Le Bourget that year. They had relocated to Dassault's Istres flight test centre to practise a routine for the show, but No. 01 broke up in the air due to airframe flutter near Fos, Marseilles, on 18 May during its 24th sortie. Bigand was fatally injured and the aircraft – distinguishable from those which followed by its blunter, Mirage IIIE-type radome – was completely destroyed.

Though unfortunate, the loss had no effect on the programme to place the Mirage F1 in military service. Lightning conversion of the AA to the Mirage F1's merits has never been satisfactorily explained, but may have more than a little to do with Dassault's belief that it was a better export prospect than the larger and more expensive Mirage F2 or the specialised F3. Further connections are also seen in Dassault's obliging financial rescue of the ailing Breguet firm, announced on 28 June 1967, and France's pull-out from the AFVG programme a week later. At a stroke, the French aircraft industry was strengthened, foreign involvement drastically reduced, employment prospects improved, and the seeds of increased profitability sown. The only one not to get what it wanted was the Armée de l'Air which, if it really needed an interceptor with no extraneous capabilities, would have been better off with the Mirage F3. The partially complete F3 prototype was scrapped in 1967, denying the AA an opportunity of comparing it with the F1 in flight test.

No official requirement had existed for the Mirage F1 until March 1967, when a specification was written round a

Dassault Mirage F1

production version of the aircraft. Jean-Jacques Samin was transferred from the now-defunct Mirage F2 to lead the F1 design team, although most of the changes were seen to be internal when No. 02, marked 'Super Mirage F1', was completed in the St Cloud experimental shop, on the Paris outskirts, in December 1968. The Melun flight test centre having by then closed, No. 02 was dismantled for road transport to Istres, where assembly was completed by 20 January, ready for vibration trials. Pending availability of the definitive Atar 9K-50 powerplant, No. 02 had a 9K-31B(3), rated at 65.7 kN (14,770 lb st) with reheat.

Development programme

Conducted by new project pilot Jean-Marie Saget, the test programme began in confident style, but a couple of weeks behind schedule. Taking off from Istres on 20 March 1967, No. 02 was airborne within 450 m (1,475 ft) and conducted trials of the undercarriage, flaps and airbrakes before 'cleaning up' for a high-level run to Mach 1.15. Landing at the end of a 50 minute-sortie, Saget brought No. 02 to a halt in 400 m (1,310 ft). The following day, Saget was again airborne to demonstrate the aircraft's speed range by flying at Mach 1.5 and then slowing to 115 kt (213 km/h; 132 mph). For landing, the approach speed was 135 kt (250 km/h; 155 mph), followed by touch-down at 125 kt (232 km/h; 144 mph).

After taking time out from its trials programme to become a prime exhibit at the 1969 Paris air show, No. 02 was stood down on 27 June after 62 flights, having completed Phase 1 testing. This had included a flight above 15240 m (50,000 ft), low-altitude operation at 1300 km/h (808 mph), carriage of military loads including wingtip Sidewinder missiles and underwing drop-tanks, and exploration of the full flight envelope. Some missions were flown by chief test pilot Jean Coreau and Captain Guillard of the Centre d'Essais en Vol official flight test centre. No. 02 was re-engined with a 70.6-kN (15,873-lb st) pre-series Atar 9K-50 and returned to flying in August.

Flight experience of No. 02 had reached 77 sorties and 80 hours when Saget flew No. 03 at Istres for the first time on 18 September 1969. The pair completed Phase 2 testing in December after 120 sorties/135 hours, following which No. 02 went to the CEV on 22 December for armament testing. The 137th flight by No. 02, on 21 February 1970, was the first with a production Atar 9K-50 installed, and was marked by achievement of Mach 2.15 at 53,000 ft (16155 m) that day. The joint 200th sortie, including 50 by No. 03, was celebrated on 11 March 1970, by which time carriage trials had begun with a MATRA R530 AAM on the centreline pylon.

Radar tests

Production avionics were the principal feature of No. 04 when it flew on 17 June 1970. This aircraft conducted interception and air-to-ground firing trials at the CEAM military test establishment in August 1971, scoring 50 per cent despite poor operating conditions. Its 210th sortie, on 2 May 1972, was the 1,000th by the three officially-funded prototypes, and by this time 47 pilots (from AA, French navy, CEV and seven foreign countries) had flown Mirage F1s. External changes during the early development phase were few and restricted to refinements to the tailfin tip shape, the addition of twin ventral fins to improve lateral stability under certain conditions and (beginning with No. 03) leading-edge slats for better combat manoeuvrability. Today, prototype

Left: This is the prototype Mirage F1B two-seat conversion and continuation trainer, for which Kuwait was the launch customer, the Armée de l'Air having previously felt happy to use Mirage IIIBs and IIIDs. Once the Mirage F1B was available, however, it changed its mind and acquired several. Greece, Morocco and South Africa never procured two-seaters, however.

No. 02 is preserved at the Musée de l'Air at Le Bourget, providing a fitting tribute to the massive development effort.

The three AA-sponsored prototypes demonstrated beyond doubt that the addition of a conventional wing and tailplane to the basic Mirage III fuselage had produced an aircraft of greatly increased capabilities, despite only a modest increase in installed thrust. The delta had been chosen for the first-generation Mirage partly because it could achieve the low thickness:chord ratio needed for supersonic flight without resorting to very thin wings, which were then difficult to construct. By the mid-1960s, manufacturing techniques had improved and the thin wing was less of a challenge. The delta's disadvantages include a high landing and take-off speed – thereby demanding a long runway – through lack of conventional moving horizontal tail surfaces and an incompatibility with the leading-edge slats which permit slow-speed flying. To take a perverse example, raising trailing-edge elevons on take-off to cause the nose of a

Left: Mystery Mirage! Masquerading as the first Mirage F1C-200, which had a stretched forward fuselage to allow a detachable inflight-refuelling probe (not shown). This instead appears to be an F1CG, with the number 200 applied to indicate its build number.

Mirage III to rotate actually increases drag and reduces lift, tending to push the aircraft down onto the runway. More recent delta-winged aircraft overcome this difficulty by using forward control surfaces to rotate the nose (actually adding to total lift) and by making the aircraft unstable in pitch so that the nose tends to be pushed upwards, level flight being maintained by computer. The slow approach speeds and

A pair of Mirage F1C-200s of EC 2/5 'Ile de France' formates with an Armée de l'Air C-135FR tanker, which already has its drogue-equipped refuelling boom deployed. Inflight-refuelling dramatically increased the flexibility and versatility of the Mirage F1, in particular allowing the aircraft to deploy abroad much more easily. These huge squadron markings were soon replaced by a much smaller insignia featuring the three yellow fleur de Lys in a tiny blue shield, with the cross of Lorraine in a black border along the top of the shield. Each aircraft carries a single MATRA R530 under the centreline. This weapon had a poor reputation, and a worse combat record, and was replaced on the F1 by the much improved Super 530.

short field length requirements which Mirage F1 test pilots were anxious to demonstrate were a direct result of the new wing.

Compared with the Mirage IIIE, an F1 requires 23 per cent less take-off run and has a 20 per cent slower approach speed, yet is 80 per cent more manoeuvrable and carries 43 per cent more fuel. This is despite having 29 per cent less wing area and 2.5 tonnes added to the take-off weight. A

shoulder-mounted wing and low tailplane eliminate the delta's tendency to violently depart, especially at high g, so that in addition to possessing a 21° per second instantaneous turn rate, the Mirage F1 can sustain over 7 g at Mach 2.2 and 8 g below Mach 1.0.

The only area in which the F1 'cheats' is that of increased power. Société Nationale d'Etude et de Construction de Moteurs d'Aviation (SNECMA) produced the 58.8-kN (13,228-lb st) Atar 09B and 09C turbojets for the Mirage III/5 family, modifying them for the Mirage IVA under the designation 09K. In the latter case, air mass flow is increased from 68 to 72 kg/second (150 to 158 lb/second) and all nine compressor stages have steel blades, instead of four being alloy. As such, the 09K is rated at 65.7 kN (14,771 lb st). Despite its similar title, the 9K-50 incorporates substantial changes to improve both output and fuel efficiency. The turbine is completely redesigned with blades cast instead of forged, and pressure ratio increased from 6:1 to 6.5:1. Arrangement of accessories is revised and control and electronic equipment improved.

Engine trials

Following an official 150-hour trial by the CEP at Saclay between 8 September and 24 November 1969, the 9K-50 was cleared for use at ratings of 49.0 kN (11,023 lb st) dry and 70.6 kN (15,873 lb st) in afterburner. By the early 1980s the 9K-50 was turning in a figure of 261 hours per failure-related removal and 1,736 hours between serious failures requiring depot-level maintenance. Regular engine overhaul interval is 900 hours, with maintenance every 300 hours. Internal fuel totals 4300 litres (946 Imp gal), of which 375 litres (82.5 Imp gal) are in integral wing tanks and the remainder in three main tanks and one inverted-supply tank in the fuselage. External fuel comprises up to three RP 35/2 drop-tanks (centreline and inboard wing pylons), each holding 1200 litres (264 Imp gal), but some F1Es and the F1CT have been modified to accept a 2200-litre (484-Imp gal) centreline tank initially commissioned by Iraq.

Structurally, the Mirage F1 airframe employs a high number of integrally-machined or chemically milled components and honeycomb sandwich structures, with assembly by flush riveting or (for secondary stringers and sealed panels) spot welding. A perforated airbrake is located on the forward underside of each engine air intake trunk. Aérospatiale at Bourges was contracted to build the nose and cockpit section (back to Station 17); SOCEA, the canopy; part of the centre fuselage (between Stations 17 and 22) was assigned to CASA of Spain; the intermediate fuselage (between Stations 22 and 25) to Latécoère at Toulouse; rear (Stations 25 to 36) to Aérospatiale (SOCATA) at Toulouse; and the tail section (Stations 36 to 41) to Avions Fairey and SABCA of Belgium. Fuselages were assembled at Dassault's Argenteuil plant, Paris, before transfer to the production line at Bordeaux. The all-moving tailplane is actuated hydraulically by electrical or

manual control and a braking parachute is stowed in a tubular fairing at the base of the rudder.

Wing structure

Mainplanes are of all-metal, two-spar, torsion-box construction, again using mainly mechanically or chemically
milled components. Swept at 47° 30', they have extended
chord on the outboard two-thirds of leading edge, giving a
distinctive 'dogtooth' discontinuity. They are fitted with
honeycomb sandwich control surfaces at the leading and
trailing edge. For landing and take-off, flaps are extended
along the entire leading edge (these can also be automatically
deployed as manoeuvre flaps, extending in combat below
834 km/h; 518 mph), while each trailing edge has two differentially operating double-slotted flaps and one aileron, the
last-mentioned compensated by trim devices incorporated in
the linkage. Roll at slower speeds is controlled by perforated
two-section spoilers on the upper surface of each wing,
ahead of the two-section flaps. These and the ailerons were
built by Potez and powered by irreversible hydraulic actuators. A complex folding mechanism by Messier-Hispano-
Bugatti allows the twin mainwheels to have a track of 2.5 m
(8 ft 2½ in), yet to be stowed in the fuselage. The nose leg,
also with twin wheels, retracts rearwards. In the lower forward fuselage is a pair of DEFA 553 cannon with 135
rounds each, firing 50 rounds per second at a muzzle velocity of over 800 m/second (2,625 ft/second).

Viewed from the air-conditioned cockpit, under its single-piece, rear-hinged canopy, instrumentation resembles
that of the Mirage III. An average-sized pilot has an arc of
vision 60° to the rear and 50° downwards, bettering NATO
minimal criteria by between 5° and 12°. Standard equipment
includes TACAN, radar altimeter, ground datalink, ILS,
VHF/UHF radio and IFF. Electrical power is provided by
two 15-kVA AC generators connected to two 100-A rectifiers and linked to a 40-Ah battery. In the event of a flame
out, the engine's windmilling is normally sufficient to provide emergency hydraulic power, but an electrical pump is
automatically activated in the case of complete failure.

Ejection seat

In the basic Mirage F1C, the pilot has an F1RM4 (Mk 4)
ejection seat, built in France by Société d'Exploitation des
Matériels Martin-Baker and effective at all altitudes when
forward speed exceeds 90 kt (167 km/h; 104 mph). Ejection
is through the canopy after explosive fragmentation. Later
French Mirage F1s received zero-zero Mk 10 seats, as specified by some export customers, while others have taken the
option to modify their Mk 4 seats to Mk 6s with the addition of a rocket pack for zero-zero escape. By 1993, only a
few Mk 4s remained in French service, the others having
been replaced retrospectively by Mk 10s. The current position regarding overseas users is: Ecuador Mk 10; Greece Mk
6; Iraq Mk 4 and Mk 10; Jordan Mk 4 and Mk 10; Kuwait

Plugged in! A Mirage F1CR spears the basket of a C-135FR with its fixed inflight-refuelling probe. The French C-135FRs have a drogue attached to the end of their booms. They have recently started to be equipped with additional flight refuelling hose drum units underwing, converting the aircraft to three-point tankers capable of refuelling more than one aircraft at a time.

Left: A 'Cornouaille' Mirage F1C-200 is caught on finals to Base Aérienne 103, Cambrai-Epinoy. Wingtip missile launch rails are empty, and no missiles are carried under the wings or centreline. Under the starboard wing, however, is a defensive ECM pod. EC 3/12's conversion to the Mirage 2000C was cancelled as an economy measure, thereby leaving it as the last remaining Mirage F1 air defence squadron.

Facing page, opposite: Laden with bombs and underwing fuel tanks, an SAAF Mirage F1AZ manoeuvres hard at low level, streaming vortices from the upper surfaces of its broad wings as it negotiates the Blyde River canyon.

Right: A South African Air Force Mirage F1AZ rolling at low level. South Africa's Mirage F1s have been in the thick of action on several occasions, and have proved popular and durable. Plans to re-engine the aircraft with Russian Klimov (Isotov) RD-33 engines reached an advanced stage, with engines delivered to South Africa and fuselages to Russia for fit checks. The SAAF's Mirage F1CZ interceptors have been retired and placed in storage, but the dedicated ground attack F1AZs continue to play a vital role.

Mk 10; Libya Mk 4; Morocco Mk 4; Qatar Mk 10; Spain Mk 6 and Mk 10; and South Africa, believed to have Mks 4, 6 and 10.

Radar options

Interceptor versions have Thomson-CSF Cyrano IV radar from the same family as Cyrano II in the Mirage III. The Mk IV is an I/J-band monopulse radar which, early in French service, was modified to Mk IV-1 standard to include a basic moving-target indication in the look-down mode. Radar has accurate ground-mapping and low-altitude modes in its Mk IV-2 configuration, while Cyrano IV-3 incorporates the improvements of the -1 and -2 series.

The pilot may select range displays on his radar scope of 110, 65 or 28 km (68, 40 or 17 miles). Radar scans ± 60° in azimuth and ±30° in elevation and automatically changes to track mode when a marker is placed against a particular target – only one of which can be tracked at any time. Indication is also given of the earliest, latest and optimum times for

firing an AAM. Air-to-air performance is degraded by poor weather, so early reports of the Mirage F1's air-defence potential concentrated on high-altitude interception, during which the aircraft can pursue a target for eight minutes at Mach 2.0 at 15240 m (50,00 ft) on full internal fuel. At low-level, particularly before the Super 530 AAM became available, the F1's interception capability left something to be desired.

Avionics fit varies according to customer requirements. As in the Mirage III/5 series, Dassault offered the F1 in three basic configurations: F1A for day attack, F1C interceptor, and F1E multi-role aircraft. Apart from the first-mentioned, these even used the same suffix letters as the first-generation Mirage, the non-radar F1A being equivalent to Mirage 5. Suggestions that the A stood for Appui (Attack) and C for Chasse (fighter) were made by Dassault during the 1970s, but these were tongue-in-cheek after-the-fact musings by the marketing men. As built for home use, the Mirage F1C is fitted with Cyrano IV fire-control radar, SFENA 505 autopi-

lot, LMT ARN52C TACAN, LMT NR-AI-4-A IFF, central air data computer, SFIM spherical indicator with ILS pointers, Sextant 63 navigation indicator and CSF HUD with field-of-view double converter.

All versions have seven hardpoints. The centreline pylon is stressed for 2100 kg (4,630 lb), inboard wing pylons to 1300 kg (2,866 lb), outboard underwing pylons to 550 kg (1,213 lb), and wingtip missile mounts to 150 kg (331 lb). A further mounting is available for Alkan LL 5020 modular chaff/flare dispensers which are scabbed to the underside of the wing inboard of the inner wing pylons. Mirage F1Cs normally carry wingtip short-range missiles, inboard underwing medium-range missiles and a centreline tank. Initially, only one medium-range MATRA R530 was carried (on the centreline), while more recently the outboard underwing positions have been used to give interceptors self-defence jamming (Barax, starboard) and chaff/flare (Phimat, port) pods.

To increase versatility, a refuelling probe was added halfway through Mirage F1C production for France and offered to export customers. Fitted to the starboard side of the forward fuselage, the distinctive non-retractable probe can only be accommodated by adding an extra 7-cm (2¾-in) plug to the airframe, increasing fuselage length to 15.30 m (50 ft 2⅛ in). The prototype was converted from F1C No. 1 and reserialled No. 201, thereby giving the probed Mirage its designation of F1-200. The probe can be installed in or removed from suitable aircraft in under two hours and has no limits on performance up to Mach 1.4, although top speed is restricted to Mach 1.9. Deliveries began on 2 March 1977, but the first demonstration of potential did not take place until January 1980 when four aircraft flew from Solenzara, Corsica to Djibouti as a show of rapid reinforcement capability.

Beginning with the 70th F1C delivered to France (No. 79), tailfins were fitted with the prominent 'bullet' fairings for a Thomson-CSF BF radar warning receiver, two side-facing antennas for which are less conspicuously embedded

in the fin structure. Of exported Mirage F1s, only the Greek aircraft were built without an RWR, although they were retrofitted, later Iraqi aircraft having a more advanced, digital Thomson-CSF TMV011 SHERLOC, recognisable by its larger, rectangular housings in the fore and aft positions. Most Mirage F1s also have horizontal aerials on the fin for a SOCRAT 6200 VOR/ILS, those in Iraqi and Libyan service also carrying an HF aerial fillet at the junction of fin leading edge and fuselage.

An operational evaluation of the F1C was compiled by its first operating *escadre* (wing), the 30th at Reims, during the mid-1970s. The cockpit was assessed to be comfortable in spite of its small size, and well planned, with a clear and rational layout of instruments and controls. Noise level and air conditioning were praised and flight controls commended for their smoothness at all speeds. Compared with the Mirage III, the aircraft exhibited a reduced angle of attack when landing, approaching at 190 kt (352 km/h; 219 mph) and touching down at around 135-140 kt (250-260 km/h; 155-161 mph). Landing roll of 800 m (2,625 ft) was reduced to 600 m (1,970 ft) when the braking parachute was used. The Atar 9K-50 engine, it was noted, had few operating restrictions and was free from compressor stall worries at high altitude.

In assessing the first integrated navigation system installed in a French combat aircraft (autopilot, VOR/ILS and TACAN), Escadre de Chasse 30 (Fighter Wing 30, abbreviated in French as EC 30) reported its satisfaction that autopilot could be used at any stage of the flight and employed for automatic approaches. On full internal fuel, the Mirage F1C demonstrated a range of 1100 km (685 miles). The F1's thin wing was found to permit better transonic performance than the Mirage IIIE and the combination of higher aspect ratio and taper ratio gave an improved steady turn performance. As expected, serviceability was poor in the early days, registering only 34.6 per cent in 1974. This rose to 45 per cent in 1975, 48 per cent in 1976 and 59 per cent in the first half of 1977. When 50,000 flying hours were exceeded late in 1977,

Dassault Mirage F1AZ

This Mirage F1AZ wears the distinctive camouflage now applied to surviving South African Air Force Mirage F1s. This consists of an overall medium grey, with only the upper surfaces of wings, tailplanes and the top-most parts of the upper fuselage decking having a disruptive dark brown and green camouflage. National insignia and squadron markings are often oversprayed, sometimes remaining just visible, sometimes becoming completely obscured.

Inflight-refuelling probe
The Mirage F1A fighter-bombers do not have a Cyrano radar in the nose, but instead have only the much smaller Aïda ranging radar, leaving more internal space available in the nose. This has allowed the installation of a neat retractable refuelling probe, covered by a flush-fitting door when not in use.

Tailfin
The modestly swept fin carries distinctive conical forward and rear hemisphere receiver antennas for the Thomson-CSF BF passive RHAWS, each giving 90° of coverage. Sideways cover is given by flush disc antennas on the sides of the fin.

Undernose fairing
South African Mirage F1AZs are equipped with a laser rangefiinder in an undernose fairing. This is almost certainly a Thomson CSF TMV-630 as fitted to many Mirage 5/50 upgrades. Use of a laser rangefinder in the ground attack role allows accurate range measurement, without making tell-tale radar emissions.

Bombs
South African Mirage F1s can carry a range of air-to-ground ordnance, some of it of French origin, some of Israeli origin and some of indigenous design and manufacture. This aircraft carries four Armscor 250-kg fragmentation bombs under the fuselage, with long-range tanks underwing.

Ventral fins
Ventral fins were added to the second prototype, and all subsequent Mirage F1s, to enhance directional stability.

Undercarriage
The undercarriage is made by Messier-Hispano-Bugatti and retracts into the intake trunks, swivelling and retracting forwards. All three undercarriage units carry twin wheels.

No. 3 Squadron
No. 3 Squadron has a long and proud tradition, having served as a fighter squadron during World War II in East Africa and the Middle East, and finally in Italy. Post-war, however, it has had mixed fortunes, with long periods of enforced inactivity. Between 1952 and 1959 the unit was a reserve 'Citizen Force' squadron flying Harvards, and was reformed in 1966 as a paper unit under the control of No. 2 Squadron, the 'Flying Cheetahs'. During this period the unit used a handful of aircraft borrowed from No. 2 Squadron, since attrition had reduced the Mirage III fleet to the extent that another squadron could not be fully equipped. Colours were awarded in 1970, and the squadron fully activated as an autonomous unit in February 1975, prior to receiving Mirage F1AZs on 4 April. Since then the squadron has been heavily committed to operations in Angola and its aircraft have flown many operational cross-border missions. The long border war remains cloaked in secrecy, and it will be many years before the full part played by the Mirage F1AZ becomes known.

Cockpit
Covered by an upward/rearward-hinging clamshell canopy and a three-piece windscreen, the Mirage F1's cockpit is deceptively spacious, although cramped by contemporary US standards. The pilot's view of the outside world is also poor by modern standards, with a very restricted view aft. The instrument panel is entirely conventional, and typically French, with small analog instruments and a shielded radar scope on those aircraft fitted with Cyrano IV.

Ranging radar
The Mirage F1A fighter-bombers carry a small EMD Aïda 2 ranging radar in the extreme nose. The radar has a fixed antenna, and provides automatic search, acquisition, ranging and tracking for air-to-air or air-to-surface targets in its 16° field of view. Information is presented to the pilot in his gyro gunsight. The radar was designed by Electronique Marcel Dassault (now Dassault Electronique) specifically for installation in the pointed noses of fighters originally designed without radar.

Air intakes
Like the Mirage III/5/50 family, the Mirage F1 has semi-circular air intakes, with a variable conical ('shock cone') centrebody. These move in and out of the intake to match intake area and configuration to airspeed. The intakes themselves stand proud from the fuselage to obviate the need for splitter plates. These are usually required to separate the sluggish boundary layer airflow, keeping airflow into the engines 'pure'. The intakes are positioned well forward of the gun muzzles, to prevent gun gas ingestion problems. When extra power is required, at low airspeed, extra mass flow to the engines is achieved via the spring-loaded 'suck-in' auxiliary intake doors mounted on the sides of the main intakes.

Flying controls
The Mirage F1 has conventional servo-actuated outboard ailerons, with two-section trailing-edge flaps inboard. These can operate symmetrically as high-lift/drag-producing flaps, or differentially for roll control. They are augmented by two-section perforated spoilers on the upper surfaces of the wing, which also act either symmetrically as lift-dumpers, or differentially for roll control. The flaps and spoilers are actuated hydraulically, using servos. The remaining primary flying controls comprise the single-piece rudder and the massive all-moving tailerons, which operate symmetrically (as elevators) for pitch control or differentially for roll control at high speeds.

Powerplant
Like the Mirage 3NG and Mirage 50, all Mirage F1 sub-variants use versions of the SNECMA Atar 09K50 turbojet. There have been serious proposals to re-engine the SAAF Mirage F1s with Russian Klimov (Isotov) RD-33 engines, as used in the Mikoyan MiG-29.

South Africa and the F1
The French government's relatively liberal attitude to arms exports during the 1960s led to the establishment of a long-standing and profitable relationship with some nations regarded as pariahs by other traditional arms-supplying nations. Thus, when Britain imposed sanctions on South Africa, Dassault stepped in to fill the breach, supplying Mirage IIIs and then Mirage F1s.

Wingtips
The Mirage F1AZ can be fitted with optional missile launch rails for the carriage of defensive AAMs. These can include the indigenous V3B Kukri, or the newer V3C Darter, both of which are extremely agile IR-homing dogfight missiles in the same class as the Magic or AIM-9. The installation of such launch rails naturally generates drag, and is therefore not automatically undertaken.

Fuel
The Mirage F1 has 14 internal bag-type tanks in each inner wing, with a centre fuselage tanks and further tanks in the fuselage walls. Total internal fuel capacity is 4300 litres (1,136 US gal) which can be augmented by the carriage of up to two external fuel tanks, each of 1200-litres/317-US gal capacity. These can either be carried singly on the centreline, or in pairs under the wing. The aircraft can use fuels corresponding to JP-4 and JP-5 (NATO F-40 and NATO F-44).

Above: A Mirage F1CR, laden with a Harold reconnaissance pod, rolls inverted during a low-level aerobatic routine, afterburner glowing. Harold has been supplied to a number of Mirage F1 export customers, adding recce capability to Mirage F1 fighter and ground attack sub-variants.

Left: This ER 33 F1CR is laden with a belly-mounted Raphäel SLAR 2000 pod. The first of these pods was delivered to the Armée de l'Air in 1986.

Below: The Raphäel SLAR 2000 is optimised for long-range stand-off reconnaissance, and utilises pulse compression and synthetic aperture techniques to maximise resolution.

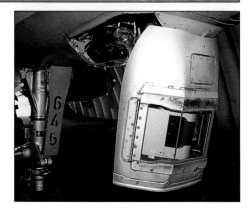

Above: The Mirage F1CR's SAT SCM2400 Super Cyclope IRLS is fitted in place of the starboard cannon, with an aperture aft of the airbrake and just ahead of a heat exchanger

Left: The ejection seat of a Mirage F1CE. These aircraft were delivered with Martin Baker Mk 4 seats, which have been modified to Mk 6 standards by the addition of a rocket pack for zero-zero escape, or replaced by Mk 10s.

Right: Under the nose of the Mirage F1CR, a bulged fairing houses the three windows of the prism for the aircraft's panoramic camera. The bulge is hinged at the front, and when swung down acts as an access panel for the camera bay.

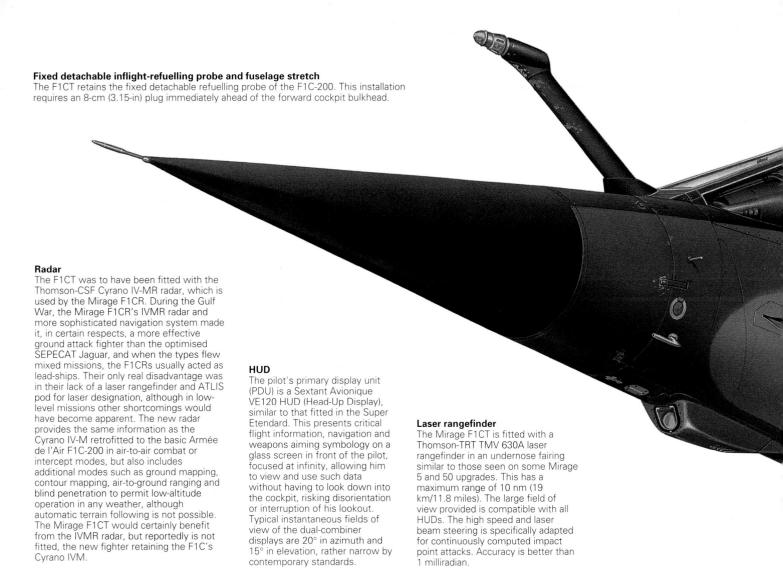

Fixed detachable inflight-refuelling probe and fuselage stretch
The F1CT retains the fixed detachable refuelling probe of the F1C-200. This installation requires an 8-cm (3.15-in) plug immediately ahead of the forward cockpit bulkhead.

Radar
The F1CT was to have been fitted with the Thomson-CSF Cyrano IV-MR radar, which is used by the Mirage F1CR. During the Gulf War, the Mirage F1CR's IVMR radar and more sophisticated navigation system made it, in certain respects, a more effective ground attack fighter than the optimised SEPECAT Jaguar, and when the types flew mixed missions, the F1CRs usually acted as lead-ships. Their only real disadvantage was in their lack of a laser rangefinder and ATLIS pod for laser designation, although in low-level missions other shortcomings would have become apparent. The new radar provides the same information as the Cyrano IV-M retrofitted to the basic Armée de l'Air F1C-200 in air-to-air combat or intercept modes, but also includes additional modes such as ground mapping, contour mapping, air-to-ground ranging and blind penetration to permit low-altitude operation in any weather, although automatic terrain following is not possible. The Mirage F1CT would certainly benefit from the IVMR radar, but reportedly is not fitted, the new fighter retaining the F1C's Cyrano IVM.

HUD
The pilot's primary display unit (PDU) is a Sextant Avionique VE120 HUD (Head-Up Display), similar to that fitted in the Super Etendard. This presents critical flight information, navigation and weapons aiming symbology on a glass screen in front of the pilot, focused at infinity, allowing him to view and use such data without having to look down into the cockpit, risking disorientation or interruption of his lookout. Typical instantaneous fields of view of the dual-combiner displays are 20° in azimuth and 15° in elevation, rather narrow by contemporary standards.

Laser rangefinder
The Mirage F1CT is fitted with a Thomson-TRT TMV 630A laser rangefinder in an undernose fairing similar to those seen on some Mirage 5 and 50 upgrades. This has a maximum range of 10 nm (19 km/11.8 miles). The large field of view provided is compatible with all HUDs. The high speed and laser beam steering is specifically adapted for continuously computed impact point attacks. Accuracy is better than 1 milliradian.

MATRA Phimat
The MATRA Phimat is a 3.6-m (11-ft 10-in) long podded electromagnetic chaff decoy system, consisting of a chaff dispenser and control unit. The 108-mm (4¼-in) cylindrical body contains the drive electronics, ejection system and up to 210 chaff packs. With a total system weight of 105 kg (231 lb), Phimat can be triggered manually or automatically. The system is also in service with Armée de l'Air Jaguars, as well as RAF aircraft including the Jaguar, Tornado and Nimrod.

Dassault Mirage F1CT
Escadron de Chasse 1/13 'Artois'
1er Commandement Aérienne Tactique
Force Aérienne Tactique
Armée de l'Air
Base Aérienne 132, Colmar/Mayenheim
France, 1992

The Mirage F1CT was developed as a result of the availability of surplus Mirage F1C-200 airframes rendered surplus by the conversion of air defence squadrons to the Mirage 2000C. The availability of a new fighter-bomber was a considerable blessing to the Armée de l'Air, which still relied on tired Jaguars, obsolete Mirage IIIEs and ageing Mirage 5Fs. Replacement of the latter, rather primitive aircraft was accorded the highest priority, and EC 13 at Colmar was targeted for conversion to the new aircraft. This Mirage F1CT of Escadre de Chasse 13 wears the hirondelle (swallow) insignia of SPA 100 on the port side of the tailfin, this having been adopted as the badge of the 2e Escadrille of EC 1/13. The 1e Escadrille badge (the chimére (dragon) badge of SPA 83) is carried to starboard. Previously the Mirage 5F OCU, 'Artois' flew the final Mirage IIIB sortie and passed its IIIBes to EC 2/13 to continue the training role on 15 January 1992, having relinquished its OCU task, The squadron's pilots then began ground school on the Mirage F1CT before transferring to CEAM at Mont-de-Marsan for type conversion, the squadron flying its final Mirage III sortie on 26 June 1992. The first Mirage F1CT to be received was the third conversion, No. 278 13-QA, which made its public debut at the Colmar Meeting Nationale de l'Air on 14 June 1992. Training at CEAM was completed on 6 November 1992, when the squadron returned to Colmar with its first batch of aircraft. It was declared operational in April 1993. Squadron badges applied to the aircraft underwent a major change during October 1993, when EC 1/13 'Artois' and EC 3/13 'Auvergne' were renamed 'Normandie-Niémen' and 'Alsace'. The wing's third squadron, EC 2/13 'Alpes', did not convert to the F1CT due to the change from a three-, to a two-, squadron wing structure. During 1995 the two squadrons will become autonomous elements of EC 30 (EC 1/30 'Normandie-Niémen' and EC 2/30 'Alsace') remaining at Colmar, where they will be joined by the surviving F1CR and F1C/F1B units. The Mirage F1CT is something of a hybrid aircraft, retaining the airframe and some systems of the F1C-200 and adding other systems developed for the F1CR and some export versions. The change in role from interception (biased towards high/medium-level navigation) to ground attack (where long-range low-level navigation is more important) necessitates a change in navigation equipment. The SAGEM Uliss 47R INS, for instance, is a modified model of the Uliss 47 system fitted in F1CR and export F1s and has a typical accuracy of 1 nm/hour circular error of probability. All Uliss systems utilise high-accuracy inertial components comprising two dynamically tuned gyroscopes and three dry accelerometers, with highly integrated circuits and a microprocessor-controlled computer. The central digital computer is a Dassault Electronique M182XR and is a modification of the normal F1C-200 unit. A Sextant Avionique AP 505 autopilot is fitted for flight management and control. Similarly, because the Mirage F1CT now has a primary ground attack role, instead of the limited and secondary ground attack capability enjoyed by the F1C and F1CR, Dassault added a laser rangefinder, while updating and upgrading other systems to cope with the demanding high-threat, low-level environment. Thus the Mirage F1CT has new chaff/flare dispensers, radar warning receivers, secure radios and a Martin-Baker F10M ejection seat.

Left: A Lacroix flare dispenser can be installed in the tailcone, in place of the normal brake parachute. A similar installation is used in the SEPECAT Jaguar.

Right: An alternative location for a chaff/flare dispenser is scabbed onto the lower part of the rear fuselage, next to the ventral fin. This one is seen on a Moroccan aircraft.

85 Tailplane pivot fitting
86 Tailplane hydraulic actuator
87 Autopilot controller
88 Port ventral fin
89 Inboard double-slotted flap segment
90 Flap hydraulic jack
91 Spoiler hydraulic jack
92 Port spoiler housing and actuating linkage
93 Port aileron hydraulic actuator

94 Outboard double-slotted flap segment
95 Port aileron
96 Wingtip missile interface unit
97 Port navigation light
98 Leading-edge flap
99 Port MATRA Magic air-to-air missile
100 68-mm rocket projectile
101 MATRA 18-round rocket launcher

102 Thomson-CSF ECM pod
103 Outer pylon attachment hardpoint
104 Wing panel multi-spar construction
105 Port wing integral fuel tank
106 Main undercarriage hydraulic retraction jack
107 Shock absorber strut
108 Twin mainwheels
109 Levered suspension axle
110 Mainwheel leg strut and leg rotating linkage

111 Leading-edge flap hydraulic jack
112 Main undercarriage wheel bay
113 Port ammunition bay, unused
114 Centre fuselage weapon pylon
115 400-kg HE bombs
116 Underwing MATRA-Corral conformal chaff/flare dispenser
117 Multiple bomb carrier

118 Thomson-Brandt BAP-100 runway cratering bomb or BAT-120 area denial/anti-armour munition
119 MATRA Belouga submunition dispenser
120 MATRA Durandal retarded concrete piercing bomb

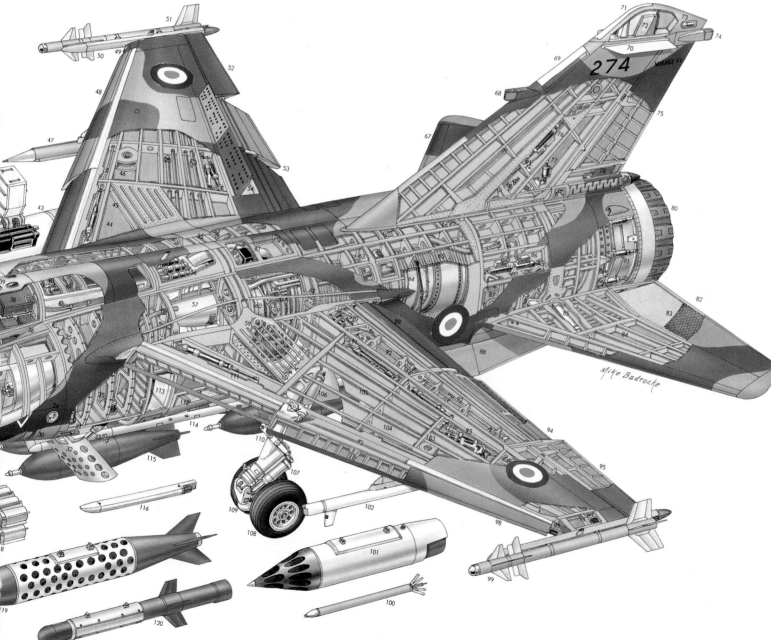

Mike Badrocke

Inside the Dassault Mirage F1

*Right: Seen from below, a Moroccan **F1EH-200** shows off its indigenous centreline reconnaissance pod. This was developed by Aero Maroc with French assistance. Windows in the centre section cover a fan of cameras which can give horizon-to-horizon coverage. Cooling airscoops and vents at the rear of the pod indicate that some electronic equipment is also carried, perhaps including a **SLAR** or **IRLS**.*

*Below: Another view of a recce-configured Moroccan Mirage F1EH-200, carrying the same pod as is pictured at right. Why Morocco opted to procure an indigenous pod, rather than one of the existing French pods, remains uncertain. Other pods compatible with and cleared for use by the Mirage F1 include the Harold, **COR-2** and Raphäel. The chaff/flare dispenser shown on the next page is not carried by this aircraft. Such chaff/flare dispensers were fitted following combat losses to Polisario surface-to-air missiles.*

Dassault Mirage F1CT

1 Pitot head
2 Glass-fibre radome
3 Radar scanner housing
4 Inflight-refuelling probe
5 Dynamic pressure sensor
6 Thomson-CSF Cyrano IVMR radar equipment module
7 Incidence probe
8 TMV 630A laser rangefinder
9 Rudder pedals
10 Control column
11 Instrument panel shroud
12 Windscreen panels
13 Thomson VE120 head-up display
14 Upward-hinging cockpit canopy cover
15 Martin-Baker F10M zero-zero ejection seat
16 Engine throttle lever
17 Side console panel
18 Nose undercarriage hydraulic retraction jack
19 Twin nosewheels, aft retracting
20 Hydraulic steering mechanism
21 TACAN aerial
22 Cockpit sloping rear pressure bulkhead
23 Canopy jack
24 Canopy emergency release
25 Central intake control actuator
26 Moveable half-cone intake centre-body
27 Port air intake
28 Air conditioning equipment bay
29 Intake centre-body screw jack

30 Intake suction relief door
31 Pressure refuelling connection
32 Port airbrake panel
33 Airbrake hydraulic jack
34 Retractable landing lamp
35 Forward fuselage integral fuel tank
36 Boundary layer spill duct
37 Avionics equipment bay
38 Power amplifier
39 Strobe light (white) and anti-collision beacon (red)
40 Fuel system inverted flight accumulator
41 30-mm DEFA cannon, starboard side only
42 Ammunition magazine, 135 rounds
43 External fuel tank
44 Starboard wing integral fuel tank
45 Forged steel wing attachment fitting
46 Inboard pylon attachment hardpoint
47 MATRA-Philips Phimat chaff/flare pod
48 Leading-edge flap
49 Starboard navigation light
50 Wingtip missile launch rail
51 MATRA Magic air-to-air missile
52 Starboard aileron
53 Two-segment double-slotted flaps
54 Spoiler panel (open)
55 Wing panel attachment machined fuselage main frame
56 Fuel system filters

57 Engine intake centre-body/starter housing
58 Wing panel attachment pin joints
59 Engine accessory equipment gearbox
60 SNECMA Atar 9K-50 afterburning engine
61 Engine bleed air pre-cooler
62 Rear spar attachment joint
63 Rear fuselage integral fuel tank
64 Engine turbine section
65 Engine bay thermal lining
66 Fin spar attachment joint
67 Starboard all-moving tailplane
68 Forward SHERLOC ECM antenna fairing

69 UHF antenna
70 VOR aerial
71 Fin-tip aerial fairing
72 IFF/VHF 1 aerial
73 Rear navigation light and anti-collision beacon
74 Aft SHERLOC ECM antenna
75 Rudder
76 Rudder hydraulic actuator
77 Rudder trim actuator

78 VHF 2 aerial
79 Brake parachute housing
80 Variable-area afterburner nozzle
81 Nozzle control jacks
82 Port all-moving tailplane
83 Honeycomb trailing-edge panel
84 Multi-spar tailplane construction

Ejection seat
The F1CT pilot has a SEM Martin-Baker F10M rocket-powered ejection seat capable of zero-zero operation. The older zero/90 SEMMB F1RM4 unit has been steadily replaced by the Mk 10 in most French Mirage F1s. Ejection is through the rearward-hinging canopy after explosive fragmentation.

Internal cannon
All Mirage F1s (except for the F1CR) are fitted with two 30-mm DEFA 553 cannon in the lower forward intake trunking. The DEFA is a single-barrelled, gas-operated revolver-type gun. It utilises the same basic design as the earlier DEFA 552 cannon as fitted to the Mirage III/5, but incorporates modifications to improve the service life of certain components. A steel cylinder drum is fitted, and other modifications permit ammunition feed from either side. Normal capacity is 135 rounds per gun with a firing rate of 50 rounds per second at a muzzle velocity of over 800 m/second (2,625 ft/second). As the cannon is mounted adjacent to the air intakes, a device is fitted to the nitro-chrome steel barrel to deflect gun muzzle gases from the engine.

Belouga CBUs
The Belouga was developed by Thomson Brandt
Armaments and MATRA SA as a ground-attack cluster
weapon for dispensing submunitions. Three types of
submunition may be carried: general-purpose
fragmentation, anti-armour and area interdiction. The
3.3-m (10-ft 10-in) long low-drag bomb body may be
divided into three distinct components: the nosecone
containing an air-driven electrical generator, sequencer,
distributor and pyrotechnic actuators; the 366-mm (14½-
in) diameter cylindrical body housing a centre tube to
which are radially fixed eight submunition launching
chambers staggered in 19 rings; and the aft finned
section with a drag chute system. A total of 151
bomblets may be carried, each of 66-mm (3-in) diameter
and 1.3-kg (2.86-lb) weight. The Belouga is cleared for
use up at a maximum speed of up to 550 kt and a
minimum release height of 60 m (200 ft). For increased
effectiveness, the bomblets are individually braked by
parachute immediately after ejection from the main
dispenser to give almost vertical target impact. Either of
two bomblet ground pattern configurations may be
selected by the pilot prior to release: a high-impact
density short carpet (5000 m²/53,820 sq ft) and long
carpet (10000 m²/107,640 sq ft).

Fuel
Most of the F1's fuel is housed in three main tanks and a
single inverted-flight supply tank in the fuselage with a
combined capacity of 3925 litres (863.5 Imp gal).
Additionally, fuel is contained in integral wing tanks with a combined
capacity of 375 litres (82.5 Imp gal), giving a total internal fuel
capacity of 4300 litres (946 Imp gal). For extended
range/endurance operations, the primary wing stations can
also carry 1200-litre (264-Imp gal) drop tanks, while the
centreline station can carry a single RP 35 2200-litre (484-Imp
gal) tank originally developed for the Iraqi Mirage F1EQ.

Left and above: A Mirage F1CE drops four retarded live 400-kg bombs. Its target is a circle of stones on a dummy airfield, complete with redundant T-33s and F-86s as targets. Its bombs explode in the centre of the circle.

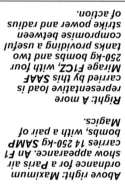

Above: Mirage F1s have been used to test a variety of modern systems which may never enter service with Armée de l'Air Mirage F1 units. These have included this early prototype Apache modular stand-off weapon.

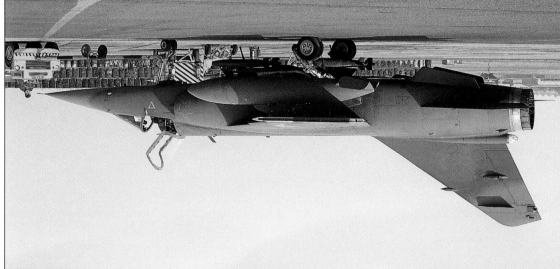

Right: A more representative load is carried by this SAAF Mirage F1CZ, with four 250-kg bombs and two tanks providing a useful compromise between strike power and radius of action.

Above right: Maximum ordnance for a Paris air show appearance. An F1 carries 14 250-kg SAMP bombs, with a pair of Magics.

Above: A Mirage F1EQ-1, armed with a pair of MATRA 400-kg laser-guided bombs. These use EBLIS seekers, based on the Aeriel unit fitted to the AS30L missile. Carriage of an ATLIS pod instead of the centreline tank would allow self-designation.

Left: The Dassault Mirage F1's
main weakness has always
been its missile armament,
though this has been
significantly improved since
aircraft entered service. The
initial **MATRA 530FE** had a v
poor combat record, and a p
reputation, and replacemen
was an urgent priority. Here
early trials aircraft, with an
undernose rearward-facing t
camera package and a
centreline test instrumentat
pod, lets loose a **Super 530** i
gout of flame and smoke. T
Super 530 is usually carried
under the wing, and only a
semi-active radar homing
version is available. It is
significantly more capable t
the **530FE** which it has repl

The basic **MATRA 530FE** is little used today, having
been largely replaced by the **Super 530**. The missile
could be carried on the centreline, or, more rarely,
under the wing. This is the **IR**-homing variant.

The standard **BVR** missile of the Mirage **F1** today is
the **MATRA S**uper **530-F1**. This has a much better
reputation than its predecessor, although it has an
unimpressive combat record.

The **R550 Magic** is a short-range, manoeuvrable
homing dogfight missile with fixed forward can
powered forward control fins and free-moving r
fins.

Powerplant

The SNECMA Atar 9K-50 was developed specifically to power the Mirage F1 and is the powerplant of all variants of the F1 and certain Mirage III/5 derivatives (Mirage 50 and Atlas Cheetah). The original single-shaft Atar turbojet was first run in 1946, and has been developed steadily since then, powering subsequent versions of Mirages and Etendards (the latter in non-afterburning form). The 9K-50 was derived from the Mirage IV's Atar 9K, which was in turn developed from the Mirage III's Atar 9C, and was designed to offer improved specific fuel consumption at subsonic speeds, increased thrust for supersonic acceleration and improved service life. The turbine section was entirely redesigned with cast (not forged) blades, while the initial stages of the compressor were redesigned to increase pressure ratio from 6:1 to 6.15:1, coupled with a slightly increased mass flow. Other modifications include a revised intake section to accommodate a rearranged accessory-drive system, and improved control and electronic equipment to increase reliability. Although these changes resulted in an increase in dry weight of 126 kg (278 lb) to 1582 kg (3,487 lb), there were commensurate improvements in performance of approximately 20 per cent in each case, the 9K-50's maximum dry thrust increasing to 49.0 KN (11,023 lb st) and maximum thrust with afterburner increasing to 70.6 KN (15,873 lb st). Specific fuel consumption at these ratings was improved by approximately four per cent to 27.5 mg/Ns (0.97 lb/hr/lb st) and 55.5 mg/Ns (1.96 lb/hr/lb st) respectively. The regular engine overhaul interval is 900 hours, with maintenance every 300 hours.

MATRA R550 Magic

The Mirage F1 entered service with the Armée de l'Air toting the initial production of the MATRA R550 Magic missile. This is a short-range AAM in the same class as the AIM-9 Sidewinder. Development of the missile commenced in 1967, with initial flight trials taking place in 1971. By 1975, MATRA had begun series production and delivered the first Magics to the French air force. The 2.72-m (8-ft 11-in) long missile has a body diameter of 157 mm (6.2 in) and a unique double canard configuration, with four fixed front delta fins followed by four moving control fins. In plan view, the latter have a rectangular forward section transposed on a delta rear section. This configuration was chosen to improve controllability by allowing the wing fins to remain effective at higher angles of incidence. The fixed rear fins have a wing span of 0.66 m (2 ft 2 in). Production of the Magic 1 ended in 1984, after development of a more advanced Magic 2 variant commenced in the late 1970s. Magic 1 was limited by its relatively insensitive IR detector to rear aspect attacks only. The externally similar Magic 2 served to address this deficiency by introducing a more sensitive IR seeker, permitting all-aspect engagements. Other changes included an improved IRCM capability, replacement of the Magic 1's IR proximity fuze with an RF fuze, a 10 per cent increase in thrust from the solid propellant rocket motor and decreased time to prepare the missile for launch. The 13-kg (28.6-lb) high-explosive warhead of the Magic 1 is retained. With a launch weight of 90 kg (200 lb), the Magic 2 has a range of approximately 5 km (3 miles) compared to the 3 km (1.8 miles) of the Magic 1.

Conversion programme

Two prototype F1CTs were funded for conversion by Dassault, of which the first (which was begun in 1989 in Biarritz-Parme) was delivered to the CEV trials unit at Istres on 3 May 1991. '273' was the first 'production' conversion from the air force's own workshops (Atelier Industriel de l'Armée de l'Air) at Clermont-Ferrand/Aulnat. The 1990 defence budget included funds for 19 conversions, with authorisation for 22 more. The 1991 budget removed funding for a final batch of 14.

The Armée de l'Air and the F1

The Mirage F1 equipped a total of 11 air defence fighter squadrons at its peak, before replacement by the Mirage 2000C began during 1988. It marked a major advance in air defence capability, although initially its radar and missiles were little better than those of the aircraft it replaced. Fast, easy to maintain and agile, the F1 also had a viable radius of action even without inflight refuelling. Upgrades to radar and avionics, and integration of the Super 530 missile further improved capability. Until 1995 EC 3/30 will remain in the French air defence role with F1Cs, with the F1C-200s of EC 4/30 in Djibouti and of EC 3/12 in the OCU role. Three further squadrons flew the F1CR until 1993, when they were reorganised into two units. Even after 1995, the Mirage F1 will have an important role to play. Effectively concentrated into a super wing at Colmar will be the ER 1/33 'Belfort' and ER 2/33 'Savoie', with EC 3/33 (formerly EC 3/30) as a conversion unit alongside the two Mirage F1CT units, EC 1/30 'Normandie-Niémen' and EC 2/30 'Alsace' (nominally autonomous parts of EC 30).

Defensive systems

In addition to R550 Magic missiles, the standard defensive fit consists of an underwing Barax ECM jammer/detector pod, as shown here, with a Phimat chaff/flare dispenser under the opposite wing and with Corail chaff/flare dispensers in conformal gondolas under the wing roots. These augment the on-board RHAWS.

Radar warning receivers

RWR is Thomson-CSF SHERLOC (TMV 011). Compared with the standard F1's Thomson-CSF BF unit (also fitted to other Mirage F1s and some upgraded export Mirage III/V/50S), it is equipped with a more comprehensive threat library, has faster processing and presents data on a CRT with alpha-numeric notations. The BF has simple direction indication plus three lights for pulse-Doppler, CW or TWS indication.

Camouflage scheme

The F1CT is currently the sole F1 variant to wear a wraparound camouflage scheme. This was adopted due to the aircraft's new low-level tactical role. The continuation of upper surface disruptive camouflage onto the lower surfaces removes the possibility of an enemy seeing 'flashes' of the lighter underside colours. The F1CR was delivered in a similar two-tone NATO grey and green camouflage but retained silver/grey undersides because of their predominantly medium-level reconnaissance tasking. Many F1CRs have also worn temporary desert camouflage colour schemes. The F1CTs carry small national markings and toned-down squadron insignia.

Keith Fretwell

Above: Usually carried on an 18-store carrier, the **BAT120** is a parachute-retarded anti-armour weapon packed with fragments which penetrate armour over a wide area. A stick of 18 can disperse 45,000 main fragments over 35000 m² (376,750 sq ft). It is closely related to the very similar looking **BAP100** runway penetrating bomb, which is carried in the same fashion by Mirage F1s.

Above right: The **MATRA F4** rocket pod contains 18 Thomson Brandt 68-mm **SNEB** rockets (or the Multi Dart 68 rockets, though these are normally fired from a **MATRA 155** pod), and is still a regular **F1** weapon. High explosive, armour piercing or incendiary warheads can be fitted.

Right: An Aérospatiale (Nord) **AS30L** is fired by a Mirage **F1C**. The twin side-by-side sustainer nozzles are clearly visible. Each contains a spoiler plate for course corrections. The missile requires illumination by an **ATLIS** designator pod.

Left: Test firing a **MATRA Armat** from a Mirage **F1**. Used operationally against Iranian air defence radars by Iraqi Mirage **F1EQ**s, the Armat is a modernised development of the anti-radar version of the Anglo-French Martel, with a new seeker and electronics. It is used by France, Iraq, Kuwait and Egypt.

Below: The Apache Container Weapon System originated as a Franco-German unpowered stand-off glide cluster-bomb, though it is now turbojet powered, with varying ranges according to sub-type up to 150 km (93 miles). The wings are stowed fore-and-aft above the rear fuselage, being spread after launch.

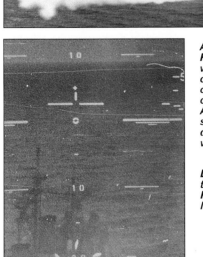

Above: Iraqi Mirage **F1EQ-5s** and **F1EQ-6s** are fitted with Agave radar which confers full anti-ship capability, while retaining air-to-air capability. This makes these aircraft compatible with the Aérospatiale **AM39 Exocet** sea-skimming anti-ship missile, which it used to devastating effect during the long war with Iran.

Left: A camera gun frame, filmed through the **HUD**, from a Mirage **F1CE** during a mock attack on a **US Navy** warship.

Friend and foe: A South African Air Force Mirage F1AZ, wearing the distinctive insignia of No. 3 Squadron, flies close escort on an Angolan MiG-17 which defected on 8 July 1981. The aircraft was evaluated before being dismantled and returned to its original owners.

the Mirage F1C was registering a creditable 85 per cent serviceability. Mirage F1s of all nations exceeded 1,000,000 flying hours in June 1989.

In place of fire control radar, the Mirage F1A sports only a small nose radome for a Dassault Electronique Aïda II ranging radar. Despite its fixed antenna and 16° cone of view, Aïda is a versatile set with search, acquisition, ranging and tracking modes for land, sea and air targets. Range against an aerial target is 10 km (6 miles), increasing to 12 km (7.5 miles) over land and 36 km (22 miles) at sea. Additional space in the F1A's nose is used for a retractable refuelling probe, a laser rangefinder and other repositioned avionics which allow the aircraft to increase the size of the fuel tank behind the cockpit. The avionics suite, known as Système d'Attaque au Sol (Ground Attack System), comprises a Thomson-CSF TAV-38 laser-ranger, Dassault Avionique Doppler navigation system, SFIM inertial navigation, a Thomson-CSF 129 HUD, Thomson-CSF map display and computers by Creuzet and Thomson-CSF. In clear weather, this allows targets to be acquired at a distance of 5 km (3 miles) for automatic bomb release.

Multi-role variants

Remaining single-seat aircraft are versions of Mirage F1E, even the misleadingly labelled F1CR and F1CT. All have additional modes to their Cyrano IV radar, the other baseline avionics including SAGEM ULISS 47 INS, Dassault Electronique 182 central computer, Thomson-CSF VE-120 cathode ray tube HUD, Sextant air data computer, and digital armament and navigation control panels. For most multi-role Mirage F1 versions, radar is either Cyrano IV or IVM, the former (as in Mirage F1CT) still being basically interception orientated, but with air-to-ground and air-to-sea modes and improved ECM resistance. Cyrano IVM is optimised for multi-sensor reconnaissance aircraft (Mirage F1CR), having the same capabilities as the IV, plus ground mapping (with optional Doppler beam-sharpening), contour mapping and blind penetration modes. Iraqi Mirage F1EQ-5s and -6s are equipped with Thomson-CSF Agave radar for compatibility with Aérospatiale AM39 Exocet anti-ship missiles. Fitted to the Dassault Super Etendard naval fighter, Agave does have air-to-air and -ground modes in spite of being optimised for naval attack.

Mirage F1CR is the designation of aircraft intended for reconnaissance and secondary attack with the French air force but, as noted above, retaining radar. An SAT SCM2400 Super Cyclope infra-red linescan system replaces the starboard gun and an undernose bay houses either a Thomson-TRT (formerly OMERA) 40 panoramic camera

of 75-mm format or a quickly interchangeable Thomson-TRT 33 vertical 150-mm camera. Unlike earlier French F1s, ejection seat is the zero-zero SEMMB Mk 10. Beginning in 1993, F1CRs were retrofitted with a FLIR in the port gun bay, providing imagery to a new HUD. They will also gain MATRA Corail underwing chaff and flare containers to partly replace the earlier self-defence fit of flares in the brake parachute housing and a Phimat pod on the starboard outer pylon. A Barax ECM jamming pod is still carried on the port outer wing position.

External sensors

Remaining F1CR reconnaissance equipment is carried in pods on the centreline pylon. A range of these is available, but France uses only the 565-kg (1,246-lb) Thomson-CSF Raphaël side-looking airborne radar and 400-kg (882-lb) Thomson-CSF ASTAC ground radar locator. The latter was tested beneath a French Mirage F1CR in 1991, prior to service acceptance. Raphaël SLAR can be operated in Alpha mode to locate objects larger than 36 m² (400 sq ft) at a distance of 100 km (60 miles), or in Beta mode for 9 m² (100 sq ft) targets at 50 km (30 miles). Medium-altitude reconnaissance is conducted with a SLAR pod and nose-mounted T-TRT 33 vertical camera in the nose – the latter having a positional matrix (derived from the ULISS 47 INS) printed on the film for post-mission correlation of imagery. Low-level sorties are flown without SLAR and only a T-TRT 40 panoramic nose camera.

Super Cyclope is available on any mission and, like Raphaël, can have its data down-loaded on landing or while still airborne. Maximum range of the real-time datalink is 350 nm (649 km; 403 mph) at high level, although operational considerations significantly reduce this in all except uncontested airspace. Each of the three French F1CR squadrons has an air-transportable SARA (Système d'Aérotransportable de Reconnaissance Aérienne) ground station comprising eight caravans containing datalinks, processing and analysis equipment. The first SARA was delivered in August 1984.

Two Mirage F1C-200s (Nos 269 and 277) were taken from the production line and converted to F1CR-200 prototypes (Nos 01 and 02), of which the first was flown at Istres by M. Fremond on 20 November 1981. The pair received 'production' serial numbers 601 and 602 around the time that No. 603 made its initial flight, at Bordeaux, on 10 November 1982. Other types of export Mirage F1 can be adapted to carry centreline reconnaissance pods, including 680-kg (1,500-lb) Dassault HAROLD (Thomson-TRT 38 long-range oblique camera with 1700-mm lens, giving 4

Left: The Mirage F1C-200 was heavily committed during Operation Epervier, the French intervention against Libyan incursions in Chad. This aircraft from EC 1/5 'Vendé' carries a centreline fuel tank, but is otherwise unarmed. EC 2/12 was also among the units which contributed aircraft to the operation.

m³/43 sq ft object resolution at 100 km/60 miles); 400-kg (880-lb) Dassault COR2 multi-purpose pod with a mixture of four Thomson-TRT 35 visual-spectrum cameras with focal lengths between 44 and 600 mm, one T-TRT 70 panoramic and one Super Cyclope IR linescan; 257-kg (567-lb) Thomson-CSF TMV 018 Syrel real-time electro-optical recce pod; 85-kg (187-lb) Dassault NORA (Nacelle Optique de Reconnaissance Aérienne) real-time video. A simpler device used by French F1Cs in Djibouti is the RP 35P pod, which is no more than a standard drop-tank equipped with a camera.

The F1CT is the latest of the Mirage F1 variants to emerge since production finished, and met a French requirement for an interim ground attack aircraft to fill the gap between Mirage IIIE/Mirage 5F and the delayed Dassault Rafale. The basis for a conversion programme lay in the availability of Mirage F1C-200s made redundant by Mirage 2000C deliveries to air defence squadrons. The Mirage F1CT derives its designation from being a tactical (*tactique*) air-to-ground version of the F1C interceptor, although retaining interceptor capability. Two prototypes were converted by Dassault at Biarritz (the first flying on 3 May 1991) and 55 more are following from the Atelier Industriel de l'Aéronautique (aviation workshops) at Clermont-Ferrand/Aulnat by 1995. The first of these, No. 273, was flown by Cdt Vinson of the CEV on 30 January 1992 and

delivered to CEAM at Mont-de-Marsan on 13 February 1992.

Launched in December 1988, the F1CT programme upgrades interceptors to a similar standard to the tactical recce F1CR, the retrofit taking a year to incorporate in the first aircraft produced at Clermont-Ferrand. Radar changes from Cyrano IV to IVMR, with additional air-to-ground modes, and is backed by a SAGEM ULISS 47 inertial platform, Dassault Electronique M182XR central computer, Thomson VE120 HUD, Thomson-TRT TMV630A laser rangefinder beneath the nose, SEMMB Mk 10 zero-zero ejection seat, Thomson-CSF SHERLOC radar warning receiver, chaff/flare dispensers and secure radio. Structurally, the cockpit is rebuilt and the wing strengthened and modified for activation of the outboard hardpoints, while the port cannon is removed to make space for the additional equipment (most notably provision for a FLIR) and the whole airframe is rewired and fitted with new dielectric panels. Strengthening of the centreline pylon permits carriage of the large 2200-litre (484-Imp gal) tank originally developed for the Iraqi Mirage F1EQ. Externally, the blue-grey air defence camouflage is exchanged for overall green and grey. The F1CT carries bombs and rocket pods to fulfil its new mission, but retains the ability to launch Super 530F-1 and Magic 2 AAMs in order to act as a pure interceptor in the air defence role.

Left: Mirage F1s were deployed to Saudi Arabia for service during Operations Desert Shield and Desert Storm (Operation Daguet to the French). These included Mirage F1C-200s for the air defence of Qatar, and F1CRs, as seen here, for tactical and armed reconnaissance. The F1C-200s were drawn from EC12, and were based at Ali Al Salem air base, while the ER 33 F1CRs were based at Al Ahsa in Saudi Arabia. French Mirage F1s were grounded for the first few days of the air war because of fears that they might be mistaken for Iraqi Mirage F1s.

Two essentially similar trainer versions of the Mirage F1 are the F1B and F1D, equivalents of the F1C interceptor and F1E export multi-role attack aircraft. Curiously, it was not France, but Kuwait, which placed the first order for a tandem-seat F1, the initial example of which flew on 26 May 1976 and was tested at CEAM before delivery. Fitting a second cockpit to the F1 increases its length by 30 cm (11½ in) and raises empty weight by 200 kg (440 lb), despite the fact that both DEFA 553 cannon and their magazines are removed. Internal fuel capacity is reduced by 450 litres (99 Imp gal) and a dummy refuelling probe can be fitted for training. For a French pilot's first practice connections with a Boeing C-135FR tanker, the radome is replaced by a metal nosecone, in case of mishaps. Trainers have SEMMB Mk 10 zero-zero seats with command ejection.

Weapons options

The wide market achieved by Dassault combat aircraft invariably results in them carrying a broad spectrum of weaponry, French and foreign. As first delivered, the F1 was an interceptor armed with the Mirage IIIE's standard weapon, the MATRA R530FE. Fitted with either an infra-red or semi-active radar-homing head, the R530FE was formally cleared for Mirage F1C application after qualification trials at the CEV's Cazaux detachment between 7 and 18 December 1977, although it had earlier been carried by squadron aircraft during training. Despite its size, the R530 had a range of only 18 km (11 miles) and an unimpressive claimed kill probability of only 35 per cent. In fact, the R530 was probably an even worse weapon than these figures might suggest. More effective was the IR-seeking MATRA R550 Magic, a Sidewinder-sized weapon, which gained IOC in 1975 and was first launched from a Mirage F1 at Cazaux in December 1976. Following trials with 5 Wing, it was issued to other units during 1978 and carried on wingtip rails. The Magic's effective envelope extends from 300 m (330 yd) to 10 km (6.2 miles). Magic 2, with a

new motor and more sensitive seeker, entered production in 1984. Most analysts rate the missile as being inferior to late-generation AIM-9 variants, however.

A considerable improvement in medium-range effectiveness occurred with the advent of MATRA's semi-active radar homing Super 530. Very different from the pointed-winged R530, the Super 530 has extremely short-span, broad-chord fins and a range of 35 km (22 miles). Its Dassault Electronique AD26 seeker head is optimised for the Mirage F1's Cyrano IV radar, in which application it is known as Super 530F-1 (not to be confused with the first-generation R530FE – and R530ZE on South African Mirages – or the Mirage 2000's Super 530D). The first guided Super 530 was fired in 1976 (from a Mirage F1 at CEV, Cazaux), deliveries to the AA following in September 1978 and formal commissioning in December 1979 with EC 12 as the first user. The wing was at that time assigned to medium-altitude interception and was best suited to utilise the Super 530's snap-up/snap-down potential of 7600 m (24,950 ft), which was later improved to 9000 m (29,550 ft). Super 530 undertook its first double launch on 7 November 1985.

Interceptor Mirage F1Cs of the French air force have a secondary attack role using two MATRA F4 rocket pods, each containing 18 missiles of 68-mm calibre. The F1CR has avionics better suited to attack, and thus can carry alternative loads of Brandt BAT 120 120-kg (265-lb) anti-armour bomblets, Brandt BAP 100 100-kg (220-lb) anti-runway bomblets, MATRA BLG-66 Belouga cluster-bombs, 195-kg (430-lb) MATRA Durandal anti-runway bombs and SAMP EU2 250-kg (551-lb) bombs. Also available for centreline pylon fitment is the Thomson-CSF ATLIS (Automatic Tracking Laser Illumination System) pod for use with SAMP T200 400-kg (882-lb) LGBs. This latter combination is little used by French F1s, but is one of many weapon options employed abroad, the Aérospatiale AS30L missile being another system compatible with ATLIS. The resourceful Iraqis even adapted their Russian X29L (AS-14 'Kedge')

Dassault Mirage F1CE

The Spanish air force uses a mix of 45 Mirage F1CE interceptors and 20 F1EE multi-role fighter-bombers, as well as six F1BE two-seat trainers. All are concentrated in Ala 14 (the 14th Wing), the F1EEs having served with Escuadron 462 of Ala 46 until 1992. Now aircraft from Ala 14 (including F1CEs) are temporarily detached to the Canaries, while remaining under the ownership of Ala 14. The new arrangement makes a great deal of sense, since in days gone by the F1EE fighter-bombers were dedicated to the air defence role, while the F1CEs based in mainland Spain had an important secondary ground attack commitment, spending 40 per cent of their time training for the latter. This aircraft wears the newly adopted light grey air defence colour scheme, with Ala 14 badges and specially applied tiger squadron markings.

Tiger stripes
Many NATO fighter squadrons which have a tiger (or sometimes some other 'big cat') as their badge take part in regular competitions and get-togethers known as 'Tiger Meets'. Aircraft participating in such events often receive extra decoration in the form of areas of tiger-stripe paint.

Pitot probe
Fighter and multi-role versions of the Mirage F1 carry their pitot probes on the tips of their nose radomes, while F1A fighter-bombers have a longer pitot probe mounted further back and slung below their noses. This gathers pitot/static data from the clean, undisturbed airflow ahead of the aircraft for the primary flight instruments, including the airspeed indicator and altimeter.

Fin antennas
Flush dielectric panels on the fin cover a notch aerial on the leading edge for the UHF communications radios and, inside the fin-top, an antenna for the VHF radio. Horizontal blade antennas on the sides of the fin are VOR localiser aerials. These receive signals from VHF omni-range ground beacons.

Nose gear
The steerable nose undercarriage unit consists of twin rearward-retracting nosewheels each shod with a 360 x 135 mm Dunlop high-pressure tyre.

Perforated airbrake
The Mirage F1 carries its airbrakes close to the centre of lift in order to minimise pitch changes when they are deployed. Each takes the form of a downward/outward-hinging door and each is perforated by a series of differentially sized holes, which minimise buffet. The airbrakes are hydraulically actuated, using a single ram.

Tail unit
The all-moving tailplane is mid-set on the fuselage and, like the fixed tailfin, is of twin-spar construction. The rudder actuator is in a fairing on the starboard side of the fin. This aircraft has prominent conical antenna fairings on the leading and trailing edges for the Thomson CSF BF passive radar warning system, and a brake chute fairing immediately below the rudder.

Radome
The radome covering the Cyrano IV radar is exceptionally long and slender, giving the Mirage F1 an unusual and distinctive nose shape.

Viability

While the Mirage F1 lacks the very high levels of agility of the latest FBW superfighters, and its primitive and cramped cockpit imposes a heavy cockpit workload, the aircraft is an effective combat aircraft, especially in the air-to-ground role, and as an air-to-air fighter compares favourably with aircraft like the F-5 and F-4. The Mirage F1's old-fashioned but well laid out cockpit has many features in common with earlier Dassault fighters, easing conversion from aircraft like the Mirage III. Simple to maintain and operate, the aircraft also has a competitive performance, and Dassault provide excellent spares support. The Spanish air force clearly feels that the Mirage F1 is still a viable interceptor and ground attack platform, since they are currently trying to purchase the F1s recently retired by Kuwait. French Mirage F1C-200s retired from the air defence role have been converted for further service as tactical ground attack aircraft.

Structure

Like most aircraft of its generation, the Mirage F1 is of all-metal construction, with no significant use of advanced alloys or composites. The fuselage is of conventional semi-monocoque construction, with integrally machined primary structure and chemically milled secondary frames and fuel tank panels, etc. Secondary structure is spot welded, the rest being bolted or flush riveted and sealed. The wings have two main spars and four auxiliary spars.

Radar

Based as it is on the basic Mirage F1C interceptor, the Mirage F1CE is fitted with Cyrano IV monopulse air intercept radar. Designed for the Mirage F1, the radar has a coaxial magnetron as a signal generator and operates in the 8-10 GHz (NATO I Band). It employs a basic flat-plate antenna since it dates from before Thomson CSF's flirtation with twist cassegrain antennas. Scanning through 120° in azimuth, and 60° in elevation, the radar provides information to the pilot via the weapons sight. The pilot can place a marker over a target, and the radar then automatically switches to its tracking mode, measuring range and relative velocity. The system can then signal both the earliest and the optimum times for weapons launch, and can indicate when a 'firing window' has ended. French Mirage F1Cs had their Cyrano IV radars upgraded to virtual IV-M standards, and this later standard of radar (with multi-role capability) was also applied to some late export Mirage F1C derivatives and most F1EEs. The further refined IV-MR is used by the F1CR and F1CT, and gives additional capabilities at low level.

Wingtip missile launch rail

The wingtip is stressed for the carriage of a variety of light stores, usually defensive AAMs, but also including Phimat chaff/flare dispensers or Barracuda ECM pods. When a missile is carried, a launch rail is fitted centrally as on the F-104 (rather than being underslung). While intended primarily for the carriage of the MATRA R550 Magic, some export customers prefer to use versions of the AIM-9 Sidewinder family. This Spanish aircraft carries a Philco-Ford AIM-9P on each wingtip launch rail. Similar launch rails can be carried on the underwing pylons, but this is unusual, since these stations usually accommodate longer-range missiles such as the MATRA R530FE or the new-generation Super 530F1.

Afterburner

The Mirage F1's SNECMA Atar 9K50 engine is fitted with an integral variable-area afterburner nozzle. This is associated with an approach control system which allows the aircraft to maintain a nearly constant airspeed during the approach. This automatically varies engine power, by altering jetpipe area, during the approach, as well as functioning as a conventional convergent/divergent afterburner nozzle.

Pylons

Two Alkan universal stores attachment points are mounted under each wing, with a further attachment point under the centreline. These are augmented by hardpoints for wingtip stores. Total warload is 4000 kg (8,820 lb). The attachment points can be used to mount a variety of pylons, including the Alkan 910, 915 and 38DN (for the R530 missile).

Actuators

Flap and aileron hinges and actuators are housed in small well-faired fairings under each wing. Leading-edge slat actuators are flush with the wing surface when the slats are retracted. The leading-edge surfaces consist of slotted flaps (slats) outboard and simple hinging flaps (leading-edge flaps) inboard. These can function automatically in conjunction with the trailing-edge flaps as manoeuvre devices.

Undercarriage

Designed to be rugged enough for operation from semi-prepared strips, the Messier-Hispano-Bugatti undercarriage is both complex and heavy. Its retraction sequence is similarly complex, the oleos swinging forwards and inwards while the wheels rotate to lie vertically fore-and aft in the sides of the intake ducts. Each unit is fitted with twin mainwheels, with 605 x 155 mm Dunlop tyres inflated to 9-11 bars (130-160 psi). Unusually, when they are extended, the lower parts of the oleos sweep forward. Messier-Hispano brakes and anti-skid units are fitted as standard. Landing and taxi lights are not fitted to the undercarriage units, a single ground-adjustable taxi light being mounted behind a flush port in the port intake cheek.

Dassault Mirage F1

Right: The two most important Armée de l'Air aircraft types during the Gulf War were the SEPECAT Jaguar and the Mirage F1CR. Although the Jaguars flew more sorties, the more accurate nav attack system of the Mirage F1CR made it a valuable complement to the Anglo-French striker. While the air defence-assigned Mirage F1Cs and Mirage 2000Cs never encountered an enemy aircraft, the pilots of 33 Escadre de Reconnaissance had a more active war, mounting joint attacks with the Armée de l'Air SEPECAT Jaguars. They amassed 264 combat flying hours spread over 114 sorties.

ASMs to function with ATLIS. In future, French Mirages may use the MATRA APACHE (Arme Propulsée A CHarge Ejectable) stand-off weapons container, the first full trial of which took place at Cazaux on 11 June 1987, launched from the CEV's Mirage F1C No. 5.

Standard weapon pylons are Alkan 910 on the centreline, Alkan 915/916 for the inner wing positions, and Dassault units outboard, all with 115A ejectors. Optional adaptors include a Dassault CLB4 for four bombs beneath the fuselage, CLB30 carrying one bomb on the outer wing pylons, CLB8 for four bombs on the inner wing, and Rafaut AUF-2 to take two Belougas.

Typical combat weights would comprise 7400 kg (16,314 lb) empty equipped, plus 5350 kg (11,795 lb) of fuel in full internal tanks and two RP 35/2 drop-tanks on inboard wing pylons, plus 3450 kg (7,606 lb) of ordnance on centreline, outer wing and wingtip pylons to bring the aircraft up to its maximum take-off weight of 16200 kg (35,715 lb). Some over-enthusiastic sales brochures quote a 6300-kg (13,890-lb) weapons load (the combined bearing strengths of all hardpoints), with which it would be impossible to fill even the internal tanks before exceeding maximum take-off weight. More practically, maximum stores load for a short-range mission would be 4000 kg (8,818 lb). Export customers have specified MATRA ARMAT anti-radiation missiles, 1000-kg (2,205-lb) bombs, CEM 1 multi-store carriers (18 rockets of 68 mm, plus either two Durandals or several BAP 100 bomblets) and Dassault CC-420 pods containing one 30-mm DEFA 553 cannon and 180 rounds. Iraq, of course, employed the Aérospatiale AM39 Exocet anti-ship missile with some success during the 1980-88 war with Iran and attempted a similar raid in the 1991 Gulf War, possibly using the Intertechnique buddy refuelling pod to extend the Mirage's range on missions towards the southern end of the Arabian Gulf.

With one Exocet on the centreline, two Magics, two ECM pods and two RP 35/2 tanks, the Mirage F1E's unrefuelled lo-lo radius is 700 km (435 miles), including the 60-70 km (37-43 miles) range of the missile. This is achieved at a cruising speed of 400 kt (742 km/h; 461 mph), apart from the first 95 km (59 miles) of the return flight which are flown at 550 kt (1019 km/h; 633 mph). Radius can be stretched to 900 km (559 miles) with one buddy refuelling. Ultimate unrefuelled radius is 1400 km (870 miles), but only if flown hi-lo-hi, without Magic and ECM protection and with only two 250-kg (551-lb) bombs.

Defensive aids available to the Mirage F1 include Thomson-CSF Barem and Dassault Electronique Barax jamming pods. MATRA Phimat chaff/flare pods are used by France, although an alternative or additional fit involves replacing the braking parachute with a 14-shot Lacroix flare dispenser.

Some export customers, including Qatar, use the MATRA Sycomor chaff/flare system in podded form or in gondolas scabbed to the wing's underside, just outboard of the roots. This same position is used for Alkan LL 5020 dispensers and their development, the Corail, now coming into use with the French Mirage F1CR.

The Mirage III's ability to turn round rapidly between sorties was demonstrated graphically by Israel in the 1967 Six Day War and was a feature which Dassault sought to perpetuate in the Mirage F1. Time between two intercept missions is claimed to be 15 minutes, including six minutes for a full refuel via the single-point pressure system, while maintenance requirements were targeted at 4.5 hours per flying hour. Replacing the engine, for example, is a three-hour job for four men. Major overhauls are required every 800 flying hours, interspersed with inspections every 200. To maintain the F1 at a high state of cockpit readiness, reducing reaction time to two minutes, a GAMO alert truck is available to supply electrical power for pre-heating systems, cooling radar

Left: One of No. 3 Squadron's Mirage F1AZs discharges an IR decoy flare. The refuelling probe cover is clearly evident on the top of the nose. South African Mirage F1s went from a factory-applied sand and olive camouflage to an overall grey, before green and dark brown was reapplied to the upper surfaces. National insignia shrank, then disappeared, and squadron markings have been progressively reduced in size and toned down.

and air conditioning the cockpit, its thoughtful extras including a parasol on a telescopic arm to shade the pilot. Selection of the engine starting procedure automatically disconnects the GAMO umbilical cord and the Mirage is ready to taxi. GAMO is air mobile, as is the trailer-mounted SDAP automatic check-out system which can examine all aircraft systems and detect any faults within 15 minutes.

'Eurofighter' bid

The export Mirage F1E now in widespread service differs in vital details from the similarly-designated machine with which France had earlier attempted to win the informal competition to supply a single, standard tactical fighter for NATO air forces, which became known as the 'Sale of the Century'. The requirement to replace a mixture of Lockheed F-104G Starfighters, Northrop F-5A Freedom Fighters and North American F-100D/F Super Sabres in the Belgian, Danish, Netherlands and Norwegian air forces was never an official joint requirement (let alone a NATO one), but the four nations acted in concert in order to get the best possible deal. The competition was held during the first half of the 1970s and promised an initial prize of 350 orders with follow-ons for at least another 200. US contenders were the Northrop YF-17 Cobra (later developed into McDonnell Douglas F/A-18 Hornet), General Dynamics F-16 (later Fighting Falcon) and projected Lockheed CL-1200 Lancer,

Below: Mirage F1CRs were deployed to Turkey in support of UN enforcement of 'No-Fly Zones' over northern Iraq. This aircraft carries defensive AAMs, chaff dispenser, ECM pod and centreline recce pod.

Dassault Mirage F1

Right: The conversion of Mirage F1C-200 units to the Mirage 2000C resulted in the sudden availability of plenty of surplus F1C-200 airframes. These were converted for further service in the ground attack role under the new designation F1CT, to replace ageing and relatively inflexible Mirage 5s. Aircraft 274 is seen during trials with CEAM, wearing that unit's 118 codes and fin badge.

Below: A Mirage F1CT of EC 1/13 'Artois' banks away from the camera aircraft, showing off its wraparound camouflage scheme. The aircraft wears the dragon badge of SPA 83 on the starboard side of the tailfin. The squadron's original SPA identities for its constituent escadrilles were changed when EC 1/13 took over the traditions of 'Normandie-Niémen'.

while Europe fielded the Mirage F1E (E for European) and outsider Saab 37 Viggen. The initially promising Dassault entry began to be overtaken by American products as the assessment progressed and so was revamped as the F1-M53, so named from the superior thrust provided by a SNECMA M53 Super Atar.

Rated at 54.9 kN (12,345 lb st) dry and 83.4 kN (18,740 lb st) with afterburning (i.e. 18 per cent more than an Atar 9K-50), the Super Atar was an 'almost turbofan' developed by SNECMA as a simpler alternative to the troublesome TF306 it worked on for the Mirage IIIG. This bypass turbojet had the same 'keep it simple and reliable' philosophy which Dassault had found so effective with Third World customers for two generations of Mirages. However, NATO was looking for something more advanced.

Having been a private venture for two years, the M53-powered F1 gained official backing on 16 March 1973 when the French government declared its support for the programme, promising to pay two-thirds of the cost. Fine words on European collaboration were backed up by a promise that the Armée de l'Air would take between 40 and 120 F1Es (and F1D trainers) if at least two other countries placed orders. Having on several previous occasions stated its lack of interest in an aircraft costing 20 per cent more than the F1C, the announcement came as somewhat of a surprise to the AA, which again faced the prospect of being landed with a Mirage variant for which it had neither asked nor budgeted. Guy Mitaux-Maurouard was aboard F1E No. 01 for its maiden flight on 22 December 1974, during which it achieved Mach 1.35 and 11582 m (38,000 ft) during a one-hour sortie. Two flights on the next day raised speed to Mach 1.65 and then 1.84, while a Christmas Eve mission touched Mach 2.05. Representatives of the four prospective purchasers were shown round the prototype on 8 January 1975.

The aircraft they saw was 23 mm (9 in) longer than a standard F1, had slightly larger air intakes and rear fuselage and was equipped with improved avionics, including Cyrano IV-100 radar, a SAGEM/Kearfott SKN2603 INS and HUD. Among performance improvements were an extra 1200 m (4,000 ft) on ceiling, initial climb rate improved by 60 m/second (12,000 ft/minute), time to 12192 m (40,000 ft)

reduced by 2.5 minutes, a further +0.7 *g* on the steady turn rate at Mach 0.95, and 105 km (65 miles) on the hi-lo-hi range with four 454-kg (1,000-lb) bombs. Reserved designations were F1EB for Belgium, F1ED for Denmark, F1EN for the Netherlands and F1FV for Norway. None was used, for the Mirage F1 was unable to offer interested air forces and potential sub-contractors a high-technology, fly-by-wire airframe nor did it have sufficient potential for future growth, although Dassault's arguments that the aircraft was faster than its rivals at high level, and better suited to withstanding European weather, proved powerful, as did the fact that the F1M-53 carried a representative weapons system and that its twin DEFA 30-mm cannon were more powerful than the single 20-mm Vulcan gun used by the F-16 and YF-17. It also attempted to point out that the YF-16 and YF-17 were mere technology demonstrators, using 'untried' fly-by-wire control systems and what Dassault chose to present as other 'immature' technologies.

An acrimonious European fighter competition was concluded when Belgium fell into line behind the other three customers and selected the F-16, having finally been persuaded that tactical, technical and military considerations were more important than the political advantages of selecting an all-European option. Cruelly, the decision was announced on home ground on 7 June 1975 at the Paris air show, where the F1E prototype was a central exhibit. No. 01 disappeared from the show for a couple of days, then returned in a defiant red, white and blue colour scheme before retreating to Istres for 18 months of storage. It then resumed flying to conduct a series of M53 engine trials in connection with the Mirage 2000 programme before disappearing without trace. Orders for a second F1E and an F1D trainer were cancelled. No move was made to offer the M53-engined Mirage for export elsewhere, even though its additional power was matched with excellent fuel economy. The Armée de l'Air commitment to buy the F1M53 was allowed to drop, since it had always been primarily a politically imposed idea intended to encourage potential overseas customers by providing a theoretical 'home customer'. It also threatened funding for the air force's preferred option, the Super Mirage 4000.

In parallel with the Eurofighter competition, Dassault attempted to interest India in the Mirage F1 for its Deep Penetration Strike Aircraft requirement against opposition from the Jaguar and the Saab 35 Viggen. The Mirage's progenitor was, by now, step-parent to the Anglo-French attack aircraft and no opportunity was lost to sway India away from the favoured Jaguar. By 1972, the Mirage F1 was the anticipated winner, but the selection process dragged on until

1978, when the IAF's will eventually prevailed and the Jaguar won.

Had it won these two competitions, the Mirage F1 would have secured the same sales figure of some 1,400 aircraft achieved by its immediate predecessor, the Mirage III/5. Even more potentially important to the size and importance of the Mirage F1 was a proposal by Boeing to licence-build a Mirage F1 derivative as a back-up, or even an alternative, to the F-15 and/or F-14. Instead, production quietly drew to a halt in 1991 at 731, including five prototypes and 20 embargoed Iraqi airframes. In the increasingly tough world of arms sales that is no mean total, and though less than the enthusiastic predictions of the early 1970s it takes nothing from the fact that the Mirage F1 is one of the most combat-experienced fighters in current service.

Mirage F1 Operators

France

Procurement of Mirage F1s by France is normally quoted as 251, although this total includes all prototypes, two of which were private ventures: Mirage F1 No. 01 and the Mirage F1E (F1-M53) 'Eurofighter'. Funding was undertaken on the usual annual basis, but within outlines laid down by successive five-year defence plans. The first-stage target of 105 aircraft was achieved between 1969 and 1973, the aircraft due for delivery by June 1977. Funding of a further quantity began in 1977 including, for the first time, Mirage F1B trainers. With replacements assured for the Vautour IIN, Super Mystère B2 and Mirage IIIC interceptors, additional aircraft were included in F1CR reconnaissance guise to supplant Mirage IIIRs and IIIRDs, bringing production orders to 225 by 1980. However, because of delays with the Mirage 2000 programme, a further 21 aircraft were added in the 1982 budget for reconnaissance, allowing the same number of earlier machines to be built as F1C interceptors. The position, after some later adjustments, was:

Budget	F1B	F1C	F1CR	F1E	Total
1969	0	30	0	0	30
1971	0	55	0	0	55
1973	0	20	0	0	20
1976	0	11	0	0	11
1977	6	24	0	0	30
1978	9	24	0	0	33
1979	5	0	18	0	23
1980	0	0	23	0	23
1982	0	0	21	0	21
Sub-total	**20**	**164**	**62**	**0**	**246**
Prototypes	0	4	0	1	5
Conversions		-2	+2		
TOTAL	**20**	**166**	**64**	**1**	**251**

Including the air-refuellable F1C-200, the Armée de l'Air (AA) received four Mirage F1 variants, to which it assigned different ranges of serial numbers. Because of diversions and conversions, these were not all consecutive. In addition, Mirage F1C-200s are being converted to F1CT standard, retaining their original serials. Funding for the first 19 F1CTs was assigned in the 1990 budget, followed by 22 in 1991 and the final 14 in 1992. For a total of 246, the aircraft were (as delivered):

Mirage F1B	20 aircraft	Nos 501-520 delivered 21 October 1980 to 1 March 1983
Mirage F1C	83 aircraft	Nos 1-50, 52, 54, 55, 58, 60, 62-64, 67-85, 87, 90 and 100-103 delivered 13 March 1973 to 1 April 1977
Mirage F1C-200	79 aircraft	Nos 202-223, 225-268, 270-276, 278-283 delivered 2 March 1977 to 22 December 1983
Mirage F1CR-200	64 aircraft	Nos 601-664 delivered 23 December 1982 to 15 June 1987
Mirage F1CT	0 aircraft	All conversions (55 aircraft) delivered from 13 January 1992

Notes:

a) F1Cs Nos 1 and 11 became F1C-200s Nos 201 and 224.

b) Nos 51, 53, 56, 57, 59, 61, 65, 66, 86, 88, 89, 91, 93, 94, 96 and 97 diverted to Greece.

c) Nos 92, 95, 98 and 99 completed as Nos 202, 203, 204 and 208, respectively.

d) Nos 269 and 277 completed as F1CRs Nos 01 (later No. 601) and 02 (later 602) respectively.

e) Mirage F1CT prototypes included No. 262; production began with Nos 273, 274, 278, 254, 267, 239, 280, 229, 237, 233 and 242, in that order.

f) During the initial-build-up phase, 16 aircraft were on charge by 31 December 1973, increasing to 48 a year later, then 63, 77, 102 and 101 (sic) by December 1978.

g) Prototypes are assembled at Istres, production aircraft at Bordeaux; the two F1CT prototypes were converted at Biarritz, but the remainder are being produced by the AA's workshops at Clermont-Ferrand/Aulnat.

h) Losses up to 1993 totalled at least one F1B, 12 F1Cs, nine F1C-200s and 10 F1CR-200s.

Administration

Mirage F1Bs and F1Cs were assigned to French Air Defence Command, CAFDA (Commandement 'Air' des Forces de Défense Aérienne), until 1 September 1991, when it was absorbed by FATac, the Force Aérienne Tactique. FATac's single component, the 1er Commandement Aérienne Tactique, has also controlled the Mirage F1CR-200 force from the outset and now administers Mirage F1CTs.

Until recently each fighter wing (Escadre de Chasse) had between two and four fighter squadrons (Escadrons de Chasse), normally comprising two – or occasionally three – flights (Escadrilles). Since 1993, however, a new force structure has resulted in a gradual change from two flights per 15-aircraft squadron to three flights per 20-aircraft squadron, usually accompanied by the disbandment of one of each wing's three squadrons. Wings occupy a single air base, which is both numbered and named for a prominent aviator as well as having a geographical name comprising the nearest village and nearest town or city. Squadrons are usually named for a district of France. Escadrilles perpetuate the traditions of prominent squadrons, often those of World War I which flew SPAD, Nieuport, Salmson, Moineau or Breguet aircraft and whose numbers are therefore prefixed SPA, N, SAL or BR. A few, prefixed ERC, recall the various Escadrilles Régionales de Chasse (Regional Fighter Flights) of 1939-40.

When two-flight squadrons were the rule, normally, No. 1 Escadrille applied its badge to the left side of the fin and No. 2 to the right, but there were exceptions, and in today's three-flight squadrons the badge situation is more confused. Squadrons without numbered flights apply the squadron badge to both sides. Aircraft are identified by a number/letter code comprising the wing number followed by one letter to indicate the squadron and another letter for the individual aircraft. As an example, 5-NA indicates the first aircraft (A) of the first squadron (N) of 5 fighter wing, those of the second squadron being 5-OA onwards, while the third squadron uses 5-AA, etc. The two letters additionally conform to the last pair of a peacetime five-letter callsign group. Two-flight squadron establishments were 15 aircraft and 18 pilots although, taking spares and executive personnel into account, the first two-squadron wings had 31 Mirage F1Cs and 41 pilots.

Colour schemes

The factory-finish colour scheme for the Mirage F1C is medium grey-blue satin (gris bleu moyen satiné) with matte silver undersides. All radomes are black, and remain so, but the red air intake lip markings have been removed. Serial numbers are 15 cm high on the fin. Cockades, originally 52 cm in diameter in six positions on the aircraft, were reduced to 48 cm during the early 1980s by elimination of the yellow outline. As part of this toning down process, squadrons were ordered in 1982 to reduce the size of their fin insignia, some of which was highly visible. The traditional tricolour rudder was abandoned before the F1C entered service and thus only appeared on the prototypes. No. 79 and subsequent F1Cs, all F1C-200s, F1Bs and F1CRs, have fore- and aft-facing bullet fairings for a Thomson-CSF BF radar warning receiver. Nos 70-78 have the modifications necessary for a BF, but the opportunity to retrofit has not been taken.

Above: One of several schemes applied to F1s, this is the 'African' scheme of sand and dark brown. The aircraft is from EC 2/30.

Below: Mirage F1Cs were delivered in this elegant dark grey scheme, with large escadrille markings. Shown is EC 1/12.

One pattern of disruptive upper/side surface camouflage is used for the Mirage F1CR-200, F1C in Djibouti and F1CT. NATO standard grey and green (matte silver below) was applied to the prototype and production F1CRs from 1981, but when the aircraft began to operate in Chad, some adopted 'sand and (dark) chocolate' colours in 1985, sand replacing grey. The same 'African' scheme was applied to Djibouti-based F1Cs of EC 4/30. For the Gulf War, the chocolate shade was significantly lightened for those aircraft newly painted, but the 'African' machines initially retained their darker markings when deployed to Saudi Arabia in late 1990. The lighter colours were used for F1CRs deployed to Turkey from 1991, some of which were repainted from 'African' to 'Iraqi' chocolate, like their Gulf War compatriots. It should be noted, however, that the 'African' scheme lightens through weathering. A further variation was the four-tone scheme used for F1CRs in the February 1987 Red Flag competition, the two additional shades filling the spectrum between sand and chocolate. In the case of the F1CT, the normal green and grey colours are extended to the underside of the aircraft.

Ordnance

Missile armament of the F1C interceptor was originally the MATRA R.530FE in either IR- or SAR-homing form; one on the centre pylon, or two underwing, as first applied to EC 30's aircraft in February 1976, although the weapon was not released for use until December 1977. Wingtip MATRA 550 Magic 1s were available from 1978. Deliveries of Super 530F-1 began in September 1978, and the missile was cleared for use by EC 12 in December 1979, the other wings following. Magic 2 deliveries began in 1984. Wings initially specialised in interception at different altitudes: EC 30, high; EC 12, medium; and EC 5, low.

The standard Mirage F1 drop tank is the RP 35/2 of 1200 litres (264 Imp gal) carried on the centreline or inner wing pylons, although aircraft deployed to Qatar during the Gulf War adopted the 2200-litre (484-Imp gal) centreline tank developed by Dassault for Iraqi Mirage F1EQs. In addition to specific recce pods for the Mirage F1CR, the F1Cs of EC 4/30 based in Djibouti use a centreline RP 35 tank fitted with a single OMERA 60 optical camera. In the alternative attack role, Mirage F1Cs (Djibouti) and F1CTs may carry MATRA LR.F4 rocket pods, BAP 100 anti-runway bomblets, BAT 120 anti-armour bomblets, MATRA BLG-66 Belouga cluster bombs and SAMP 250-kg (551-lb) bombs. For target-towing, F1Cs are equipped with a SECAPEM PR-53 or TAC-100 centreline pod. The former deploys sleeve targets; the latter tows solid, tubular targets containing an audio proximity detector. These R-85 targets are mounted on the wingtip rails, allowing the Mirage full manoeuvrability and use of afterburner until launch.

Outer, underwing hardpoints of the F1C/-200 interceptor are occasionally activated for self-defence equipment, such as a Phimat chaff/flare dispenser (port) and Barax jammer (starboard). F1CRs regularly fit the same equipment, but in reversed positions. The F1CT carries Phimat to starboard and a Barem jammer to port. All Mirage F1s deployed abroad operationally can carry a Lacroix flare dispenser in place of the braking parachute. The modular Alkan Corail chaff/flare dispenser is being issued to F1CR squadrons in 1993, fitted to a new position inboard of the inner wing pylons. Depot maintenance is at Clermont Ferrand/Aulnat with the Atelier Industriel de l'Aéronautique, which began Mirage F1 modifications in 1977 and progressed to full overhauls from 1980 onwards.

Operational use

Mirage F1s have been employed in overseas operations: twice in Chad, and in the Gulf War. For Operation Manta, four Mirage F1C-200s and four Jaguars were deployed from holding positions in Gabon and the Central African Republic to N'Djamena, capital of Chad, on 21 August 1983. Initially, the detachment was assigned to escort visiting French transport aircraft and did not interfere with Libyan air raids supporting rebels invading northern Chad. However, on 25 January 1984 a Mirage was damaged and a Jaguar shot down while attacking a rebel convoy. The French force was withdrawn from 25 September 1984.

Operation Epervier was launched on 16 February 1986 when 12 Jaguars, with four Mirage F1s of EC 5 for cover, attacked the new Libyan-built airfield at Wadi Doum, in northern Chad, from bases in the Central African Republic. Mirage F1CRs of ER 33 provided reconnaissance support, wearing their new 'African' camouflage. Two Mirage F1s

The two-seat conversion trainer was not procured in large numbers, and was not delivered until some way into the single-seat production run. The variant retains full combat capability.

transferred to N'Djamena on 17 February and six more the next day. Jaguars made a further raid on Wadi Doum on 7 January 1987, at which time the Mirage detachment comprised six F1Cs and two F1CRs. The F1Cs of EC 5 provided top cover for this mission while the F1CRs conducted pre- and post-raid reconnaissance. The Mirage presence had grown by early 1988 to 12 F1Cs provided by EC 5, 12 and 30, plus two Mirage F1CRs, seven of this total remaining until 1990 when they were replaced by Mirage 2000Cs. These eventually withdrew on 1-April 1992 after the defeat of the Chad government in a rebel coup.

In connection with preparations for the Gulf War, Operation Salamandre, accomplished between 10 August and 5 October 1990, included deployment of an extra Mirage F1C and a Transall C.160 (tanker version) to reinforce Djibouti. EC 12 provided F1Cs for Operation Méteil, requested by the United Arab Emirates government to boost its air defences. EC 1/12 deployed to Doha on 17 October 1990 with eight aircraft, 12 pilots and 33 ground staff, and EC 3/12 arrived on 18 December with eight aircraft, 12 pilots and 42 ground crew to officially replace its companion on 30 December. When it returned to France on 17 March 1991, EC 3/12 had flown 492 sorties in 434.30 hours, of which 280 sorties/246 hours were operational. EC 2/12 was in Qatar from 15 March with a further eight Mirage F1Cs, 12 pilots and 41 staff, generating 334 sorties in 270.50 hours, much of it supersonic training in air combat zones south of Qatar. The aircraft returned between 2 and 10 May and the last personnel arrived home by civil airliner on 23 May.

The main French action, Operation Daguet, was initiated on 16 September and included four Mirage F1CRs of ER 33 deployed to Al Ahsa, Saudi Arabia, in two groups on 3 and 8 October to support a Mirage 2000C and Jaguar detachment. One aircraft was lost in a fatal accident on 7 December and replaced. The F1CRs had flown 731 hours in 442 sorties, doing useful work in SLAR reconnaissance up to the beginning of hostilities on 17 January 1991, at which time they were grounded to avoid confusion with Iraqi F1EQs. The four returned to action in the fighter-bomber role on 26 January, leading Jaguar raids with use of their navigation radar and carrying four 250-kg bombs in addition to Barax, Phimat, two Magic 2s and a 1200-litre (264-Imp gal) centreline tank. On 5 February photographic and radar reconnaissance was resumed, and intensified after a further pair of F1CRs arrived two days later. During hostilities, which ended on 27 February, the F1CR force flew 114 sorties in 264.40 hours, including 51 reconnaissance sorties, the latter covering bombed bridges over the Euphrates and surveying Route Texas, the advance axis of French ground forces towards As Salman. Mirage F1CRs returned from Saudi Arabia early in March 1991.

Operational Aconit began on 25 July 1991 when four Mirage F1CRs deployed from Istres to Incirlik, Turkey, to join the international force (US Operation Provide Comfort and UK Operation Warden) protecting the Kurdish people of northern Iraq. Four more F1CRs were quickly added, the force making four sorties per day (two camera; two SLAR), each lasting 3½ hours with C-135FR tanker support. Maintained by all three squadrons of ER 33, the detachment was still in place early in 1993, having lost an aircraft near Irbil, Iraq, on 1 June 1992, because of technical failure.

French users

French wings and squadrons operating the Mirage F1 are listed below. Details of the mixture of F1Cs and F1C-200s within fighter squadrons are given for 1991, just prior to F1C-200s beginning progressive withdrawal for conversion to F1CTs. The unprobed F1C will remain with just one wing, EC 30, until it disbands in 1995. The main programme of F1C/-200 deliveries equipped three and one-half wings with two squadrons each, followed by three further squadrons. In chronological order, these were EC 2/30, 3/30, 1/5, 2/5, 3/12 (originally 2/12), 1/12, 2/12, 1/10 (later 1/30), 3/5 and 4/30. During 1981-82, nine of the 10 squadrons constituting CAFDA operated Mirage F1Cs. EC 12 and EC 30 perpetuated the tradition of squadron colours by painting the conical covers to the braking parachute housing: 1/12 and 1/30 both blue; 2/12 and 2/30 both red; 3/12 green; and 3/30 yellow. In the case of the Mirage F1CR, colours are ER 1/33 blue; 2/33 red; and 3/33 black. There are, however, numerous exceptions to the above rules.

Various units have adorned their Mirage F1s with special marks. EC 1/5 painted this aircraft to celebrate its 50,000th F1 hour.

A 'Normandie-Niémen' special – the lions are the badge of Normandy, while the white arrow is that of the 303rd Fighter Division, Soviet air force.

Mirage F1 Operators

5e Escadre de Chasse

EC 5 has been based at Base Aérienne 115 'Capitaine Maurice de Seynes' Orange/Caritat since GC 5 was renumbered on 1 April 1951. It was equipped with two squadrons of Mirage IIICs when, late in 1974, it began passing equipment to EC 10 at Creil in order to become the second Mirage F1C wing. Declared operational (although with only 27 aircraft) on 1 January 1976 under Lt Col Lartigau, it received its 31st and last Mirage F1C in March 1976, establishment at that time also including 41 pilots and some 560 other personnel. Initial aircraft allocation was Nos 38-77, less Greek diversions Nos 51, 53, 56, 57, 59, 61, 65 and 66. The wing began using hardened aircraft shelters from 1 September 1975. EC 5 recorded its 100,000th Mirage F1 hour in December 1985. A probe-equipped F1C-200, No. 202, was received for evaluation early in 1977, both squadrons re-equipping thereafter. A simulated long-range mission was flown by four aircraft in January 1980, involving a non-stop flight from Solenzara (Corsica) to Djibouti to demonstrate rapid deployment capability. In July 1981, EC 5 celebrated its 2,000th aerial victory, the 50,000th Mirage F1 flying hour and the addition of a third squadron.

Escadron de Chasse 1/5 'Vendée'

Aircraft: Mirage F1C/-200
1e Escadrille: SPA26 insignia - cigogne de Saint-Galmier (stork), starboard
2e Escadrille: SPA124 insignia - Jeanne d'Arc (Joan of Arc), port
Codes: 5-NA to 5-NZ (radio call FUGNA/FUGNZ)

In April 1974, 'Vendée' squadron sent its first batch of technical personnel to Mont-de-Marsan to convert to Mirage F1Cs under the guidance of EC 24/118. In June of that year, the first six pilots were transferred to Reims to receive four weeks of ground instruction from the Echelon Mobile d'Instruction F1 before undergoing a flying conversion course with EC 24/118 at Mont-de-Marsan. The first Mirage F1C was delivered on 6 August 1974 by EC 5's commander, Lt Col Denis Letty, and the last Mirage IIICs released to EC 10 at the end of September. Ground training for the rest of the squadron then followed at Reims, the pilots between 15 October and 8 November, technicians from 1 October to 15 December. Groups of pilots then received their flying conversion at Mont-de-Marsan, while the others kept up their flying currency on the Mirage IIICs of EC 2/5.

It was 19 March 1975 before the initial eight aircraft were transferred from Marsan to Orange. Deliveries were completed in April 1975, the squadron being formally commissioned on 26 March. F1Cs initially wore large fin flashes containing the escadrille badges, but these were reduced in size by early 1976 to comprise a pennant superimposed upon a diagonal bar. A further reduction took place with the general order to tone down unit markings in the early 1980s. From July 1977, EC 1/5 was re-equipped with Mirage F1C-200s, the first air-to-air contact with a French Boeing C-135F tanker being made by Capt Pariat on 1 February 1978. EC 1/5 flew its 50,000th Mirage F1 hour on 12 June 1987, but the squadron relinquished its Mirage F1s in January 1988 to begin converting pilots to Mirage 2000Cs, the first of which was received on 20 July that year.

Escadron de Chasse 2/5 'Ile de France'

Aircraft: Mirage F1C/-200
1e Escadrille: Paris
2e Escadrille: Versailles
Insignia: a cross of Lorraine and three fleurs-de-Lys (port and starboard)
Traditions: No. 340 Squadron, Royal Air Force
Codes: 5-OA to 5-OZ (radio call FUGOA/FUGOZ)

Training for a first party of six pilots and 20 technicians of EC 2/5 began with ground school at Reims in June 1975, a further five pilots following in August. The last Mirage IIICs were withdrawn at the end of the month, by which time their predecessors were undertaking flying conversion with EC 1/5. A first deployment to Solenzara took place in August 1966 for air-to-air gunnery and ground attack practice with bombs and rockets. 'Ile de France' re-equipped with -200 refuellable aircraft in 1977, receiving its first Mirage 2000C on 18 April 1989 and currently operating that aircraft type.

Escadron de Chasse 3/5 'Comtat Venaissin'

Aircraft: Mirage F1B and F1C
1e Escadrille: ERC571 insignia - pirate (Algerian pirate flag and scimitar), starboard
2e Escadrille: SPA171 insignia - dragon sable (black dragon), port
Codes: 5-AA to 5-AZ

After seven years as a two-squadron wing of Mirage F1s, EC 5 gained a third component on 1 April 1981. 'Comtat Venaissin' had been EC 3/5 when it disbanded as a Mystère II unit on 30 October 1957, and had remained dormant since then. It was assigned all 20 Mirage F1Bs, three of which had been received by the time of the formal commissioning ceremony on 3 July 1981. Aircraft were allocated the codes 5-AA to 5-AT in serial number order, with reservations for those employed by CEAM. The final F1B was handed over to the AA on 1 March 1983, giving the squadron a complement of 19, plus three F1Cs (coded 5-AU, -AV and -AW). A tragic accident on 18 April 1985 resulted in the loss of No. 508/5-AH and the 1984 and intended 1985 Mirage F1 display pilots. During a low pass with 'everything down', the latter raised flaps instead of undercarriage and the Mirage stalled over the airfield at Orange.

The squadron was re-organised with three flights in December 1985, adding SPA62. This had last disbanded in December 1963 as a flight of the Thunderstreak-equipped EC 2/1 'Morvan'; this was particularly appropriate as its partner flight in 'Morvan' was SPA94, which became the third flight of the Mirage III OCU (EC 2/2) in 1972. In preparation for the conversion of EC 5 to Mirage 2000Cs, 'Comtat Venaissin' was earmarked for brief service as a regular Mirage F1C squadron, which guise it adopted on 1 July 1988, passing the two-seat F1Bs and SPA62 to Reims, where they joined EC 3/30 a month later. After two years, EC 3/5 flew its final Mirage F1C mission on 25 July 1990 and stood down for Mirage 2000C conversion.

Above: EC 1/5 'Vendée' was in the vanguard of F1C refuelling operations, receiving the first F1C-200. The entire wing subsequently upgraded to the Mirage 2000C.

Above: Worn on the port side of EC 1/5's aircraft (for 2e Escadrille) is the Joan of Arc badge, originally carried by SPA124.

Above: The black dragon on the port side of EC 3/5's fin is the badge of SPA171, adopted by the 2nd flight of the squadron.

Below: On EC 3/5's starboard fin is ERC571's Algerian pirate flag. The squadron performed the Mirage F1 OCU role.

Below: EC 2/5 wore the same badge on both sides of the fin of its F1Cs. Its traditions rest in No. 340 Sqn, RAF, the aircraft wearing the cross of Lorraine badge of the Free French.

10e Escadre de Chasse

EC 10 was established as a fighter wing at Base Aérienne 110, Creil/Senlis on 1 December 1954, re-equipping with Mirage IIICs in 1974 as a result of EC 5's conversion to Mirage F1Cs. The wing's second squadron, EC 2/10 'Seine', remained as such until EC 10 disbanded on 1 April 1985, while a third squadron formed abroad with Mirage IIICs in 1979, as explained under the entry for EC 4/30.

Escadron de Chasse 1/10 'Valois'

Aircraft: Mirage F1C/-200
Base: BA112 Reims-Champagne
1e Escadrille: N84 insignia - renard (fox's head), starboard
2e Escadrille: SPA93 insignia - canard (duck), port
Codes: 10-SA to 10-SZ (radio call FUISA/FUISZ)

'Valois' began its conversion to Mirage F1Cs in May 1981 when its pilots transferred to Reims to receive instruction from ETIS F1, flying their first sortie there on 27 May. The squadron's Mirage IIICs were officially transferred to sister squadron EC 2/10 on 1 June, while on 28 August the first six F1Cs were flown to Creil. Among them was No. 27/10-SO, the first to wear a revised form of the SPA84 insignia with fox's head in white (instead of red) within a red rectangle, the latter soon being dropped. Remaining pilot conversion was undertaken at Creil where, by the end of the year, the squadron had received all its 15 aircraft and flown 1,700 hours. In March 1982, it deployed to Istres for a training programme in supersonic flying and in July flew to Greece for an exchange with the Mirage F1CG squadrons at Tanagra. First Magic missile firings were not conducted until late February 1984 during a detachment to Mont-de-Marsan. Also

available to the squadron were MATRA R.530FE AAMs, one of which was carried on the centreline pylon. Initially with a mix of F1Cs and F1C-200s, the squadron had relinquished all the latter by the end of 1984. With the disbandment of 10 Wing in April 1985, the squadron moved to Reims, becoming EC 1/30 'Valois'.

Right: EC 1/10 had a short F1C career in the early 1980s before becoming EC 1/30. The starboard side badge was that of N84.

Below: EC 1/10 F1C armed with an inert Super 530F missile, displaying the SPA93 duck badge.

12e Escadre de Chasse

Installed at Base Aérienne 103 'Commandant René Mouchotte', Cambrai/Epinoy on 1 September 1953, EC 12 received Dassault Super Mystères in 1959 and Mirage F1Cs from 1976, initially under Lt Col Claude Solanet, as the third wing to convert. In the course of working up, the wing's Mirages launched their first Magic AAMs during an armament camp in October 1978 and the first Super 530s in November 1980, the latter confirming the missile's performance against drones flying over 70,000 ft (21335 m). A third squadron was added to EC 12 in June 1980. Initial airborne refuelling training was begun in September 1983, allowing the wing to take part in operations in Africa during the following year. The wing's secondary role is ground attack. Early in 1989, each of the three components received a Mirage F1B from EC 3/30 for training new pilots and applied individual squadron badges and codes, even though all three aircraft were officially assigned to EC 1/12, which accordingly reduced single-seater strength to 12 F1Cs.

Escadron de Chasse 1/12 'Cambrésis'

Aircraft: Mirage F1C/-200
1e Escadrille: SPA162 insignia - tête de tigre (tiger's head), starboard
2e Escadrille: SPA89 insignia - abeille (bee), port
Codes: 12-YA to 12-YZ (radio call FUHYA/FUHYZ)

Conversion to Mirage F1Cs began for EC 1/12 on 16 May 1977 when the first seven pilots were posted to Reims to receive training with EC 30. Deliveries of Mirage F1Cs had actually begun on 31 January 1977 when No. 13 (secondhand, ex-EC 30) arrived and was temporarily held on the charge of EC 2/12, coded '12-ZY' but with tiger and wasp badges (SPA89's badge depicts a wasp, but the certificate of

approval [A-527 of 30 June 1953] describes it as a bee). Transition was completed in September 1977, making it the second – and at that time, last – unit of EC 12 to re-equip. Having been the first squadron to fly Dassault Super Mystères, it was also the last when the final three machines were retired on 9 September 1977.

EC 1/12 was a founder member of the Tiger Squadron association, and attended the first Meet at Woodbridge, England, in July 1961. Application of tiger stripes to one of the squadron's aircraft for such meetings was a regular feature of the Mirage F1 and previous eras. Meets were held at Cambrai in 1964, 1972, 1979 and 1986. Conversion to Mirage 2000Cs resulted in 'Cambrésis' standing down when its pilots were temporarily transferred to Dijon for familiarisation with the new type in October 1991, strength at that time including seven F1C-200s and one F1B. EC 1/12's first Mirage 2000C arrived at Cambrai on 14 April 1992.

Above: One of the best known French squadron badges was worn by the Mirage F1Cs of EC 1/12 'Cambrésis' before the unit's conversion to the Mirage 2000C. The wasp insignia was originally worn much larger on the fin.

Above and below: EC 1/12 was well known around Europe as the French tiger squadron, having been a staunch supporter of Tiger Meets with its Super Mystères. The tradition continued with the F1C and to a lesser extent with the 2000.

Mirage F1 Operators

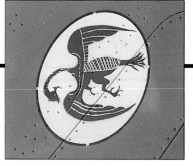

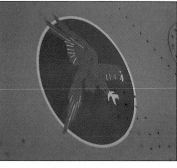

Escadron de Chasse 2/12 'Cornouaille'

Aircraft: Mirage F1C/-200
1e Escadrille: insignia - scorpion (scorpion), starboard
2e Escadrille: insignia - dogue d'Ulm (bull mastiff), port
Codes: 12-ZA to 12-ZZ (radio call FUHZA/FUHZZ)

Formerly EC 3/12, 'Cornouaille' squadron was redesignated EC 2/12 in August 1959, when the Cambrai wing converted from three squadrons of Mystère IVAs to two of Super Mystères. Working up on Mirage F1Cs began at Reims in February 1976 with two pilots receiving conversion by EC 30, followed by four in April and seven between June and September. Others were trained at Cambrai by their compatriots. The first eight aircraft for EC 12 (including one flown by the CO, Cdt Jean Moschetta) arrived at their home base from Reims on 1 October 1976.

The squadron was declared operational on 1 January 1977, although it was not until October 1978 that the wing conducted its first armament practice camp for live firings of Magic AAMs. 'Cornouaille' was the first to have F1Cs fitted with radar warning receivers, beginning with No. 79 '12-ZA'. The allocation, Nos 79-85, 87, 90, 100-103, comprised the last unprobed F1Cs in the AA, but they were dispersed to other squadrons in 1980-81. EC 2/12 spent the next few years recoding its aircraft every six months in a doomed attempt to keep them in alphanumerical order, but constant interchange between squadrons resulted in the practice being abandoned. In anticipation of forming a third squadron, EC 12 renumbered 'Cornouaille' from 2/12 to its old designation of 3/12 on 1 June 1979.

Escadron de Chasse 2/12 'Picardie'

Aircraft: Mirage F1C/-200
1e Escadrille: SPA173 insignia - oiseau d'azur (bluebird), port
2e Escadrille: SPA172 insignia - perroquet (parakeet), starboard
Codes: 12-KA to 12-KZ

'Picardie' was a natural choice when re-alignment and expansion of CAFDA during the late 1970s required EC 12 to add a third squadron. Designated EC 2/12 in the days of the Mystère IVA, 'Picardie' had disbanded in November 1957 and then briefly been assigned to a Mirage IVA

squadron (EB 3/93) before falling dormant. After training of its personnel at Orange, the squadron reformed on 1 June 1980 under Cdt Bartholomy as the third Mirage F1C element of the Cambrai wing, although its was 15 May 1981 before the unit received its standard. Most of the early aircraft were on loan from other squadrons until new machines could be supplied by Dassault. The squadron's complement included about eight F1C-200s in 1991. EC 2/12 stood down on 1 November 1992 to start Mirage 2000C conversion.

EC 2/12 'Picardie' sent its Mirage F1Cs to Doha, Qatar, just after the Gulf War (below). Shown above is the starboard side of the fin.

Above: The port side of the 'Picardie' F1s featured the parakeet of SPA172. The 'SPA' prefix signified the use of SPADs in World War I.

Escadron de Chasse 3/12 'Cornouaille'

Aircraft: Mirage F1C/-200
1e Escadrille: insignia - scorpion (scorpion), starboard
2e Escadrille: insignia - dogue d'Ulm (bull mastiff), port
Codes: 12-ZA to 12-ZZ (radio call FUHZA/FUHZZ)

On 1 June 1979, EC 2/12 was redesignated EC 3/12 without undergoing any change of markings. In 1991 it was operating four F1C-200s and F1B among its 15 aircraft. The squadron, often erroneously referred to as 'Cornouailles', was due to re-equip with Mirage 2000Cs during 1993, but defence cuts will result in its retaining F1s until disbandment in the mid-1990s.

Above and right: 'Cornouaille' renumbered from EC 2/12 to EC 3/12 in 1979, taking its scorpion and mastiff badges with it. They were originally presented on a fin-stripe.

Below: EC 3/12 retains the F1C, having been passed over for Mirage 2000 conversion because of defence cuts. The modern badge presentation is very muted.

13e Escadre de Chasse

EC 13 moved into newly-completed BA132 Colmar/Mayenheim on 1 April 1957, and by the early 1990s was a three-squadron wing with Mirage 5Fs in two attack squadrons (16 aircraft each) and an OCU flying 15 Mirage IIIEs, six IIIBs and six IIIBEs. In 1991, the wing began conversion to Mirage F1CTs. EC 1/13 and EC 2/13 were assigned a secondary interception role in 1987, EC 3/13 being similarly tasked soon afterwards. EC 1/13 and EC 2/13 were renamed on 13 October 1993, as EC 1/13 'Normandie-Niémen' and EC 3/13 'Alsace'. EC 13 will disband in 1995, allowing its two squadrons to become autonomous elements of EC 30 but remaining at its present base.

Escadron de Chasse 1/13 'Artois'

Aircraft: Mirage F1CT
1e Escadrille: SPA83 insignia - chimère (dragon), starboard
2e Escadrille: SPA100 insignia - hirondelle (swallow), port
Codes: 13-QA to 13-QZ (radio call FUHQA/FUHQZ)

On 15 January 1992, having relinquished its OCU task, 'Artois' flew the final Mirage IIIB sortie and passed its IIIBEs to EC 2/13 to continue the training role. Pilots then began ground school on the Mirage F1CT before transferring to CEAM at Mont-de-Marsan for type conversion, the squadron flying its final Mirage IIIE sortie on 26 June 1992. The first Mirage F1CT to be received was the third conversion, No. 278 13-QA, which made its public debut at the Colmar Meeting Nationale de l'Air on 14 June 1992. Training at CEAM began on 1 September 1992 and was completed on 6 November 1992, when the squadron returned to Colmar with its first batch of aircraft. It was declared operational in April 1993, renaming on 13 October as detailed below.

Escadron de Chasse 1/13 'Normandie-Niémen'

Aircraft: Mirage F1CT
Base: BA132 Colmar-Mayenheim
1e Escadrille: not named
2e Escadrille: not named
Insignia: two gold lions passant guardant above a silver lightning flash on a red shield (port and starboard)
Codes: 13-QA to 13-QZ (radio call FUIQA/FUIQZ)

On the disbandment of EC 2/30 the 'Normandie-Niémen' name and tradition was passed to EC 1/13 (formerly 'Artois') at Colmar. The name will be retained after the squadron becomes EC 1/30 in 1995.

Escadron de Chasse 2/13 'Alpes'

Aircraft: Mirage 5F and Mirage IIIBE
1e Escadrille: insignia - chevalier et cheval gris (knight on grey horse), starboard
2e Escadrille: insignia - chevalier et cheval bai (knight on bay horse), port
Codes: 13-PA to 13-PZ (FUHPA/FUHPZ)

Having taken over the small Mirage 5/III OCU commitment in January 1992, 'Alpes' was due to be the last of three Mirage F1CT squadrons. However, with the adoption of a new 20-aircraft squadron/two-squadron wing structure, its conversion was cancelled, and the Mirage 5F unit disbanded in June 1993.

Escadron de Chasse 3/13 'Auvergne'

Aircraft: Mirage F1CT
1e Escadrille: SPA85 (GC II/9-3e) insignia - folie (jester), port
2e Escadrille: GC II/9-4e insignia - écu et épée (shield and sword), starboard
Codes: 13-SA to 13-SZ (FUHSA/FUHSZ)

Replacement of EC 3/13's Mirage 5Fs by

Right: EC 1/13 'Artois' wore the badges of SPA83 (illustrated) and SPA100 before adopting the 'Normandie-Niémen' tradition.

Mirage F1CTs began early in 1993 with the squadron standing down for conversion in January and with Cdt Herve Buchler flying the first F1CT sortie on 23 April. The squadron was renamed 'Alsace' on 13 October 1993.

Escadron de Chasse 3/13 'Alsace'

Aircraft: Mirage F1CT
Base: BA132 Colmar-Mayenheim
1e Escadrille: Strasbourg
2e Escadrille: Mulhouse
Insignia: six gold crowns separated by a gold band on a red shield (both sides); some aircraft seen with SPA85's jester holding a trident (port), perhaps indicating that this will become the third escadrille
Codes: 13-SA to 13-SZ (radio call FUISA/FUISZ)

On the disbandment of EC 3/2 the 'Alsace' name and tradition was passed to EC 3/13 (formerly 'Auvergne') at Colmar. The name will be retained after the squadron becomes EC 2/30.

Right: The historic 'Normandie-Niémen' badge is currently carried by the F1CTs of EC 1/13.

Below: EC 3/13's F1CTs only carried the badges for 'Alpes' briefly in 1993, renaming as 'Alsace' in October.

Right: Resplendent in newly-applied wraparound camouflage, this EC 3/13 Mirage F1CT proudly wears the arms of Alsace, a tradition to be continued when the squadron becomes part of EC 30.

Below: Badge of SPA100, EC 1/13.

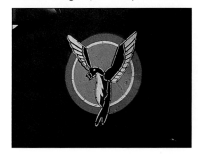

30e Escadre de Chasse

The last remaining Vautour IIN night-fighter wing, the 30e Escadre de Chasse Tous Temps (All-Weather Fighter Wing) had been based partly, then wholly, at Reims/Champagne (Base Aérienne 112 'Marin la Meslée') since February 1961. Nominated as the initial two-squadron Mirage F1C wing, it deleted the 'Tous Temps' from its title on 20 December 1973, the date that the first new aircraft arrived for Escadron 2/30. The last Vautours left Reims on 18 April 1974 when conversion began of EC 3/30.

A total of 10,000 hours of safe flying was celebrated in July 1975, and 15,000 hours in March 1976, including 1,850 hours (1,500 sorties) at night. Not until 31 March 1977 was the first aircraft (No. 7 30-MD) lost in an accident. From the outset, only pilots experienced in air defence were allowed to fly the F1, minimum flying time stipulation being 700 hours. Transition took the form of 11-14 handling flights and 25 operational evaluation sorties, all in a single-seat aircraft, as the F1B was not available. The first non-air defence pilots to fly the Mirage F1C were posted to Reims in the first half of 1976, comprising 12 direct from training and four former instructors. They were able to solo after a one-month course including 12 simulator sorties.

Mirage F1Cs began carrying a pair of MATRA R.530s beneath their wings from February 1976, the wing's air defence task being the constant provision of one pilot and aircraft at seven minutes' readiness and one at 15 minutes'. EC 30 was raised to a three-squadron wing when its vacant first squadron position was filled by 'Valois'. In the wake of the Iraqi invasion of Kuwait in August 1990, EC 30 detached about 50 technical personnel to Saudi Arabia to assist the Kuwait air force Mirage F1 squadron to maintain its aircraft while in exile. Following the use of the Global Positioning System by Jaguars in the Gulf War early in 1991, Mirage F1Cs of EC 30 were fitted with the same equipment. The wing's identity will be used by EC 1/13 and EC 3/13 which will become EC 1/30 and EC 2/30 at Colmar in 1995. EC 3/30 will become EC 3/33 while EC 4/30 will remain in Djibouti.

Escadron de Chasse 1/30 'Valois'

Aircraft: Mirage F1C/-200
Base: BA112 Reims-Champagne
1e Escadrille: N84 insignia - renard (fox's head), starboard
2e Escadrille: SPA93 insignia - canard (duck), port
Codes: 30-SA to 30-SZ (radio call FUISA/FUISZ)

Closure of Creil as a combat aircraft base resulted in disbandment of the 10e Escadre de Chasse and transfer of its Mirage F1 squadron to Reims in June 1985. The position of 1/30 had lain dormant since Vautour IIN-equipped 'Loire' disbanded on 31 March 1965, so EC 1/10 'Valois' became EC 1/30 and merely changed the '1' in its aircraft codes to '3'. At the time of the

Right: EC 1/30 was created by the movement of EC 1/10 to Reims. The squadron retained its badges and traditions.

Below: The flying duck of EC 1/30 graces this Super 530F-equipped Mirage F1C-200. The squadron disbands in 1994.

move, all were unprobed F1Cs. Early in 1990, the squadron added a single Mirage F1B trainer (No. 509 '30-SO'), the remaining aircraft being evenly divided between F1Cs and F1C-200s. EC 1/30 will disband in 1994, but the designation will be taken over by F1CT-equipped EC 1/13 'Normandie-Niémen', currently at Colmar, in 1995.

Escadron de Chasse 2/30 'Normandie-Niémen'

Aircraft: Mirage F1C/-200
Base: BA112 Reims-Champagne
1e Escadrille: not named
2e Escadrille: not named
Insignia: two lions passant guardant above a silver lightning flash (port and starboard)
Codes: 30-MA to 30-MZ (radio call FUIMA/FUIMZ)

The first operational Mirage F1C squadron is slightly unusual in that the second element of its name is not a French geographical feature, but a Russian river. 'Normandie' fought on the Eastern Front in World War II, equipped with Soviet fighters, and was awarded a battle honour by Stalin in November 1944 for supporting the crossing of the Niémen. Links with the Soviet air forces were resumed after France left NATO in 1966, resulting in reciprocal

visits by the 'Neu-Neu' squadron and MiG-21s, MiG-23s, MiG-29s and Su-27s based at Kubinka, near Moscow. The first Mirage F1C deployment to Kubinka, of six aircraft, took place between 24 and 29 July 1977, followed by a further visit between 26 and 29 August 1979. Most recently, six F1s (including two F1Bs wearing EC 3/30 codes, but 'Neu-Neu' badges) visited Kubinka in June 1990. The squadron's two

Above: EC 3/30 is the current F1 OCU, and has a large number of F1Bs. The aircraft are marked with the arms of Lorraine.

flights are neither named nor have their own badges, and its aircraft carry the two lions of the province of Normandy, plus the arrow-headed lightning flash of the 303rd Fighter Division, Soviet air force, applied to

Left: Indicative of previous service in Africa, this EC 2/30 'Normandie-Niémen' machine wears the sand and chocolate scheme.

Above: EC 2/30 was the first operational Mirage F1 escadron.

the unit's Yak fighters in World War II.

Formerly equipped with Vautour IINs, EC 2/30 began despatching groups of pilots to Cazaux from May 1973 onwards to convert to the Mirage F1C. Operational working-up was under the auspices of EC 24/118 at Mont-de-Marsan before the first 11 Mirage F1Cs (including four belonging to CEAM, brought to make up numbers) arrived at Reims on 20 December 1973, their pilots including the squadron's CO, Cdt. Pagès (although Cdt. Prost landed the first F1 at Reims, an hour before the remaining 10 aircraft). With the first five production aircraft assigned to CEV and CEAM, EC 2/30's machines began at No. 6 '30-MA' and ran through to No. 21, although not with consecutive codes. The squadron became the first to employ the F1C in an air defence exercise when it participated in the annual Datex of 1974, but the Mirage F1C did not undertake its first intensive air-to-air cannon training course until deployed to Cazaux from 1 to 26 March 1976. The 14-aircraft detachment flew at least 50 (and a record 70) sorties per day, 10 per cent of them against ground targets. EC 3/30 followed immediately with its own four-week course, beginning 26 March 1976.

Following receipt of the F1C-200s, airborne refuelling practice began early in 1984 and was put to good use the following September for deployment to Chad to participate in Operation Manta. Illustrating the continued effectiveness of the Mirage F1C, a two-man team from EC 2/30 won the Coupe Air-Air (Air-to-Air Cup) in the 1992 weapons competition, putting Mirage 2000Cs of EC 1/5 into second place. EC 3/12, another Mirage F1C outfit, came third. Prior to disbandment on 1 August 1993 some 11 of the squadron's aircraft were F1C-200s. The unit's distinguished name was then passed to EC 1/13, which is based at Colmar with its F1CTs, becoming EC 1/30 in 1995.

Escadron de Chasse 3/30 'Lorraine'

Aircraft: Mirage F1C/-200; later Mirage F1B and F1C/-200
Base: BA112 Reims-Champagne
1e Escadrille: Metz
2e Escadrille: Nancy
3e Escadrille: SPA62 insignia - coc Gaulois (cockerel)
Insignia: three alerions on a yellow shield (port and starboard)
Codes: 30-FA to 30-FZ (radio call FUHFA to FUHFZ)

Vautour IINs of EC 3/30 were exchanged

Above: An EC 3/30 'Lorraine' F1B in standard scheme.

Right: The Mirage F1C adopted sand and chocolate for service in the French garrison in Djibouti with EC 4/30. The squadron maintains 10-12 aircraft, supported by EC 12 and EC 30.

for Mirage F1Cs during the spring of 1974 and the two squadrons then in EC 30 completed their re-equipment on 5 July 1974. EC 3/30's aircraft were Nos 23-37, coded '30-FA' to '30-FO' in sequence. Impending conversion of EC 5 at Orange from Mirage F1s to Mirage 2000Cs resulted in EC 3/30 being assigned the role of the type OCU. The transfer formally took place on 1 August 1988 and the squadron's F1Cs were exchanged for F1Bs, which modified their 5-A* codes to 30-F*. At the same time, an increase in personnel strength associated with the new role qualified the squadron for a third flight, this being SPA62 which was inherited, like the Mirage F1Bs, from EC 3/5 'Comtat Venaissin'. In a change from usual practice, however, some F1Bs were transferred to other squadrons early in 1989, leaving EC 3/30 with an establishment (1993) of 12 F1Bs and three single-seat F1Cs, plus 19 instructor pilots.

New pilots from advanced training on Alpha Jets at EC 8 receive a three-stage conversion programme at EC 3/30, the first being 45 sorties in the Mirage F1B. This is followed by night and instrument flying experience in three or four flights and, finally, eight weeks of operational training involving 36 sorties using the aircraft's weapon system. The introductory phase is also undertaken by pilots destined for the Mirage F1CR and F1CT. EC 3/30 also

provides inflight refuelling courses and is responsible for the annual instrument flying checks for all Mirage F1 pilots. It will become EC 3/33 in 1995.

Escadron de Chasse 4/30 'Vexin'

Aircraft: Mirage F1C/-200
Base: BA188 Djibouti
1e Escadrille: ERC3/561 insignia - mousquetaire gris (grey musketeer), starboard
2e Escadrille: ERC4/561 insignia - mousquetaire bleu (blue musketeer), port
Codes: 30-LA to 30-LZ (radio call FUILA/FUILZ)

'Vexin' has been based in Djibouti since formed with 10-L*-coded Mirage IIICs as EC 3/10 on 1 January 1979. It became an autonomous squadron after EC 10 disbanded on 1 April 1965, but with retirement approaching for the veteran IIICs a Mirage F1 squadron was assembled as a replacement, its first four aircraft (all F1C-

200s formerly with EC 1/5) leaving France on 6 June 1988 for a six-hour delivery flight. Officially formed on 1 July 1988, the new 'Vexin' became operational on 9 August 1988, having by then received four more non-refuellable aircraft.

Its Mirages, though nominally F1C interceptors, are regularly seen carrying air-to-ground ordnance or reconnaissance pods and wearing tropical camouflage, although air defence colours were carried by early machines. The former colour scheme is the same pattern as the Mirage F1CR overseas scheme of 'chocolate and sand' but employs a darker shade of sand. The first operational test of the new aircraft of EC 4/30 was participation in the combined forces training exercise Operation Hippocampe between 26 February and 13 March 1989. Since mid-1989, both EC 12 and EC 30 have been jointly responsible for supporting the Djibouti squadron, its current strength being 11 aircraft, including seven F1C-200s. Desert-camouflaged aircraft awaiting their turn to serve in Djibouti are occasionally seen wearing the codes of other squadrons.

33e Escadre de Reconnaissance

France's sole reconnaissance wing has been partly or wholly based at BA124 Strasbourg/Entzheim since September 1959, attached for most of that time to the Force Aérienne Tactique. During the 1960s, two squadrons were equipped with Mirage IIIRs and a third received the IIIRD. Two of

the three squadrons have a secondary attack role. ER 33 has been involved with several overseas operations, for which reason many of its Mirage F1CRs have received tropical camouflage since the first was thus marked late in 1985.

Each squadron has a SARA

reconnaissance ground station, the first delivered in August 1984 and the second late in 1986. Pilot training now includes familiarisation with the F1CR's nav-attack system on a specially modified Mystère 20 at CITac 339. Podded sensors used by the F1CR comprise the Raphaël SLAR and ASTAC emitter-locator.

Squadrons carried the insignia of a single World War I escadrille on both sides of the

fin, but modified in the case of ER 1/33. Since the disbandment of ER 3/33 the surviving escadrons each have three escadrilles (with World War I identities) and so the aircraft wear an unpredictable mix of fin badges. Two flights, simply numbered 1

Battered-looking F1CRs of ER 1/33. Note the weathering difference between the two aircraft.

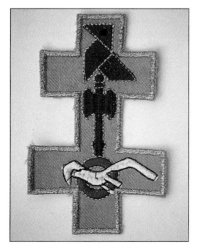

Above: Wing patch of ER 33.

For most of their existence the squadrons of ER 33 wore only one badge, this being the seagull of ER 2/33. In 1993 the disbandment of ER 3/33 saw the redistribution of traditions so that both ER 1/33 and 2/33 picked up more badges.

Escadron de Reconnaissance 2/33 'Savoie'

Aircraft: Mirage F1CR-200
Insignia: SAL6 - mouette (seagull)
From 1.8.93 **1e Escadrille:** SAL6 - mouette
2e Escadrille: BR 11 - cocotte (paper bird)
3e Escadrille: C-53 - pennant
Codes: 33-NA to 33-NZ (radio call FUINA/FUINZ)

Selected to be the first recipient of Mirage F1CRs, ER 2/33 began converting its Mirage IIIR pilots with a ground course at the ETIS F1CR at Reims early in 1983. Training on the squadron's aircraft under EC 24/118 at Mont-de-Marsan followed in April-June 1983, before the first F1CR arrived at Strasbourg on 1 July. Some 80 ground crew passed through Reims between April and June. By the time it was commissioned, on 7 September, the squadron had seven of an intended 15 aircraft and 15 of a planned 18 pilots. Allocations to the squadron were Nos 603-617, coded 33-NA to 33-NO, but these had an interim equipment fit and were soon returned for installation of Super Cyclope IR sensors. ER 2/33 therefore received a further batch in the spring of 1985, Nos 620-636 as 33-NA to 33-NQ, but these have also been dispersed with the passage of time. The squadron re-organised into three escadrilles when it became autonomous on 1 August 1993.

Escadron de Reconnaissance 3/33 'Moselle'

Aircraft: Mirage F1CR-200
Insignia: BR11 - cocotte (paper bird)
Codes: 33-TA to 33-TZ (radio call FUITA/FUITZ)

Re-equipment of ER 33 was completed early in 1988 when 'Moselle' discarded its Mirage IIIRDs in favour of Mirage F1CRs. One of the first to be noted – No. 664 33-TU, the last production aircraft, in March 1988 – was the only new-built Mirage F1CR to go straight to ER 3/33. Formation of the squadron resulted in a considerable interchange of aircraft, with the result that all three units comprising ER 33 had aircraft from throughout the production run. ER 3/33 stood down on 1 July 1993 and disbanded on 30 August 1993.

Mirage F1CR-200s from all three squadrons from Strasbourg (ER 3/33 illustrated) were very active in the Gulf War, flying from Al Ahsa, Saudi Arabia. In addition to reconnaissance missions, they flew bombing missions late in the campaign.

Above and right: Pre-August 1993 badges of ER 33's three escadrons. The wing itself has disbanded, leaving ER 1/33 and ER 2/33 as autonomous units.

and 2 Escadrilles, initially comprised the flying element of each squadron, ground support being in the form of an interpretation section and a first-line servicing section. Total ER 33 personnel strength was 800. ER 3/33 disbanded on 30 August 1993, and the Wing HQ disbanded on the same date, leaving the surviving squadrons as autonomous units. Closure of Strasbourg/Entzheim is due in 1995.

When delivered, Mirage F1CRs wore a grey-green disruptive pattern. This is an ER 2/33 aircraft.

Escadron de Reconnaissance 1/33 'Belfort'

Aircraft: Mirage F1CR-200
Insignia: SAL33 - hache (battle axe)
From 1.8.93 **1e Escadrille:** SAL33 - hache
2e Escadrille: EALA 9/72 - Petit Prince
3e Escadrille: BR 244 - leopard
Codes: 33-CA to 33-CZ (radio call FUICA/FUICZ)

ER 1/33 was the second squadron to receive Mirage F1CRs, the first aircraft (No.

607 33-CP) arriving on 27 November 1985 after modifications by Dassault. Deliveries to ER 33 of new machines had reached 48 by the end of that year, although not all were available due to the refit programme. In the event, ER 1/33 received eight early production aircraft from the batch 603-617 after they had been modified with addition of internal Super Cyclope sensors. The squadron was the first to lose an F1CR: No. 621 33-CM on 3 September 1987.

The battle axe of SAL33 appeared in traditional form on the starboard side, but to port it is carried by the Petit Prince character created by author Antoine de Saint Exupéry, killed in action with GR II/33 'Belfort' in 1944.

Centre d'Expériences Aériennes Militaires

CEAM has its main base at BA118 Mont-de-Marsan 'Col K.W. Rozanoff', where it is a direct-reporting unit of the AA High Command responsible for trials of equipment. Its components include a fighter trials squadron assigned to both long-term development and administering the working up of the first squadrons to operate a new type or variant of aircraft. The squadron was originally designated EC 24/118, but became EC 5/330 on 15 October 1987 to reflect an administrative change by which aircraft are now 'owned' by CEAM 330 instead of Base Aérienne 118.

Escadron de Chasse 24/118 and Escadron de Chasse 5/330 'Côte d'Argent'

Insignia: CEAM (athlete hurling an arrowhead to the stars), both sides for EC 24/118, starboard for EC 5/330; tiger pailleux (tiger), EC 5/330, port only

Mirage F1 evaluation by CEAM initially centred on prototype No. 02, delivered early in 1970 after trials at CEV, and No. 04, which remained uncoded during 1972. Production F1Cs Nos 2-4 were delivered as 118-AK to -AM, the first on 14 May 1973 (Cdt Chretien, later the first French astronaut, was the delivery pilot). These aircraft remained in service for over a decade, No. 4 eventually becoming 330-AM. No. 22 118-AN was added in 1976 and probe-equipped No. 201 118-AZ in March 1977, followed by No. 225 118-AO in 1978. F1B No. 502 118-AT was delivered in 1981 for medium-term trials, but has since been replaced by others of the type.

The first two-seat F1 to be evaluated was the Kuwaiti machine, 771, in 1976-77. First F1CR-200 was No. 603 118-AA in early 1983, one of several soon passed to ER 33, but longer-term residents have been Nos 618 and 619 118-AA and -AC, which later received 330- prefixes. In the spring of

Below: The second production F1C wearing EC 24/118 codes and high conspicuity marks for photography during missile work.

1992, CEAM was supervising the conversion of EC 1/13 to Mirage F1CTs, having received No. 273, the first 'production' conversion ,on 13 February, followed soon afterwards by No. 274 330-AJ. The normal holding is an average of six or seven Mirage F1s of various types in the permanent trials fleet, the 1992 position being three F1C-200s, three F1CR-200s and one F1B.

Above: A fair proportion of the Mirage F1s have passed through CEAM at one time or another for test and conversion training purposes, this being the first F1B two-seater. It wears the original cockade with yellow outline, a feature eliminated in the early 1980s to reduce conspicuity.

Below: EC 24/118 became EC 5/330 in October 1987, adopting the tiger badge on the port side of the fin to complement the CEAM badge on the starboard. This aircraft is a standard F1C fighter being used for trials of a camera pod. CEAM retains a small fleet of aircraft dedicated to ongoing trials work.

Centre d'Essais en Vol

CEV is the airborne testing component of the Direction Technique des Constructions Aéronautiques, a military agency responsible for airworthiness testing and certification. Its main base is at Brétigny-sur-Orge, but Dassault fighters are normally evaluated by the unit's two out-stations at Istres (where Dassault's flight test unit is stationed) and Cazaux, for proximity to weapons ranges. CEV evaluated Mirage F1 prototypes Nos 02 (delivered 22 December 1969) and 03 (and 04 after CEAM), as well as the first production F1C – No. 1, delivered on 13 March 1973 – and No. 5, used for trials including the APACHE stand-off weapons dispenser. No special markings are carried, apart from infrequent application of the eagle's head logo combining the three letters 'C', 'E' and 'V'. The CEV fleet now includes three F1CRs, Nos 601, 602 and 614, the other F1s having been transferred or withdrawn.

Centre d'Instruction Tactique 339

Playing a valuable role in Mirage F1CR pilot training, the CITac is equipped not with Mirages but Dassault Mystère XXs (Falcon 20s). Centre du Prédiction et d'Instruction Radar 339 was formed at BA116 Luxeuil/St Sauveur 'Lt Col Papin' with two Mystères equipped to instruct Mirage IIIE pilots, and subsequently increased to five aircraft to embrace the Mirage F1CR and Mirage 2000N. The unit changed its name to the present title on 1 July 1988 when SEPECAT Jaguars were added to its fleet.

Mystère XX SNAR (Système de Navigation, d'Attaque et de Reconnaissance) No. 451 first flew as F-WRQC on 4 May 1984 and entered service with the CPIR on 1 May 1985, coded 339-WN (radio call FUGWN). Named 'Fil d'Ariane' it carries the CPIR/CITac badge of a bat atop the globe. The aircraft's starboard pilot's seat has Mirage F1CR instrumentation and a fighter-style control column, throttle and HUD, while a safety pilot to port has the usual Falcon 20 flight deck. Cyrano IVMR radar in

an extended nose provides the student pilot with fully realistic displays on his radar scope. Conversion courses take up to two weeks and include eight flights in No. 451.

This photograph depicts the flight deck of Mystère XX No. 451, the sole aircraft in the CITac 339 fleet equipped with Mirage F1CR avionics. The left-hand console has the standard Mystère XX flight instruments for the safety pilot/instructor, while the right-hand station is a replica of the F1CR's cockpit, with fighter-style stick, HUD and radar screen. The latter is served by the F1CR's Cyrano IVMR radar, which is grafted on to the Mystère's nose in a lengthened radome.

Ecuador

Fuerza Aérea Ecuatoriana

Escuadrón 2122 is the maintenance unit for Grupo 211's Mirage F1s.

Unable to buy the preferred IAI Kfirs because of a US embargo on the transfer of their General Electric J79 engines to Latin America, Ecuador turned to Dassault for Mirage IIIs or 5s, but ended by announcing an order for Mirage F1s late in 1977. These comprised 16 Mirage F1JAs (based on the multi-role F1E) and two F1JE trainers. After initial pilot training by EC 5 at Orange, the aircraft were delivered between December 1978 and December 1979 (the trainers in September and November 1980) to Base

Aérea Taura, Guayaquil, where they replaced Cessna A-37B Dragonflies within Escuadrón de Caza 2112, a component of Grupo 211, Ala 21. First flights in South American skies were made during April 1979, and by 15 December 1980 experience totalled 2,000 hours. Just a

month later Ecuador and Peru were involved in a 13-day border skirmish, during which the Mirages mounted standing air patrols. Only once were Peruvian Sukhoi Su-22 'Fitter-Fs' sighted, and the one MATRA Magic 1 launched from a Mirage's wingtip rail was released outside parameters and failed to strike home.

Serialled FAE801-816 and FAE830-831, the Ecuadorian Mirages have green and brown upper surface camouflage in the French pattern (brown replacing grey) with light grey undersides. Fins contain VOR aerials and bullet antennas for a Thomson-CSF BF radar warning receiver. Also tasked with ground attack, the F1JAs were upgraded with Israeli assistance in the late 1980s and early 1990s with the ability to carry eight Israeli P-1 bombs (four beneath the fuselage and the remainder under the wings), as well as other armament. One F1JE was lost in an accident, although the

training programme is assisted by a simulator. At least three single-seat aircraft have also been destroyed, including one on 23 June 1980. Esc 2112 won the Copa Taura (Taura Cup) air combat competition in 1983, yet for the remainder of the 1980s was defeated annually by its co-resident Jaguars and Kfirs, the latter acquired after the US relaxed the J79 veto in 1979.

Ecuador's single-seat Mirages are designated F1JA, similar to the F1E. They have a multi-role tasking, using MATRA Magic missiles for air-to-air and Israeli-supplied bombs for air-to-ground work. The unit badge is carried on the intakes of most aircraft, including the one remaining F1JE trainer.

Greece

Elleniki Polemiki Aeroporia

As in the case of Ecuador, US political policy forced Greece into the arms of Dassault when Washington's disapproval of the military government of the early 1970s caused it to reject a request for replacement aircraft for the nation's ageing Convair F-102 Delta Daggers. In place of what would probably have been McDonnell Douglas F-4E Phantoms, Greece ordered 40 Mirage F1CGs on 16 June 1974 as a matter of urgency because of increasing tension with Turkey, their delivery being expedited by transfer of the first 16 from the Armée de l'Air F1C contract while they were still on the production line. No two-seat aircraft were supplied. The initial 16, Greek serials 101-116, would have been AA Nos 51, 53, 56, 57, 59, 61, 65, 66, 86, 88, 89, 91, 93, 94, 95 and 97; the remainder, 117-140, were new-built. All had the French grey-blue air defence colour scheme (later receiving silver undersides) but none was fitted with a BF radar warning receiver, despite some coming off the French line. VOR aerials are standard. Prime armament for the air defence role was the AIM-9J

Sidewinder AAM, augmented from 1980 by AIM-9Ps.

The first example was handed over in France on 29 January 1975, two being lost in training before the first deliveries began to Greece on 5 August 1975. In April 1978, the 40th was received, and soon afterwards the small serial numbers on the rear fuselage were increased in size and repeated on the fin. All were supplied to 114a Pterix Mahis (Combat Wing) at Tanagra, north-west of Athens, for 334 'Thalos' and 342 'Sparta' Mire Anagaitiseos

Mirage F1CGs were supplied to 114 Pterix for 334 (badge above) and 342 Mire. The colour scheme has remained the slate grey in which they were originally delivered straight from Armée de l'Air production.

(Interceptor Squadrons). This is part of the main combat command, Arghio Taktikis Aeroporias (NATO's 28th TAF/6th ATAF), although fluctuating relationships with the alliance resulted in Greek aircraft being withdrawn from SACEUR command between 1974 and 1980 and from 1985.

Major servicing has been undertaken locally at Tanagra since 1981 by Hellenic

Aerospace Industry. During overhauls, the aircraft belatedly received BF radar warners. By the early 1990s, those of 342 Mira (at least) were marked on the nose with the name of a Greek Island.

A dispute with Turkey over ownership of Aegean islands resulted in Mirage F1CGs and Turkish Phantoms engaging in mock dogfights in April 1987 before NATO mediation calmed a potentially explosive situation. More recently, on 18 June 1992, a Mirage F1CG crashed into the Aegean while attempting to intercept a pair of Turkish F-16 Fighting Falcons.

Availability of Mirage 2000s for the defence of Athens allowed 334 Mira to move to Iraklion, Crete, by early 1990, where it formed the first air component of the 126a Smirna Nakis (Autonomous Group). The transfer was anticipated of 342 Mira to the island of Skiros, augmenting Mirages regularly detached to Lemnos. Instead, 342 Squadron is now expected to move to Agrinion, in western Greece. About eight have been lost in accidents.

The F1CGs of 342 Mira carry names of Greek islands on the nose, this being 'Rodos' (Rhodes). The unit is expected to move to Agrinion.

Iraq

Al Quwwat al Jawwiya al Iraqiya

After placing large arms contracts with the USSR, Iraq turned to the West for further supplies. Negotiations for the sale of 50 Mirage F1s had first begun in January 1970, but were broken off shortly afterwards. Renewed interest eventually led to agreement with France in June 1987 for 36 Mirage F1s (plus 36 options) and associated Super 530F-1 and Magic 1 AAMs. The first

F1EQ single-seater flew on 28 May 1979, followed by the F1BQ on 6 February 1980, and deliveries began in April 1980 to CEAM at Mont-de-Marsan for training. By the time that the aircraft were ready to leave France, Iraq had attacked Iran and was embroiled in what was to become an eight-year war. France declined to join the international arms embargo and allowed the first four aircraft to pass through Larnaca, Cyprus, on delivery on 31 January 1981, disguised as deliveries for Jordan. Further orders were placed in late 1979 (24), February 1982 (30), September 1985 (23) and 1988 (15). In total, Iraq ordered 110 single-seat and 18 two-seat Mirages, not all of which were received.

Above: Iraq's first F1BQ trainer. A total of 15 was delivered.

Below: One of the first batch of F1EQs, complete with Magic 1 AAMs.

Variant	First-last acceptance	Serials	Quantity
F1EQ	26 Aug 80 - 14 Oct 81	4004-4019	16
F1EQ-2	9 Apr 81 - 10 Mar 82	4020-4035	16
F1EQ-4-200	31 Dec 82 - 11 Jul 84	4500-4503, 4506-4529	28
F1EQ-5-200	19 Dec 83 - 28 Feb 85	4560-4579	20
F1EQ-6-200	13 Jan 88 -	4600-4608, 4615-4623	18
F1EQ-7-200	nil	4650-	12
F1BQ	27 Aug 80 - 11 Sep 80	4000-4001	2
F1BQ	17 Jun 81 - 24 Jul 81	4002-4003	2
F1BQ	15 Apr 82 - 14 Dec 84	4504,4505, 4556-4558	5
F1BQ	13 Jan 88 - ?? 89	4609-4614	6
F1BQ	nil	465.-	3

All have an HF fillet aerial at the forward joint of fin and fuselage plus BF radar warning receivers on the fin. VOR/ILS aerials are fitted from 4560 onwards, but not to the two-seat aircraft. The Series 200 aircraft have refuelling probes, as do all except the first four trainers (only dummies for practice in the case of F1BQs from 4504 onwards). The F1EQ-4, Iraq's first multi-role Mirage, appears to have had a radar altimeter and provision on the centreline pylon for COR-2 and HAROLD reconnaissance pods as well as Intertechnique buddy refuelling pods. F1EQ-5s (first flown on 7 July 1983) have Thomson-CSF Agave radar in place of the normal Cyrano IV for their anti-shipping role with Aérospatiale Exocet missiles.

Although handed over in France for training in December 1983, the first eight F1EQ-4s were not delivered until October 1984. The last few F1EQ-5s had blue-grey upper surfaces in place of the usual Iraqi colour scheme of sand and chocolate with light grey undersides. Further improvements resulted in the F1EQ-6, which had BF RWR replaced by Thomson-CSF SHERLOC, which was retrofitted to EQ5s, and blue-grey camouflage. All the EQ-6s, also fitted with Agave for Exocet compatibility, had been built by late 1987, although delivery did not begin until early in the following year. In 1989, Dassault terminated deliveries when funds from Iraq were not forthcoming, having supplied 93 F1EQs and 15 F1BQs. The remaining five, plus the follow-on batch of 12 F1EQs and three F1BQs, were placed in storage and overtaken by the UN arms embargo which followed the August 1990 invasion of Kuwait. For test flying and delivery, Mirages carried Iraqi five-letter callsigns in full on the fin, the 'last two' repeated on the forward fuselage. Examples included Y-IBLU (on

Iraq's Mirage F1EQ interceptors saw much action against Iran, claiming 35 kills including an F-14.

4526, 4566 and 4578), Y-IBLV (4563), Y-IBLW (4579), Y-IREE (4570) and Y-IREF (4528).

The first 32 Mirage F1EQs (up to 4035) were assigned to interception during the war with Iran and had claimed 35 aerial victories with 100 Super 530s fired (in pairs) up to mid-1983, although cannon were used more often thereafter. Iranian aircraft claimed were mostly McDonnell Douglas F-4 Phantoms and Northrop F-5E Tiger IIs, but a Grumman F-14A Tomcat was confirmed on 22 November 1982. Mirages escorted bombing missions and also undertook reconnaissance with COR-2 pods, flying from Qayyarah West and temporary bases closer to the front line. By 1990, 15 single-seat F1EQs and EQ-2s remained, based at Qayyarah West, Kut al

Hayy East and Al Asad, and 11 of the 15 two-seaters were also in use. The -4, -5 and -6 versions were assigned to attack, operating from Al Sahra, Qayyarah South, Tikrit and Tallil. Early in 1990, Iraq and Jordan proposed establishing a joint Mirage F1 squadron at H-3 airfield, just on the Iraqi side of their border, but this did not form.

Mirage F1EQ weapons included MATRA ARMAT anti-radar missiles, Thomson-Brandt 68-mm and 100-mm rockets,

Aérospatiale AM39 Exocets and Aérospatiale AS30L laser-guided missiles (plus ATLIS designator pods). Only 240 of the required 568 AS30Ls had been received by mid-1988, when Aérospatiale stopped deliveries because of non-payment. Undaunted, the resourceful Iraqis persuaded Russian X29L (AS-14 'Kedge') ASMs to function with the ATLIS guidance system by 1989. In late 1989, *Flight International* was reporting that the

The F1EQ-4 featured an inflight refuelling probe and enhanced air-to-ground equipment. The centreline pylon could be used for reconnaissance pods or buddy refuelling equipment.

The fitment of Agave radar resulted in the F1EQ-5 (illustrated) and -6, both Exocet-compatible for maritime strike. The slate grey camouflage was adopted for overwater operations.

payment dispute had been solved, that Iraq was ordering 346 more missiles, and requesting local assembly, as a prelude to possible licence-construction. Iraq also was the first operator to receive oversize 2200-litre (484-Imp gal) centreline tanks. Five EQ-4s and six EQ-5s had been lost by 1990.

Exocet/Agave-equipped Mirages were acquired to continue the 'Tanker War' in the Gulf, begun with Aérospatiale SA 321 Super Frelon helicopters and continued by five loaned Dassault Super Etendards in 1983-85. Missile interface problems resulted in failure of the first Exocet-armed Mirage mission on 3 December 1984, delaying the first successful anti-ship attack until late February 1985. A little over 100 vessels were attacked by Iraq between mid-1984 and the end of hostilities in August 1988, many of them by Mirages. Exocets were credited by independent analysis with all but four of the 41 ships written off. Their best-reported raid was an accidental attack on the frigate USS *Stark* on 17 May 1987, which resulted in the ship being severely damaged and 37 sailors losing their lives. Mirages also participated in the sporadic and poorly managed air war against Iran's army.

At the start of Operation Desert Storm, Iraq had 62 Mirage F1EQs and 11 F1BQs. A defending Mirage F1 was the first aircraft shot down in the conflict, by a USAF F-15C Eagle using AIM-7 Sparrow at 0320 on 17 January. Three were lost later in the day: two to F-15C/AIM-7 and one which crashed avoiding an unarmed General Dynamics EF-111A. Two were destroyed by AIM-7/F-15Cs on 19 January and a Saudi F-15C used the same weapon against two attempting an Exocet strike on 24 January. The last fell to a USAF Eagle/AIM-7 combination on 27 January. An RAF Tornado destroyed an alleged MiG-29 on Al Asad airfield during a JP233 cluster-bomb attack on 17 January, later analysis suggesting the aircraft was a Mirage F1. The nearest the Mirage F1 came to retaliation was when the falling wreckage of one shot down by an F-15 almost hit a low-flying Boeing B-52. Beginning on 26 January, 24 Mirages were among 134 Iraqi aircraft which took refuge in Iran, where they were impounded, remaining thus in early 1993. Other Mirages may have been destroyed in LGB attacks on HASs.

Jordan

Al Quwwat al Jawwiya al Malakiya al Urduniya

Having picked up Greek and Ecuadorian contracts, Dassault was further indebted to the US when it refused to supply Jordan with requested General Dynamics F-16 Fighting Falcons. Instead, Saudi Arabia bought the RJAF a first batch of 17 Mirage F1CJ interceptors and two F1BJ trainers in mid-1979 as replacements for ageing Lockheed F-104A Starfighters. Later, 17 multi-role F1EJs were funded by the same source. All three variants have BF radar warning receivers and VOR aerials, but the CJs and BJs have light blue upper surfaces and light grey below, while tops of the EJs are sand, chocolate and green. The first Mirage F1CJ was handed over in January 1981 for training with CEAM at Mont-de-Marsan, the batch serialled 2501-2517 (in Persian characters only) to signify No. 25 Squadron at Shaheed Mwaffaq as-Salti AB, Azraq. The trainers are 2518-2519 (delivered March-April 1981), while No. 1 Squadron's Mirage F1EJs – delivered between June 1982 (when the last F1CJ arrived) and June 1983 – carry 101-117 in Persian.

Weapons include MATRA Super 530F-1s and 550 Magic 1s for air defence, plus laser-guided Aérospatiale AS30L ASMs for precision attack. The aircraft are kept in hardened shelters and two are maintained at five minutes' readiness, several pilots taking one-hour turns in the cockpit. Mirage pilots are usually transferred from Northrop F-5E Tiger IIs and take a 73-sortie/four-month conversion course. Plans to obtain a further 13 were discussed in 1985, but Jordan ordered Mirage 2000s in April 1988 and decided to have its 15 remaining F1CJs converted to F1EJs. Both plans fell apart when Saudi Arabia withdrew funding after Jordan declared for Iraq in the Gulf War of 1991.

Above: Jordan was supplied with a total of 17 F1CJs for service with No. 25 Squadron. They are dedicated to the air defence mission, hence the light grey camouflage which distinguishes them from the F1EJs.

Left: The second batch of Mirages consisted of 17 multi-role F1EJs, which wear a three-tone scheme for the attack role with No. 1 Sqn.

Below: Only two F1BJ trainers were supplied to Jordan. As they were from the first interceptor batch they were painted in air defence grey.

Kuwait

Al Quwwat al Jawwiya al Kuwaitiya

Prompted by the 1973 border clashes with Iraq, Kuwait ordered 18 Mirage F1CK interceptors and two F1BK trainers on 16 April 1974 as replacements for the BAC Lightnings which it found too complex to operate. Supplies of MATRA R.530 and 550 Magic AAMs were also secured. Yet again, the US played into French hands by offering Kuwait nothing more potent than leased, refurbished Vought F-8 Crusaders. Pilot training began in France during February 1976, deliveries to Kuwait taking place over a 12-month period beginning that July, apart from one lost in an accident on 15 January 1977. Kuwait's first trainer (serialled 771 in Persian) was the prototype two-seat Mirage F1 and flew on 26 May 1976, followed by the second (772) on 20 December 1976. Both left France on 28 October 1977 and arrived in Kuwait on 3 November. A follow-on order was announced in February 1983 as comprising nine F1CK-2s and four F1BK-2s, deliveries of which began in December 1974. The early aircraft (701-718 and the first two trainers), like those which followed, had VOR and BF radar warners, but all were painted in two-tone sand camouflage with light grey beneath. However, Dash 2s (serialled 719-727 and two-seat 773-776) were overall light grey, the undersides marginally paler. Despite this and their F1C designation, they were to essentially F1E multi-role standard, to which the earlier machines were raised. New armament included MATRA Super 530F-1 and MATRA ARMAT anti-radar missiles bought in 1983; plus Thomson-CSF Remora jamming pods mounted on the starboard outer underwing pylon.

Nos 18 and 61 Squadrons were equipped with Mirage F1s at Ali al Salem, having lost at least eight aircraft by the time of the Iraqi invasion of 2 August 1990.

Another Free Kuwait Mirage at Dhahran. The sand camouflage identifies it as one of the original F1CK batch. These were later upgraded to F1CK-2 standard with better multi-role capability.

Others were destroyed by Iraqi shelling, although as the surviving 15 took off one of them was able to shoot down an enemy helicopter. Assembled at Taif, Saudi Arabia, the Mirages were painted with the prominent titles 'FREE KUWAIT' and began training for the liberation of their homeland. In January 1991, when Desert Storm began, they moved to Dhahran. In the build-up phase (Desert Shield) the aircraft flew 429 sorties (425 hours), following this with 128 sorties (200 hours) during Desert Storm. The Kuwaitis were assisted by a team of technicians provided by France's EC 30. None was lost during hostilities, and 15 were refurbished by Dassault at Bordeaux-Mérignac and Biarritz (in three five-aircraft batches) post-war, the first five being redelivered during May 1992. However the type was withdrawn from use in mid-1993 and offered for sale, one potential purchaser being Spain.

Left and below: Two views of a Mirage F1CK-2 of the Free Kuwait air force at Dhahran, Saudi Arabia, from where the 15 aircraft which survived the Iraqi invasion flew 128 combat missions over their homeland. The aircraft is armed with Mk 82 retarded bombs and carries a Remora ECM pod.

Libya

Al Quwwat al Jawwiya al Jamahiriya al Arabiya al Libyya

Following on from large Mirage 5 orders, Libya contracted for 38 Mirage F1s in 1974. With South Africa, Libya was one of only two customers to order the non-radar Mirage F1A, which has a retractable refuelling probe. Numbered 401-416, the 16 of this variant were delivered between January 1978 and April 1978, accompanied by six F1BD trainers, 201-206 (April 1978 to October 1979). Both have green and sand upper surface camouflage on the French pattern, but with the greens juxtaposed. VOR and BF RWR aerials are installed. The 16 Mirage F1EDs, 501-516, were finished to the same standard and delivered from January 1978 to October 1979.

All were based at Okba ibn Nafa AB, near Tripoli, from where they were regularly

The Mirage F1EDs of the Libyan air force are primarily tasked with air defence duties, although they have air-to-ground capability. In the 1980s they were used in raids against Chad, but declined to face up to deployed French Mirages.

Libya's order for 16 F1ADs and 16 F1EDs was accompanied by six F1BD two-seaters, supplied following the first batch from April 1978.

detached to Maaten as-Serra in southern Libya and, briefly, Faya-Largeau in occupied northern Chad. Mirages were used on several attacks into Chad during the 1980s, although air activity was reduced during French air force deployments to Chad and the prospect of F1 versus F1 combat was never realised. In defence, the Mirage F1ED can carry MATRA R.530 and Magic AAMs. Many Libyan air force F1 pilots are believed to be French and Pakistani

mercenaries, while ground crew are from several nationalities. The Mirage F1 fleet underwent overhaul in France during the 1980s – an intermittent process due to hostile activities in Chad – the last F1 being released in early 1990 in return for French hostages. Serviceability is unlikely to be high.

Right: Photographed by a US Navy aircraft near Libya on 18 August 1981, a Mirage F1ED shadows US fleet manoeuvres. The next day, F-14s downed two Libyan Su-22s.

The needle nose identifies this aircraft as one of the Mirage F1ADs. The squadron badge is that of the ground attack squadron, since removed.

The other Libyan squadron is the interceptor unit with F1EDs. This picture shows the unit's badge.

Morocco

Al Kuwwat al Jawwiya al Malakiya Marakishiya

Morocco's Mirage F1 order was placed in December 1975 in the form of 25 F1CH interceptors and an option on 50 more. In November of the same year, Morocco annexed the Western Sahara territory vacated by Spain and so entered a little-reported war with Algerian- and Libyan-backed guerrillas. Half the option was exercised in 1977 and deliveries expedited by transferring some aircraft from the French air force production line and training pilots with EC 5 at Orange.

It thus transpired that the RMAF received 30 Mirage F1CHs (126-155 between February 1978 and December 1979), 14 Mirage F1EHs (156-169 between December 1979 and July 1982), and six Mirage F1EH-200s (170-175 between July 1980 and July 1982). Production was completed in mid-1980, the delay in delivery resulting from shortage of funds.

Painted green and sand (as per French camouflage, but with greens juxtaposed) with light grey beneath, all had VOR and BF RWR. Flare dispensers were later scabbed to the rear fuselage above the ventral fins

Above: A Moroccan Mirage F1CH on patrol over the Sahara, armed with Magic 1 IR missiles on the wingtips and a single R.530 SARH missile.

Below: Following its F1CHs, Morocco received 20 F1EHs, including six with refuelling probes. The fleet flies from Sidi Slimane.

and an ECM pod fitted on one wingtip. Other specific optional features were added, including underwing RP 35 tanks modified to contain an Alkan 5030 grenade launcher (152 rounds of 74-mm calibre) and a centreline reconnaissance pod developed locally by Aero Maroc Industries with help from Dassault.

Mirages are based in hardened shelters at Sidi Slimane, from where detachments were made to El Aïoune for combat operations against Polisario guerrillas in Western Sahara until Morocco relinquished its territorial claims on August 1988. In air defence roles, Mirage F1s armed with MATRA R.530 and Magic AAMs are linked to a new American-built radar and communications network which also included French-built Crotale missile batteries. F1EHs have undertaken attack

operations during which several have been lost to Polisario ground fire. Documented cases include two on 13 October 1981 and another on 14 January 1985. The first pair was hit by SAMs during a rebel attack on the garrison at Guelta Zemmour, at least one of the aircraft being at 30,000 ft (9145 m) when struck. The January 1985 loss was also by a SAM – apparently fired from Algerian territory – during a clash with Polisario forces, which claimed to have destroyed three Moroccan aircraft of unknown type.

Morocco's Mirage F1s were used in actions against Polisario guerrillas in Western Sahara, where at least three aircraft were downed by groundfire.

Qatar

Al Quwwat al Jawwiya al Emiri al Qatar

Mirage procurement by Qatar was a protracted affair, beginning with an order placed in 1979. The first of these was handed over in France for pilot training under Armée de l'Air tutelage at Orange. With this complete, all were delivered to the Middle East in July 1984. Equipped with VOR and BF RWR aerials, the aircraft wore unusual camouflage colours of dark sand and dark green upper surfaces with medium blue beneath, using the standard French disruptive pattern, green-for-green. Serials were applied in Western-style characters and each aircraft wore a Roman code letter on the fin. Twelve Mirage F1EDAs (QA71 to QA81) are 'A' to 'L' and two Mirage F1DDA trainers are QA61 'T' and QA62 'U' (the last-mentioned handed over in April-May 1983). One additional aircraft, F1DDA QA63, was delivered in 1981 as an attrition replacement, having been ordered in late 1988.

Operated by No. 7 Squadron, the Mirages are based at Doha Airport where, together with the Alpha Jets of No. 11 Squadron, they form No. 1 Fighter Wing. Their equipment includes MATRA Magic AAMs and COR2 reconnaissance pods. A French arms contract of 1987 was reported to include upgrading of the Mirage F1 force with unspecified Mirage 2000 avionics. Mirage F1s of the Qatar Emiri air force began flying operational missions in the Gulf War on 22 January 1991, although

Above: Qatar's defence is spearheaded by the Mirage F1EDA, which can undertake reconnaissance missions in addition to the primary interception role. The aircraft serve with No. 7 Sqn, No. 1 Fighter Wing at Doha.

Right: The QEAF supports its fleet with two F1DDA two-seaters.

these were apparently limited to local air defence and did not involve combat over Kuwait or Iraq, as the aircraft have no refuelling probes.

South Africa

Suid-Afrikaanse Lugmag

South Africa was the first of only two air forces to procure the non-radar Mirage F1A,

No. 3 Squadron at Waterkloof was the first SAAF Mirage F1 unit, equipping with the air defence-optimised F1CZs. Below is its moth badge.

although that was not disclosed when first mention was made of orders for an unspecified number of Mirages. In all, the SAAF obtained 48 aircraft, of which 32 were F1AZs serialled 216-247 and delivered between November 1975 and October 1976. The balance comprised 16 F1CZ interceptors, 200-215, handed over between September 1974 and July 1975, the initial acceptance into the SAAF taking place on 4 April 1975 when two arrived

from France inside an SAAF Lockheed Hercules transport. Camouflage colours were olive drab and deep buff, plus light grey beneath, using the standard French pattern, olive-for-green. F1CZs later adopted a medium-altitude camouflage of overall (including radomes) light grey, after successful trials during 1991. VOR/ILS and BF RWR are on both variants, the F1AZs additionally having a blade aerial on the spine, to the rear of the cockpit, replacing

that under the F1CZ's forward fuselage. Normal F1A features include a laser-ranger and Aïda II ranging radar in a small nose radome.

Mirage F1s were first revealed in an air display in October 1975, but not officially acknowledged to be in SAAF service for a further 13 months. F1CZs were assigned to No. 3 Squadron, which had formed at Waterkloof in August 1966 using Mirage IIIEZs on loan from No. 2 Squadron. By

The F1AZs were assigned to No. 1 Sqn, initially at Waterkloof but from 1981 at Hoedspruit. The squadron saw much attack action.

airframes stripped to parts to equip two new airframes with the same serial numbers, produced by Dassault at Bordeaux. The same was done locally with 205 (crash landed 8 February 1985) and 206 (damaged by SAM over Angola on 27 September 1987) to make a 'new' 205. Also lost were 200 (15 February 1979), 208 (4 November 1980), 214 and 215 (28 December 1987).

Operational use by the SAAF has included air defence and attack, although published reports of military operations rarely specify aircraft types. Mirage F1CZs shot down Angolan MiG-21s on 6 November 1981 using cannon fire and on 5 October 1982, using a MATRA Magic AAM. The same SAAF pilot, Major Johann Rankin, was involved in both shootdowns, using 213 and 203 respectively, the latter aircraft now being preserved in the SAAF museum. Also available is the indigenous Armscor V3 Kukri, which is externally identical to the Magic and can be directed by a helmet-mounted sight. A developed version, the Armscor Darter, entered service in 1988, while for longer-range interception MATRA R.530ZEs are available. Mirage F1AZs, possibly with F1CZ top cover, have almost certainly been involved in the major South African offensives into Angola and anti-guerrilla strikes in the administered territory of South-West Africa until it achieved independence in 1989 as Namibia. Weapons for the ground attack role include MATRA F4 rocket pods, four of which may be carried in addition to a centreline RP 35 drop tank. Locally produced CFD-200 chaff/flare dispensers are also employed.

February 1975, when the squadron officially reformed on Mirage F1s, it was operating IIIEZs, IIIDZs and IIID2Zs, all of which were passed on to No. 85 Advanced Flying School. No. 3's badge of a moth in plan view appears on the fin. Late in 1975, No. 1 Squadron left its Canadair CL-13 Sabres at Pietersberg and moved to Waterkloof to accept the first Mirage F1AZs. These were not publicly shown until February 1980, by which time No. 1 was the largest unit in the SAAF with all 32 machines on strength.

No. 1 Squadron did not at first decorate its aircraft, but later applied the badge of an eagle with outstretched wings alighting upon a shield.

Both squadrons were part of Strike Command until included in the newly formed Air Defence Command (Lugruimbeheerkommandement) in January 1980. No. 1 moved to Hoedspruit on 14 January 1981, while No. 3 remained at Waterkloof until disbanded as an economy measure on 30 September 1992. The

Mirage F1CZs are reported to have been placed in storage, although it is likely that some will be flown by No. 1 Squadron. As insurance against France joining the UN arms embargo, South Africa's Armaments Development & Production Corporation (Armscor) obtained licences to built both the Mirage and its Atar engine. These have not been used, apart from building Atars to re-engine Mirage IIIs as Cheetahs. Two F1CZs, 203 and 204, were destroyed in a collision in February 1979 and their

No. 1 Sqn is the surviving SAAF Mirage F1 unit, its aircraft having adopted a toned-down scheme.

The Mirage F1CZs of No. 3 Squadron also received a low-visibility scheme prior to the unit being disbanded during defence cuts in 1992.

Spain

Ejercito del Aire

Three variants of Mirage F1 have been obtained by Spain, the first in 1972 when 15 F1CE interceptors (reduced from the planned 21 because of financial constraints)

were ordered under the local designation of C.14A. A further 10, including one attrition replacement, were added in 1978, followed by a batch of 48 during the next year. This last-mentioned contract, agreed after Dassault undertook to promote the CASA C.212 light transport, included six F1BE (CE.14A) trainers and 22 multi-role F1EE-200s (C.14B), giving Spain three squadrons, each with 22 single-seat and two tandem-seat Mirage F1s. These were:

Type	Spanish serials	Delivered between
Mirage F1CE/C.14A	C.14-1 to C.14-15	March 1975-May 1976
Mirage F1CE/C.14A	C.14-16 to C.14-25	June 1978-May 1979
Mirage F1BE/CE.14A	CE.14-26 to CE.14-31	October 1980-November 1981
Mirage F1CE/C.14A	C.14-32 to C.14-51	March 1980-December 1981
Mirage F1EE/C.14B	C.14-52 to C.14-73	October 1981-March 1983

Above: Spain's Mirage F1s are being painted in this smart light grey air defence scheme, complete with false cockpit painted underneath. Escuadrón 142 of Ala 14 is a NATO tiger squadron, this aircraft bearing special markings.

Left: The F1CEs were delivered in this three-tone tactical camouflage, despite their air defence role. The type is known by the local designation C.14A, all of which serve with the two squadrons of Ala 14 at Albacete.

Above: Under the local designation CE.14A, Spain acquired six F1BE conversion trainers, two of which were assigned to each squadron.

All three versions have VOR/ILS and BF RWR aerials. C.14As and CE.14As were delivered in upper surface camouflage of sand, brown and green, with light grey below; C.14Bs with French air defence blueish-grey above and light grey below, the fixed refuelling probes black. In 1989, C.14As began rotating through the maintenance unit, Maestranza de Albacete (Ala 52), to adopt new air defence colours of overall light grey with roundels of reduced size and a low-visibility wing badge.

Two squadrons of Mirage F1CEs are assigned to air defence of Spain, flying from Albacete/Los Llanos with Ala de Caza (Fighter Wing) 14. Initially a component of Mando de la Defensa Aérea, the wing was absorbed into Mando Aéreo de Combate (Air Combat Command) in 1977 and then regrouped within Mando Aérea de Estrecho (Straits [of Gibraltar] Air Command) on 1 July 1991. Ala 14 formed in June 1974 to operate the Mirage F1 and established its first squadron, Escuadrón de Caza 141, with the initial aircraft, which it coded 141-01 to 141-15. The wing badge of Don Quixote saluting a flight of three Mirage F1s is applied to engine air intakes.

Escuadrón 142 formed on 1 April 1980 with the later C.14As, which received codes beginning 142-25. The squadron has a tiger badge (not applied to its aircraft), with the result that since 1986 it has regularly attended NATO Tiger Meets, Spain having joined the alliance in 1982. The 31st Meet, in May 1992, was hosted by Spain for the first time. Since early 1987, the Ejército del Aire has had a new aircraft coding system, with the result that Mirage F1CEs are coded from 14-01 to 14-49, without reference to the individual

Above and right: The badges of Ala 14 and its two constituent squadrons.

squadron. Following the standing down of Spain's Mirage IIIEEs on 1 October 1992, Ala de Caza 11 at Manises re-equipped 111 Escuadrón with 12 Mirage F1s within Mando Aérea de Levante (Eastern Air Command).

In the Canary Islands, the self-contained miniature air arm of Mando Aéreo de Canarias contains the Mirage F1EEs of Escuadrón 462, Ala 46 at Las Palmas/Gando. The wing received all 22 C.14Bs, marked 462-01 to 462-22, and trainers CE.14-30 and -31, 462-23 and -24. All prefixes were changed in 1977 to 46-. Escuadrón 462 formed on 1 April 1982, replacing the CASA/Northrop SF-5As of Esc

464, which had disbanded on 14 January that year. As Ala 46's other squadron operates Aviocars, Mirages are permitted to wear their squadron badge of an eagle's head. Following the disposal of Mirage IIIs during 1992 the entire Mirage F1 fleet was re-coded between 14-01 and 14-74. A mix of F1CEs and F1EEs is detached to Ala 11 and Ala 46, as required.

Ground attack weapons include the CC-420 30-mm cannon pod and CEM1 multi-store dispenser holding 18 rockets, plus either six BAP100 bomblets or two Durandal dispensers for destroying runways. F1CEs have flare dispensers scabbed to each side of the lower rear

fuselage. Either version can be armed with AIM-9P Sidewinders or MATRA 550 Magics at the wingtips, plus MATRA R.530s for medium-range interception. Spain had lost 15 Mirage F1s by 1993, including six in paired accidents: two collisions and an unusual incident over the Bardenas Reales range on 13 June 1989 when faulty ammunition exploded in the gun breeches of two individual aircraft.

The Mirage F1EE (C.14B) batch initially served exclusively with Ala 46 in the Canaries, distinguished by the slate-grey camouflage.

Above: Badge of Escadrón 462, the Las Palmas-based F1EE unit.

Philippine Air Force
Hukbong Himpapawid ng Pilipinas
Photographed by Peter Steinemann

Since the overthrow of the Marcos regime in February 1986, the Philippines have struggled towards full democracy, with several coup attempts. In the distant parts of the archipelago there has been long-running guerrilla warfare. Factions of the air force have been involved in all the fighting, mostly on the side of the government, but on at least one occasion aircraft supported rebel forces. Today the air force's warfighting ability is sorely depleted, with no replacements for the fighter force and only limited procurement in other areas. The eruption of Mount Pinatubo further hastened the PhilAF's decline.

Above: *The PhilAF's interceptor force consists of the few survivors of 19 Northrop F-5As and three F-5Bs delivered in 1965. In the mid-1980s the air force attempted to buy F-5E/Fs from South Korea, but the inability to sell the Crusaders denied funding for the Tiger II purchase. The four F-5As still in service fly with the 6th Tactical Fighter Squadron, part of the 5th Fighter Wing at Mactan. Previously based at Basa, the F-5s moved after the latter base was covered in volcanic ash after the eruption of Mount Pinatubo.*

Left: *Most active of the Philippines' aircraft were the North American T-28D Trojans, which were retired in late 1992. They served with the 17th Attack Squadron of the 15th Strike Wing.*

Above: *Resplendent in a smart paint scheme, this Sikorsky S.76 Spirit is the sole example of its kind in service with the 252nd Helicopter Squadron at Villamor Air Base. Its role is VIP transportation.*

Right: *Training for the Philippine Air Force is undertaken at Fernando Air Base, home of the 100th Training Wing. Basic training is accomplished on the SIAI-Marchetti SF-260MP with the 102nd Pilot Training Squadron. The unit is known as 'Musang' and features a tiger's head as its badge.*

One of four F-5As left in service at Mactan (left), painted in light grey with high-visibility national markings. Aircraft are armed with the ancient AIM-9B Sidewinder missile as their primary weapon. The sole F-5B surviving (above) is heavily used by the 6th TFS for its conversion/continuation training requirements.

Below: Battered T-28Ds prepare for a mission in 1992, just prior to their retirement. Deliveries from the US totalled 60, but they were retired in the early 1980s. Fourteen were returned to service in 1985, although only four were still active at the end of their career. Note the GP bombs and 81-mm cluster grenades carried under the wings.

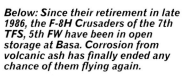

Left: Until their retirement, the T-28Ds were operating from the Tactical Advanced Command Post at Cauayan on front-line duties. During their career the T-28s saw much action.

Below: Since their retirement in late 1986, the F-8H Crusaders of the 7th TFS, 5th FW have been in open storage at Basa. Corrosion from volcanic ash has finally ended any chance of them flying again.

Philippine Air Force

Above: Philippine Air Force flying students begin their career on the Cessna T-41D Mescalero with the 101st Primary Pilot Training Squadron 'Layangs' at Fernando, part of the 100th Training Wing. The unit has a hawk's head as its badge on which is superimposed a sword, a genie lamp and the PhilAF insignia.

Right: One Lockheed RT-33 remains in storage at Basa, but like the Crusaders it has been extensively corroded by volcanic ash following the Pinatubo eruption, and will not fly again. It previously flew with the 105th CCTS at the same base.

Above: Having moved from Basa, the 105th Combat Crew Training Squadron now operates from Puerto Princesa under the aegis of the 570th Composite Tactical Wing. Three Lockheed T-33s remain on strength, but only two are serviceable. They continue to operate in a combat training role, preparing pilots for the F-5 or OV-10.

Left: To revamp its forces, the PhilAF procured 18 SIAI-Marchetti S.211 jets, split between the advanced training role at Fernando with the 100th Training Wing and weapons training from Basa with the 5th Fighter Wing. The Dayglo-painted trainers serve with the 103rd Pilot Training Squadron. The first four S.211s were built in Italy, but the remaining 14 were assembled locally from kits by PADC.

Right: The camouflaged S.211s originally intended for the 105th CCTS at Basa are currently operated by the 100th TW at Fernando. Note the addition of underwing pylons for the light strike and weapons training roles. A 0.50-in (12.7-mm) machine-gun can be fitted in a pod under the cockpit.

Above and left: The counter-insurgency force received a considerable boost in 1992 with the delivery of 24 ex-USAF Rockwell OV-10A Broncos. Delivery was by sea, the first 15 arriving in January and the remainder following later in the year. They serve with the 16th Attack Squadron, part of the 15th Strike Wing and based at Sangley Point. This unit previously operated Sikorsky S.76 gunships, which were used during the 1986 overthrow of President Marcos. The 16th AS badge features a stylised bird and the number '16'.

Above: A dozen GAF N22B Nomad Mission Masters were received in the mid-1970s, equipped with underwing hardpoints and self-sealing tanks for use on tactical airlift and casevac duties. The survivors continue to fly with the 223rd Airlift Squadron 'Nomads', part of the 220th Airlift Wing at Mactan.

Right: Partnering the Nomad in the 220th Airlift Wing is the Pilatus Britten-Norman BN-2A Islander, locally assembled by PADC. The first was received in March 1976, the second in April 1978 and the remaining 20 in 1980-81. Most wear this drab camouflage, but at least one wears an all-black scheme and markings for the 15th Strike Wing at Sangley Point.

Left: The principal transport of the Philippine Air Force, as with so many other air arms, is the Lockheed Hercules, a mix of C-130B and C-130H being on strength. They wear two distinctive camouflage styles, illustrated here. All Hercules are operated by the 222nd Heavy Airlift Squadron, partnering the Nomads and Islanders in the 220th Airlift Wing. The wing's badge consists of a winged head of a buffalo above a globe, with a lightning flash and olive branch either side. The Hercules are also based at Mactan, the PhilAF's premier base situated near Cebu.

Above: Formerly operated by Philippine Airlines, nine Fokker F27 Friendships were transferred to the air force in 1971. Most serve on general transport duties with the 221st Transport Squadron at Villamor (illustrated), but one also flies with the Presidential wing.

Above: Three Fokker F27MPA maritime patrollers were supplied in 1981 for surveillance of the seas to the west, but only one remains in service, flying with the 221st Transport Squadron. The aircraft retains its ventral radome, and has provision for auxiliary fuel tanks underwing.

Below: The stretched fuselage distinguishes this aircraft from the C-130 Hercules as a civil model L-100-20, three of which were built new for the Philippine Air Force. Two of these aircraft are unserviceable, and are withdrawn from use on the ramp at Mactan with most markings removed.

Above: Partnering the OV-10s in the 15th Strike Wing at Sangley Point are the McDonnell Douglas MD500MG Defenders of the 18th Tactical Air Support Squadron, whose badge depicts the head of a hawk and an image of an MD500. These light helicopters are highly effective in counter-insurgency operations, featuring armament of gun pods (port) and rockets (starboard). The initial order was for 22 aircraft, later increased to 30 with deliveries being completed during 1992.

Right: Also at Sangley Point with the 15th SW is the 20th Air Commando Squadron, which flies Sikorsky S.76s armed with FN Herstal HMP 0.50-in (12.7-mm) machine-gun pods and other light weapons. Its badge is a silhouette of an S.76 superimposed on a red eagle. The original order covered 17 aircraft, 12 armed aircraft and five S.76 Mk IIs for VIP transportation and SAR duties.

Above: A trio of Hueys from the 205th Helicopter Wing at Villamor, whose badge depicts an eagle hovering over the front view of a Huey and the number '205'. In the foreground is a Bell 205A-1, one of 14 supplied in 1984 and used by the 210th Helicopter Training Squadron for rotary-wing instruction. In the centre is an essentially similar Bell UH-1H, one of a large number (including at least eight delivered in armed gunship configuration) supplied by the United States over the years through FMS channels. It is used by the 505th Air Rescue Squadron, as is the aircraft in the background, the sole Bell 214 on PhilAF strength. A pair of these aircraft was supplied in 1984, initially for VIP transport with the Presidential wing. Today the survivor's extra power is valued on rescue work. Sharing the same basic cabin layout and pointed nose profile as the Model 212, the 214 is distinguished by having one engine with a prominent exhaust.

Above: Another type licence-built locally by the Philippine Aerospace Development Corporation is the MBB BO 105C, used for a variety of tasks by government forces. Some serve on SAR duties (with light armament), while others were supplied to the small naval aviation organisation and to the civil-registered police air wing. This example, though bearing civil marks, is on the strength of the Presidential Airlift Wing at Villamor Air Base.

Right: One of the more unusual aircraft in PhilAF service, this was one of three Cessna T210G Turbo Centurions supplied for meteorological reconnaissance with the 901st Weather Squadron, part of the Villamor transport wing. This is the only one left in service, and still used primarily for its original role. Its name ('Rainmaker') alludes to its use as a 'weather modifier', sowing rain-clouds with pellets of silver iodide or other chemicals to induce precipitation.

Above: Two Sikorsky S-70A-5 Black Hawks were delivered to the Philippine Air Force. One was used for SAR work, while the other now flies with the 252nd Helicopter Squadron at Villamor, wearing the smart colours of the 250th Presidential Airlift Wing.

Right: Another smart helicopter serving with the 250th Presidential Airlift Wing is this Bell 212. It is equipped to a very high standard, with excellent communications and weather radar for IFR flight.

Below: The largest Presidential wing helicopter is this Aérospatiale SA 330 Puma. In addition to the aircraft of the 252nd Helicopter Squadron, the 250th Wing also operates two fixed-wing aircraft in the VIP role – single examples of the Fokker F27-200 Friendship and F28-3000 Fellowship.

'Fight to Teach, not Fight to Win'

VMFT-401 'Snipers'

Less well-known than the US Navy's adversary squadrons and the world-famous 'Top Gun' School, but no less important, VMFT-401 (Marine Fighter Training Squadron 401) is the US Marine Corps' only adversary unit. Formed only in 1986, and initially equipped with the Israeli Kfir, VMFT-401 currently flies second-hand ex-USAF F-5E Tiger IIs. Nicknamed the 'Snipers' (after the highest Soviet pilot grade), VMFT-401 trains Marine aircrew by simulating the threat, be it former Soviet or Soviet-trained. The squadron's operations officer, Lieutenant Colonel Mark Lauritzen, recently described the squadron's vitally important role.

Above: One of VMFT-401's F-5Es gets airborne from Yuma, its flimsy-looking landing gear already folding away. The red tail star and Soviet-style Bort number denote the unit's adversary mission.

Below: A gaggle of F-5Es cruises over the Californian desert. The squadron can respond to any training need, putting up single aircraft or multi-bogey formations.

"I joined the Marine Corps in 1975 and have accumulated approximately 4,300 military flying hours. About 2,200 of these are in the F-4, another 1,000 in the A-4 Skyhawk and 900 plus in the F-5. I flew as a Reservist out of NAS Dallas before coming to MCAS Yuma, converting from the Phantom to the F-5 here.

"The uniqueness of the airplane and this squadron has made it a worthwhile decision for me. Transitioning to the F-5 was not a problem at all. It is a simple aircraft with high performance. Systems-wise, it is simple to learn and an honest fighter to fly. One of the problems that almost every pilot encounters when first flying the F-5 is that when you have 15-20 hours in it, you feel like you have 500. It has a lot of favourable flight qualities and is very forgiving.

"I had experienced the F-5E prior to coming to the squadron several times, though not as a pilot! I used to work with the guys from 'Top Gun' when they had the F-5, and also have been fortunate enough to fly against the 64th and 65th Aggressor Squadrons at Nellis. . . . when they had the aircraft. By the way, we are flying some of their aircraft today. It is a remarkable little fighter, to say the least. . . .

Above and right: This is what every VMFT-401 F-5E has to try to simulate, every day – the Mikoyan MiG-29 'Fulcrum', Russia's hottest lightweight fighter and for sale to all interested parties, worldwide.

very good performance. Against the F 4, it has a little better turning performance. When you get engaged with the F-5, he can intimidate you very much with his turn, but if you know the performance of it and fly a smart fight, you can do quite well against it even in the F-4 and especially in the Hornet. My personal encounters with the aircraft I can remember very well. . . . flying against the 'Top Gun' guys and getting beat up severely a couple of times, because I tried to work the vertical with them at higher altitudes in my F-4 and it would not turn as well. I learned very quickly to drag the fight down low and to stay in a two-circle type of sustained energy fight against the F-5. If I was flying the F-4 again today, that's exactly what my game plan would be. I'd meet the F-5 head-on, turn across his tail and try to drag him down in low so I could

optimise my aircraft's performance, and I would have a better sustained *g* capability than the F-5 has down low.

Small size

"The F-5 is a very small aircraft when compared to some of the state-of-the-art types that are flying today, such as the F-14 and F-15. It is sometimes referred to as the 'flying razorblade'. Sometimes when you are out there in the arena, it is a tough aircraft to see and this drives the mid-air potential up quite a bit,

especially in multi-aircraft scenarios. It is very hard to track in a close-in fight. You assume the other pilot sees you when in fact he doesn't. You always have to assume he does not!

"We try to present a realistic scenario, and the F-5 can replicate the MiG-21 quite easily. . . . you

Below: The squadron's aircraft wear a variety of camouflage schemes to allow them to more accurately replicate the threat posed by a number of undefined unfriendly nations.

Fight to Teach, not Fight to Win

can overlay the performance characteristics of both aircraft and show that they are almost identical. With regard to the MiG-29, a newer-generation aircraft, some of the capabilities of the -29 will exceed that of the F-5's performance and weapons systems. However, it depends on the scenario . . . if someone wants us to fly, say, a 4 vs 4 like MiG-29s, we can do a pretty good job of doing that if we have ground control intercept (GCI) to help us with our pre-merge game plan. There are definite things that both sides will do, as far as what they see on their radar scopes, decoy tactics, different tactics of elements in groups and, without getting into classified areas, I think some of the versatility of the F-5 will allow you to fly in a similar way to a newer-generation threat airplane just by the tactics they use. Obviously, if you go 1 vs 1 you can't fly as well, performance wise. You just cannot replicate his performance. If he turns at 25° per second and you are turning at 16° per second, you can't turn with him, but for the most part, the battle is won beginning 20 miles before the merge. I think, with state-of-the-art weapons, you win the fight far beyond visual range.

An underfuselage fuel tank allows the F-5E to go much further, but only at the expense of agility. Such tanks are, by consequence, rarely carried.

"Of course, to counter that threat, there are certain ways you fly, using decoy elements and ensuring you know when you are targeted. For example, if a MiG-29 pilot knows he is targeted a certain distance from his threat, he will turn in order to defeat that radar missile that may be coming his way. There are a lot of different ways he can do that and in that regard . . . yes, we can simulate that threat pretty easily."

Early MiG simulator

The squadron commmander, Lieutenant Colonel Jerry Breen, has similar opinions about the F-5. "The F-5 replicates the MiG-19, MiG-21 and MiG-23 quite adequately. Some of the capabilities of the MiG-29 (like its look-down/shoot-down capabilities) we cannot replicate. The F-5 is, however, the best aircraft for the role, as it is very cost efficient and easy to maintain. The cost per flight hour is phenomenally low."

Lauritzen continues: "Although the Soviet Union of a few years ago no longer exists, we still try to replicate the Soviet tactics. There is a very definite style of tactics that former Eastern Bloc countries use and train to, and these have proliferated throughout the world, primarily through training. A lot of

those tactics consist of just overwhelming the enemy with numbers and flying in a very offensive manner. For example, always shooting first and asking questions later, whereas the Western world is preoccupied with positively identifying the target they are going after. The Eastern Bloc's mind-set is to sort it all out after they shoot and their tactics are based on this. We will continue replicating that threat because we all know what the Western world's tactics are. The best thing we can do for our guys is to fly absolutely the best aircraft we can fly, using strange or Communist-style tactics! Those may be somewhat broken up now, but they are still considered a potential threat. They are very cagey in how they fly their fighters and are excellent at decoy tactics, and we do a good job at duplicating them. We ask our customers what they want to see: a Soviet pilot on his first formation flight, or a Russian advisor that has a couple of hundred hours in type, or do you want to see a Soviet MiG-29 type that has 3,000 hours and knows what he is doing? We'll style our flying to what they want to see.

"The future of -401 looks very good, and we have a great track record. There has been a pronounced need for the squadron. We've been integrated into a lot of the training syllabuses of many squadrons. Will the F-5 be around forever? I doubt it. Realistically, we can fly these aircraft for four or five more years without too many problems, but that is depending on the support we have. The follow-on

aircraft is unknown and there is nothing in the works right now . . . only rumours. The Navy is 'looking' at Hornets to fill the role of their adversary aircraft.

Selection procedure

"Most all of the pilots in -401 have a fighter background. It is a very selective squadron in that we recruit within the Marine Corps. These pilots are all capable of being instructor pilots or Air Combat training instructors. All have graduated from the 'Top Gun' course as F/A-18 or F-4 pilots. They are all at least second-tour aviators. The selection process for full-time pilots is usually done by a board in Washington. They rely heavily on inputs that the various squadron commanders give them. Currently, the average age and rank with VMFT-401 is major (32-35 years of age). There is very little turnover on the squadron and some of the pilot have been here since its inception. Most of the top timers are part-timers that have a career as airline pilots, and the turnover rate among the full-time pilots is very low.

"The average flight time is about 2,500 hours. The range would be approximately 1,800 hours for the least experienced pilot to about 4,500 hours for the senior pilots in the squadron. This experience has played a major factor in our safety record. Currently, we are approaching 20,000 hours of accident-free flying and should hit that mark within the next six months. The average flying time (among 13 part-time pilots) would be to fly eight days a month (flying twice a day). This would equal 12-14 hours a month and about 120 hours per year. The full-time pilots in the squadron will fly at least once a day and many times twice a day. This gives them about 28-35 hours per month and a total of 300 plus hours a year. The average length of a sortie is 0.8 hours.

Annual deployments

"Road trips . . . we don't do much cross-country. We deploy about three times a year on a squadron basis (eight or nine aircraft), to support the East Coast Marines (at Beaufort, Cherry Point, etc). In addition to this we will have four or five mini-deployments to the West Coast (Miramar, El Toro, etc). We'll take five or so aircraft for

a week. We do not leave CONUS. With our external centreline tanks, we can fly about 900-1,000 miles in VFR conditions. We are not capable of inflight refuelling with our F-5s.

"Before we had an adversary tactics squadron the Marines had a definite need for these services from the Navy squadrons, both East and West Coast, and the problem was that as the tactics became more

complex and the Marines got more and more into the F/A-18, the Navy just could not provide what we needed either through 'Top Gun' training classes or supporting the bi-annual WTI exercises. There

Maintaining the Tiger II

Fred King is one of VMFT-401's civilian crew chiefs, and has a great respect for the F-5E. "I am a retired gunnery sergeant with the Marine Corps. The majority of my experience has been with the F-4 Phantom, including the B, J, N and S models. After retiring, I went to work for General Dynamics and VMFT-401. They were using the F-21 Kfir, manufactured by the Israeli Aircraft Industries. The pilots love this fighter because of its speed. We transitioned from the Kfir to the Northrop F-5 Tiger II. The F-5 is a tremendous tactical fighter, based on what I have heard from the many pilots who have flown it. Engineering-wise, to a certain degree it is maintenance-free. When a problem crops up with the F-5, we can usually solve it quickly, and engine changes, etc., are fast. It was designed to work in a very simple manner, especially compared to some of the larger fighters. The F-5 dates back to the mid-1960s and has been flown by numerous air forces, including the South Vietnamese. All three branches of the US military have flown it. It is still used by several foreign countries as a front-line fighter.

"My aircraft, No. 12 'Excaliber', has a unique camouflage paint scheme that makes it almost impossible to spot when it is hugging the deck, in desert terrain. All of the crew chiefs, here at MCAS Yuma, have their own assigned aircraft and we all take great pride in them. In my opinion, the most formidable trait that the Tiger II has is its turn-around time. In a critical situation, these aircraft could be in the enemy's face several times a day!"

Above: Fred King, one of VMFT-401's unsung heros, is a member of the dedicated team of ground crew who keep the squadron's elderly aircraft on top line. A former Marine gunnery sergeant, King is now a civilian contractor, but as a crew chief takes a proprietary pride and interest in 'his' F-5E.

Left: VMFT-401 transitioned to the F-5E from the IAI Kfir, the conversion being made possible by the disbandment of several USAF aggressor units. Here an ex-USAF F-5E undergos a major overhaul in the 'Snipers' maintenance hangar at Yuma.

maintenance, etc. Our aircraft are owned by the Navy, as are all Marine aircraft. 'Top Gun' provides the mainstay of the tactics, the standardisations, etc. that we use. We'll follow all of the tactics laid down by 'Top Gun', their category system of missiles and aircraft, what they consider to be representative of what the real world threat may be, according to the country in the scenario. We will send out pilots to the 'Top Gun' Adversary Training Course to train them in what we consider to be the common threat tactics. There is not a lot of difference, philosophically or conceptionally, between how we see things and how 'Top Gun' sees things! There is a lot of rivalry, but this is because we are different squadrons.

Multiple roles

"The squadron has a wide range of tasks. To exercise front-line units we try to hit MCAS Beaufort (East Coast) at least four times a year. Our biggest event here at home is supporting VMFAT-101, which is the major fleet reserve readiness squadron for the F/A-18, operating out of MCAS El Toro. They are here about once a month, depending on their schedule, and that takes up most of our flying time, training those young guys in dissimilar ACM.

"Another chunk goes into WTI exercises that last about six weeks and, after that, support goes out to the Marine fleet squadrons, for example, a support of their ACTI (Air Combat Tactics Instructor) programme. What that means is that after a guy has been in a squadron and has got 500-1,000 hours in the aircraft, he needs to become an ACM Instructor. To achieve this, he'll go through a very stringent course (academic as well as flight build-up) and finally the certification part of that is conducted through our MAWTS team here at Yuma. They'll go out and administer a test to this pilot and, if he passes the exam, there is a series of three flights that he'll fly.

"The focus is primarily on the pilot's ability to brief, instruct, create a game plan and execute that plan in the air, according to what the threat is, what missiles he has available, how he employs his radar and his wingman. Then, of course, it is reconstructing or debriefing that tactical flight in such a way that the learning points are brought out in a very low-key way (egos are not part of it). You reconstruct a scenario, you take a look at what your learning objectives were and you evaluate the execution part of the

was a real market for a Marine adversary squadron. So, our niche is the uniqueness of our squadron. Not only would we support the F/A-18 squadrons, but also the Harrier units and even the guys on the ground. We fly a lot of missions over Twenty-Nine Palms where we will simulate an airborne threat that flies over the ground troops in a mock strafing attack; or we will run

surface attack profiles on the Hawk missile batteries that are operated by the Marine Corps; or we will fly strike intercept scenarios with C-130s, AV-8B Harriers, OV-10s, etc; or we'll do EVMs with the helicopters. We'll be down on the deck trying to attack them and they'll turn towards us and simulate firing Sidewinders at us. So, we have many unique missions that the

Navy squadrons do not have and, realistically, they could not support these if we requested it from them. They just don't have the assets or resources available."

Lauritzen's commanding officer, Jerry Breen, is quick to point out that the unit's unique status has its disadvantages, too. "The biggest problem for -401 is being the only adversary squadron in the Corps, supporting three air wings. We are maxed out at this level. Picking up more F-5s would not solve the problem, as you would be getting into certain manpower restraints for the Reserve Forces."

This is not to say that the Marine adversaries at VMFT-401 do things differently than their Navy comrades, as Mark Lauritzen explains: "The Navy Adversary Tactics programme and our programme run parallel. We come under the Navy's Omnibus of Adversary Squadron concept and use the same type of contract

Left: In the baking desert sun, cockpit temperatures would soon become impossibly high, so when not flying, between sorties, VMFT-401's aircraft are parked under huge platforms.

Left: The blue-painted airframe identifies this AIM-9 as an acquisition round, a missile with a live seeker and an inert rocket motor. It can lock on, but cannot be fired, making it a superb training aid.

Above: The pilots of VMFT-401 use their training, skills and knowledge to present fleet fighter pilots with a credible enemy, compensating for the age and simplicity of their aircraft.

flight according to what you briefed. If there is a way to do it better, you put your heads together and try to get it on the next flight. So this pilot gets his ACTI Certificate and he is now able, within his squadron, to be a flight lead and a mission commander for any dissimilar ACM events including from single (1 vs 1) scenario to multi vs multi packages.

"Right now we don't do anything with Red Flag. Red Flag is well known for the type of training they do, and the USMC has participated over the years and still does. VMFT-401 supporting Red Flag would pose some problems, however. If we go up to Nellis AFB as a Marine adversary squadron, in support of an Air Force unit, that means there are Marine fleet units that are not getting the support that they are tasked with. There are some times during the year that we'll have slack periods, but not many. We are alloted 3,900 flight hours per year and we use every single one of them!

"There may be times when we have low activity, maybe a couple of

Right: The cockpit of a VMFT-401 F-5E. Nothing short of primitive, the F-5E has only a simple ranging radar (often removed), making it difficult to fully simulate the threat posed by BVR-capable fighters like the MiG-29.

Fight to Teach, not Fight to Win

Above: A line-up of F-5Es shows some of the camouflage schemes applied to -401's aircraft. These are a compromise between effective camouflage and represent potential enemy colours.

weeks, but when the word gets out the phone is ringing off the wall with other Marine units waiting to use our services. Whatever we do, it must benefit the USMC!

"In most of the briefs we have, the flight leader will go to a customer, sit down and get the 'bogey' brief (and that is just a matter of 10-15 minutes where the F-5 flight leader goes over all the specifics of frequencies, altitudes, areas, etc., what the customer wants by way of threat and any restrictions he may put on us to help him in his training). After he gets that, he'll come back to our ready room and then, as a flight, we'll get together and brief that mission. Most of our missions are multi-ship, 2 vs 2 or 2 vs unknown. The latter might involve two Hornets vs six to eight F-5s. We'll throw the opposition a mixed bag so that they are always trying to figure out how many of us there are going to be. Some of the more difficult type scenarios are 4 vs 4 vs unknown. We do quite a few of those with the Marine Hornets.

"Generally, the entire flight will go to the debrief because of the dynamic nature of ACM. This is the only way of being able to piece everything together in a complete, clear picture. The flight lead will not usually have the resources to be able to reconstruct everything,

Right: The twin-stick F-5F is used for adversary training, and for standardisation and instrument flying training for squadron pilots. During the Kfir era, the squadron had no two-seaters.

because the fight may take place over a 10 sq mile area and he's likely to have his hands full. He can't always look across the circle and remember what everyone else was doing, so it is best to get together and reconstruct that in a debrief.

Contracted maintenance

"As far as what my pre-flight procedures are when I walk out to the aircraft, things are very simple. Thanks to the General Dynamics people that maintain our aircraft, there is very little to do. The F-5s are always in perfect working order and have an overall immaculate appearance. Before you get to the flight line, the crew chief is already on the way to meet you. The planes very seldom leak, as can be attested

to by the clean parking areas in the covered revetments. These General Dynamics crew chiefs all have their own aircraft assigned. If you look at the nose gear doors, his name is painted on each one. For example, one of the most dedicated crew chiefs, Fred King, has No. 12 'Excalibur'. He and I served on the USS *Coral Sea* together many years ago. His aircraft is the pride of our 'fleet' and we call it the 'Neon Earthpig' because it is green and brown. He always keeps it so clean that even the tailpipes are always shining. Everyone should know about Fred King and his fellow crew chiefs because it doesn't get any better.

"Regarding the characteristics of the F-5 on the ground – taxiing is

very easy. It has a nice nosewheel steering system, and it's got a wide stance. The tendency in this aircraft is to get to taxiing too fast. The one thing I'll demo on familiarisation flights with new pilots is just how effective the rudder is! We can be going down the taxiway at about 25-30 kt, and you can stick in full right rudder and in three or four seconds the fighter is veering right. But you don't use the rudder too much on the ground because you have the nosegear steering system.

"When the aircraft is configured like we fly them, it will take off with approximately 3,000 ft of ground roll, depending on temperature and altitude density. Once you're airborne it accelerates nicely, especially in afterburner. You have very good directional control after 30-40 kt, with the rudder. It is a delightful aircraft to fly in crosswind situations, very easy to control. You rotate the nose of

the F-5 at 150 kt and you set a take-off attitude, and very shortly you are airborne. Very easy, honest. You have very good sensation in the stick. There is a little bit of forward stick pressure through the bungee feel system in the aircraft, and it is a pure delight to fly. At rotation speed you start to ease back on the stick at 145 to 150 kt. The nose will get light and then it'll rise slowly on you. The F-5 is airborne at about 160 kt. We always use afterburner in our take-offs. As soon as the plane lifts off the gear is coming up; at about 180 kt the flaps are coming up; and at about 200 kt we come out of afterburner to full military power until we reach 350 kt. At that time we adjust our nose position to maintain a 350-kt climb. When we hit our en route altitude, we power back to around 300 kias."

Lieutenant Colonel Jerry Breen, who took over command on 4 February 1992, should have the last

word. A career fighter pilot, with 4,000 hours on the A-4, F-4 and F/A-18 (more than 1,100 hours on the Hornet alone), Jerry Breen clearly enjoys his new job: "The most memorable missions for me are when we fly against the air superiority types and throw up a large number of fighters against a couple of them, in a 4 vs 8 or 2 vs 8. What makes such sorties so memorable and rewarding for me is getting a set of Marine fighter pilots that can sort that out, realise that they are outgunned and outnumbered, and take the appropriate moves to get out untouched. It pleases me no end when I see that! They have gained the knowledge to see what we are doing and to avoid being beaten."

As the unit's handout states, under 'Philosophy': "'Fight to teach' not 'Fight to win': In our business it's not *who* wins an engagement, it's *why* that counts."

Above: An F-5E rolls inverted before pulling through in pursuit of some hapless Marine Hornet driver.

Below: Lieutenant Colonel Jerry Breen is the commanding officer of VMFT-401. The unit's 'Snipers' nickname reflects the top Soviet pilot grade.

Saab 35 Draken
Variant Briefing

Nordic Dragon

Entering its twilight years, the J 35 Draken remains in small-scale service with the Austrian and Finnish air forces, and with two-thirds of one of Sweden's front-line fighter wings. Denmark retired its last half-dozen Drakens at the very end of 1993. With its remaining users, however, the Draken is extraordinarily popular. A fighter pilot's aeroplane, its narrow but comfortable cockpit is still a sought-after posting, and pilots are justifiably proud of remaining competitive in their workload-intensive but rewarding hot rods. And they don't need more than the 'NATO Standard 45-minute fighter pilot bladder!'

Above: One of the last J 35F-1s in Swedish service pulls hard, vapour streaming off the upper surfaces of the wings, and afterburner blazing. With half the engine power of an English Electric Lightning, the Draken proved to have a very similar performance, with similar handicaps of inadequate range/endurance and, by the end of its career, a primitive weapons system and high-workload cockpit. The red fin and white ghost badge mark this aircraft as belonging to the commanding officer of the 1st Division of F10 (wing), which has now converted to the newer Viggen.

The 1950s were a particularly exciting era in the history of the fighter aircraft. Superpower confrontation was a prime motivating factor behind many of the advances in the USA, where the celebrated Century Series of fighters dominated developments. Design bureaux in the Soviet Union were also working away madly, their most enduring creation being the MiG-21 'Fishbed'. France and Great Britain conceived outstanding fighters in the form of the Mirage III and Lightning respectively, but one of the most distinctive and durable machines of this period originated from a nation that stood apart from the military alliances of east and west.

That nation was Sweden and the aircraft concerned was Saab's Model 35, more familiarly known as the Draken (Dragon). Despite the fact that it entered service as long ago as 1960, the Draken is still very much alive today, more than

three decades later, and presently serves with the air arms of Finland, Denmark and Austria, as well as Sweden, where the ultimate J 35J development only entered the operational inventory as recently as 1987.

Even a smart new air superiority grey colour scheme and AIM-9 Sidewinders cannot fully transform the Draken into a truly modern fighter, although the package of modifications comprising the J 35J conversion has given the aircraft a measure of credibility for service into the 1990s and perhaps beyond. In Sweden, two of F10's three divisions look set to retain Drakens for some time to come.

Below: The prototype Saab Model 35 Draken in flight shows off the type's unusual double-delta wing planform. The first prototype made its maiden flight on 25 October 1955. The weapons being carried here are 135-mm Bofors rockets, carried in piggy back pairs. The first prototype was also used for AIM-9 trials.

Left: This line-up comprises J 35 prototypes and an early production J 35A. The initial three prototypes were powered by imported Avon 200 series engines, and as a consequence had a unique tailcone/nozzle arrangement. They are identifiable in this picture by their different canopy arrangement, with tiny square windows behind the main glazing. The third aircraft in the line-up is the first J 35A, the first true production Draken.

largely hypothetical, since no specific requirement existed, but that situation changed during 1949 when the Flygvapen air staff drew up a new specification for a fighter to succeed the J 29, even though that portly fighter did not enter service until 1951. By the standards of the day it was a fairly tough specification, and it was to become even tougher in 1956 when it was significantly revised. In its original form, the requirement stipulated an interceptor that would be capable of a maximum level speed of the order of Mach 1.4-1.5, figures that rose to Mach 1.7-1.8 in 1956.

In addition, the aircraft was also expected to possess an outstanding rate of climb and yet be operable from the same facilities that would soon be used by the J 29. Since this in turn dictated that the new fighter be compatible with the numerous highway strips that dotted the Swedish countryside, it followed that the aircraft would need to possess good short-field characteristics, an aspect that might well compromise performance at the upper end of the envelope. As it transpired, Saab could legitimately claim to have surpassed the requirement, for the Draken eventually achieved a maximum speed in clean configuration of Mach 2 and could motor along quite happily at Mach 1.7 with a full load of missiles.

Launching the project

Other features laid down by the Flygvapen called for a rugged and yet easily maintained and supported fighter that was both economical to procure and inexpensive to operate. It was, by any yardstick, a tall order, especially as Sweden's avowed neutral stance would almost certainly curtail export potential, with the consequence that Saab could not look to massive production as a method of reducing unit cost.

The difficulties were compounded by the fact that Sweden was still technologically in the doldrums and possessed little of the highly specialised equipment that would facilitate a project which was clearly just as ambitious as anything being tackled elsewhere. A good illustration of this is the lack of supersonic wind tunnel facilities, which meant that Saab had to undertake some research in the USA. Government support eventually helped to overcome this difficulty, but it all took time to come together and, for Saab, time was another commodity that was in short supply.

Nonetheless, Saab set to work enthusiastically,

The type is, however, in decline, Denmark having recently reduced the number of aircraft still in service and Sweden now having just one Draken-equipped unit. In consequence, the Draken is very unlikely to see out the present decade with these air arms. Finland's recent selection of the F/A-18 Hornet seems certain to pave the way for that country's withdrawal of the Draken, leaving only Austria to continue flying into the next century this distinctive and attractive example of the fighter designer's art.

The initial impetus for development of what eventually materialised as the Draken dates back to the immediate post-World War II period and,

more specifically, to late 1947 when Saab engineers were alerted to the fact that flight at Mach 1 was possible. At that time, the company was already heavily committed to the J 29 Tunnan programme and was soon to initiate development of the J 32 Lansen, both of these types eventually seeing extensive service with the Kungliga Svenska Flygvapnet (Royal Swedish Air Force). The design staff were sufficiently forward-looking to begin considering proposals for a supersonic fighter, and much of the work undertaken at this time found expression in the Model 35.

In 1947-48, the main thrust of the effort was

Left: Draken weaponry: an early J 35 is displayed behind an array of the armament it could carry. Working outboard from the centreline fuel tank are weapons which include AIM-9B Sidewinders (also built under licence in Sweden as the Rb24), underwing fuel tanks, indigenous Bofors 70-mm 19-round rocket pods, ADEN 30-mm cannon, reconnaissance/night bombing flares, 250-kg bombs and clusters of six 135-mm rockets. Since early J 35As had only four hardpoints for the carriage of weapons, this array of stores is somewhat over optimistic.

assembling a design team under the capable leadership of Erik Bratt. Initial studies – collectively referred to as Project (R) 1200 – examined a number of options, including swept and delta wing planforms, but it soon became fairly obvious (to Bratt and his colleagues, at least) that the latter appeared to be the most promising avenue of exploration.

At first, they opted for a basically delta wing planform, similar to that adopted by Dassault for the Mirage III. Factors which exerted influence on the design process included a desire to minimise wave drag, this in turn dictating the necessity of employing the thinnest possible aerofoil surfaces in conjunction with a low thickness/chord ratio. Operational aspects that impinged on the design included the desired ceiling (which affected span) and mission duration (which affected fuel capacity and, in turn, root chord).

Delta drawbacks

While the pure delta looked to have a definite edge over the more conventional swept-wing, wind tunnel testing of models soon revealed that even this possessed a number of drawbacks, most notably concerning the aircraft's centre of gravity

Right: A pair of early J 35As from F13 is seen in flight. The J 35A was identifiable by its short rear fuselage and lack of a tailwheel, though both of these features were applied to late production As and retrofitted to some early aircraft. Lack of compatability with Sweden's STRIL 60 semi-automatic air defence ground control system left the J 35A an inferior interceptor by comparison with its better-equipped successors. Nevertheless, a handful of J 35As survived into the 1970s as advanced trainers with F16, then the Draken conversion and training unit. Some of these aircraft received a primitive IR seeker fairing below their radomes.

and centre of pressure. A variation of the planform known as the double delta looked much more satisfactory, since this allowed the C of G and C of P to be much closer to each other. That was by no means the only benefit that accrued; the chosen configuration cut frontal area while simultaneously permitting optimum wing area to be adopted, allowed a more suitable wing sweep angle to be used on the inner wing section, gave more favourable area distribution, reduced supersonic drag and resulted in more favourable low-speed drag.

Further wind tunnel tests soon verified the validity of a double-delta layout, and this was progressively refined under the designation Project (R) 1250. There were some who harboured reservations about this radical concept, especially among the higher echelons of the Flygvapen air staff. This was one reason, though by no means the only one, why Saab expanded its test activity to include practical trials as well as wind tunnel assessment, entailing the use of models of various scales and configurations. At

Above: No fewer than 16 J 35As take shape on Saab's assembly line at Linköping. The Cold War was raging and Sweden seemed to be facing a real threat from the East, so the re-equipment of Swedish fighter squadrons with an all-weather Mach 2 interceptor was seen as a high priority. Few would have imagined that two squadrons would still be equipped with Drakens in 1994, pending first deliveries of the fourth-generation JAS 39 Gripen.

first, the models were built of wood and powered by a small ramjet or pulsejet engine that was capable of generating about 4.5 lb st (0.02 kN). Control was rudimentary, being accomplished by means of piano wire manipulated by an operator at a centre post.

Early trials and tribulations

Unfortunately, inadequate control responses resulted in at least two models being damaged beyond repair and another being destroyed when it caught fire, so it was necessary to develop a new series of more robust models. These were fabricated from aluminium sheeting and

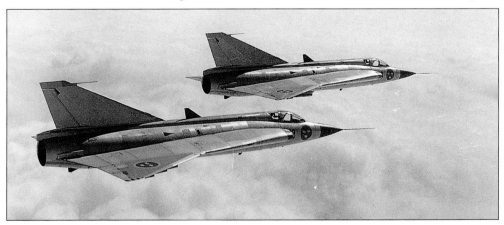

Above: The J 35D switched to a licence-produced version of the more-powerful Avon 300 series turbojet, with a redesigned afterburner, and introduced lengthened engine intakes. This aircraft carries an Rb05 anti-ship missile under the centreline, a weapon more usually associated with the later Viggen.

also used more reliable engines which, in concert with extra fuel capacity, increased flight duration to a maximum of about two minutes. Typically, these models had a wing span of about 3 ft (0.9 m) and a take-off weight of around 13 lb (6 kg). As with earlier trials, the flight path was circular, with the 'pilot' maintaining control from a centre post that was also fitted with an rpm counter and an elevon angle indicator, plus a movie camera to provide a film record of flight characteristics. Flight path radius slightly exceeded 60 ft (18 m) and the normal time to perform a complete revolution was roughly five seconds. Some 'pilots' suffered a novel variation of motion sickness, in

Below: Carrying a test camera under its centreline, a J 35F fires an Rb27 from its port underwing launch rail. The Swedish Rb27/Rb28 programme involved about 100 such firings from Drakens. The Rb27 and Rb28 were respectively semi active radar- and IR- homing versions of the US AIM-4/AIM-26 Falcon. The J 35F, with its Ericsson PS-01/A radar, was the first Draken variant to be equipped with the new missile.

that pronounced dizziness could ensue.

Experimentation with these models allowed Saab engineers to examine a variety of ideas and configurations, as well as prove the basic soundness of the design, but a much more critical and valuable role was played by the Saab 210, this seven-tenths scale flying testbed making a massive contribution to company knowledge of the double-delta planform. In October 1955 the full-size article became available with the maiden flight of the first prototype, and from that point Saab never looked back, ultimately building no fewer than 612 examples of the Draken before production terminated in 1977.

The Draken described

While the Draken may have been innovative in so far as the wing planform was concerned, it was otherwise fairly conventional and the following remarks (which pertain specifically to the J 35F) are generally applicable to all versions. The basic structure is of all metal-construction, making extensive use of light metal stressed skinning. The fuselage consists of two main sections (fore and aft), with the break point occurring directly ahead of the small dorsal fin and virtually adjacent to the front face of the engine. Numerous other smaller sub-assemblies comprise the nose radome, cockpit canopy, dorsal spine,

tailcone, air intakes and undercarriage doors.

Attachment of fore and aft main fuselage sections is by means of bolts, permitting disassembly to be accomplished relatively easily, while the tailcone is a separate component which is secured to the aft section by four quick-action locking devices. The tailcone also serves as an anchor point for the locally-designed afterburner unit and the extended and kinked exhaust pipe of the Svenska Flygmotor RM6 turbojet – removal of this entire assembly gives access to the engine bay, thus simplifying the task of changing a powerplant.

Both fuselage sections are also integral with the inner wing panels, which have a leading-edge sweep angle of 80°. Outer wing panels are separate assemblies, with a more modest 57° of sweep at the leading edge. These may also be removed for ground transportation, reducing span from a maximum of 30.85 ft (9.40 m) to a more manageable 14.42 ft (4.40 m). Moveable surfaces at the trailing edge extend across virtually the full span, with the four elevon segments (two on each wing) operating in unison for pitch control and differentially for roll control. Actuation of the elevons (and the rudder) is accomplished hydraulically and is integrated with a three-axis automatic stability unit which embodies artificial feel for the pilot's control column and rudder pedals.

Draken landing gear

The Draken's tricycle undercarriage arrangement features a steerable forward-retracting nose gear unit, two outward-retracting main gear assemblies that are hydraulically shortened during the retraction cycle so as to permit stowage in the main undercarriage bays, and an aft-retracting tail wheel bumper assembly. Nose and main wheel tyres are inflated to 142/185 psi (979/1275 kPa) and 171/242 psi (1179/1668 kPa) respectively, while the aft unit features solid rubber tyres. Goodyear single-disc brakes and a Dunlop anti-skid system are used on the main undercarriage units. The Draken also possesses a drag chute which is housed in a compartment at the base of the fin and has two hydraulically-powered airbrakes located on the upper fuselage sides, more or less adjacent to the trailing edge of the wing.

Nine hardpoints for the carriage of weapons

and external stores were provided on the J 35F: three beneath the fuselage and three under each wing, with the fuselage and inner wing stations being stressed for loads of up to 1,102 lb (500 kg). Outer wing stations can accommodate up to 220-lb (100-kg) loads. A typical configuration usually includes a mixture of fuel and weapons, with the most widely used auxiliary tank being the 280-Imp gal (1275-litre) type. J 35Fs often carry a pair of these beneath the fuselage, leaving wing hardpoints free for missiles, while the J 35J (which has two extra missile pylons beneath the inboard wing section) is frequently seen with four. Smaller 110-Imp gal (500-litre) tanks may also be fitted.

Interceptor missions

In the interceptor role, weaponry primarily comprises air-to-air missiles. The J 35F is compatible with two versions of the Falcon, namely the semi-active radar-homing Rb27 and the IR-homing Rb28; alternatively, it may employ a different heat seeker in the form of the Rb24 Sidewinder. There is also a single ADEN M/55 30-mm gun (with 90 rounds) as a weapon of last resort, this being buried in the starboard inner wing section. Space occupied by the second cannon on older versions has been given over to extra avionics equipment.

For air-to-ground missions, the Draken can carry up to a dozen Bofors 135-mm unguided rockets, a pair of 1,102-lb (500-kg) bombs or as many as nine 220-lb (100-kg) bombs. Additionally, the gun may be employed for strafe attacks.

The J 35F has the most advanced radar of any Draken, being fitted with an Ericsson PS-01/A search and ranging unit. Older Drakens were less sophisticated in this respect, with the original J 35A having only an Ericsson-built version of the relatively simple Thomson-CSF Cyrano gun ranging radar.

The pilot is housed in a pressurised and air conditioned compartment which is equipped with a Saab 73SE-F rocket-assisted ejection seat that is effective throughout virtually the entire envelope. A particularly interesting feature of this seat is that it is angled aft in order to increase pilot tolerance to *g* forces, an idea that was subsequently adopted by General Dynamics on the F-16 Fighting Falcon.

The cockpit is dominated by the central radar display scope, around which other key instruments are grouped. Emergency instrumentation, communications equipment and controls for the autopilot, engine and radar are all located to the pilot's left, while the right-hand side of the cockpit contains controls associated with navigation, weaponry and the fire control system, as well as warning and caution panels and circuit breakers.

Dual hydraulic systems are provided, with each being entirely self-contained and fully able to produce sufficient power to drive all associated systems independently. Thus, total failure of one system does not result in loss of the aircraft. In the extremely unlikely event of both systems being rendered useless, such as would occur in a case of engine failure, a pop-out ram-air turbine is fitted. This deploys automatically in emergency situations and can generate sufficient hydraulic power to allow a pilot to land safely if he is fortunate enough to be within gliding dis-tance of a runway.

The electrics comprise AC and DC systems, 200/115 V 400 Hz power for the former being furnished via a 20-kVa engine-driven generator, while DC power is obtained from AC systems via a pair of rectifiers which produce 2.2 kW at 29 V. Again, an emergency power source is available in the form of a 3.5-kVA generator unit.

A licence-built Rolls-Royce Avon turbojet is fitted to all Drakens, with later models relying on the RM6C version, which is fundamentally similar to the Series 300 Avon. In conjunction with the locally-developed Model 67 afterburner unit, this has a maximum thrust rating of 17,637 lb (78.46 kN), sufficient to propel the Draken at a top speed of Mach 2 (1,320 mph; 2125 km/h) at an altitude of 36,000 ft (10973 m). Sea level rate of climb is 39,370 ft/min (12000 m/min) and service ceiling 67,000 ft (20420 m).

Saab 35 Draken Variants

Saab 210

Originally known as the Draken and subsequently as the Lill-Draken (Little Dragon), the unique Saab 210 was fundamentally a seven-tenths scale prototype of the definitive article. Part of that uniqueness stemmed from the fact that it was the first double delta to get airborne, making its maiden flight from Linkoping on 21 January 1952.

Of much greater significance was the contribution that it made to the full-scale Draken, for the Saab 210 eventually logged over 1,000 flights before being permanently grounded and placed in the Flygvapen museum collection at Malmslatt. During that extensive programme of flight testing, it explored basic handling qualities and also functioned as a practical testbed. In the latter

area, probably the most valuable contribution was that it allowed assessment of various nose and intake configurations before Saab's engineering team finally settled on the design adopted for the production fighter.

Powered by a single Armstrong Siddeley Adder turbojet engine rated at a modest 1,000 lb (4.5 kN), Lill-Draken was underpowered. Field performance on hot days was marginal, to say the least. This failing was unlikely to have endeared the type to its pilots, since they occasionally had to fly during the small hours, sometimes launching for test hops as early as 0200. It cannot be denied that the Model 210 was a valuable research tool, nor that it played a major role in the subsequent success of the Draken project.

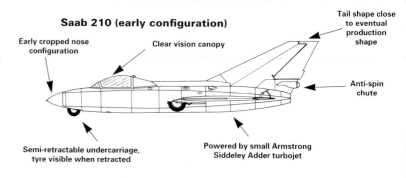

Saab 210 (early configuration)

- Early cropped nose configuration
- Clear vision canopy
- Tail shape close to eventual production shape
- Anti-spin chute
- Semi-retractable undercarriage, tyre visible when retracted
- Powered by small Armstrong Siddeley Adder turbojet

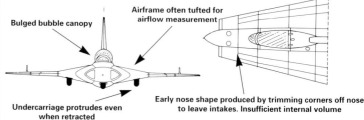

Saab 210 (early configuration)

- Bulged bubble canopy
- Airframe often tufted for airflow measurement
- Undercarriage protrudes even when retracted

Saab 210 (early configuration)

- Early nose shape produced by trimming corners off nose to leave intakes. Insufficient internal volume

Above: The Saab Model 210 Lill-Draken in flight. The world's first double-delta aircraft, the Model 210 was essentially a 7/10 scale prototype of the full-size J 35 Draken, and was uniquely valuable in gathering data on handling characteristics, and testing different nose/intake configurations.

***Right:** Seen in its final, long-nosed configuration is the Model 210. It survived 1,000 flights.*

Saab 210 (interim configuration)

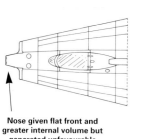

- Nose given flat front and greater internal volume but generated unfavourable

Saab 210 (interim configuration)

- Flat fronted nose has greater internal volume.

Saab 210 (interim configuration)

- Nose contours similar from absolutely side on

Saab 210 (final configuration)

- Definitive nose shape with bifurcated engine intakes and massive internal volume

Saab 210 (final configuration)

- Undercarriage extended

Saab 210 (final configuration)

J 35

In March 1952 the Flygvapen authorised the design of a full-scale prototype of the new fighter. Further milestones in the process of transforming a clearly promising concept into reality were passed in October 1952 when the first tooling drawings were released, in January 1953 when the type specification was finalised,

and in March 1953 when work on production tool design began.

In August 1953 Saab's unique double-delta concept was rewarded by a firm contract covering an initial batch of four prototype full-scale aircraft (including a non-flying fatigue test specimen) and three pre-production examples. Work on the

fabrication of the prototypes began almost immediately at Saab's Linkoping factory and culminated in the formal roll-out of the first (construction number 35-1) in the late summer of 1955.

Ground testing kept the Saab team occupied for a period of several weeks and autumn was well advanced when the

prototype eventually left the ground for the first time, company test pilot Bengt Olov being in the cockpit for the uneventful maiden flight on 25 October 1955. This machine was duly joined in the development effort by the second (c/n 35-2) and third (c/n 35-3) prototypes in January and March 1956 respectively and, for the

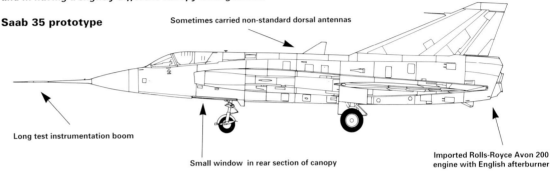

next two years, these three aircraft continued to explore and expand the flight envelope. One very noteworthy hurdle was satisfactorily negotiated on 26 February 1956 when the original prototype exceeded Mach 1 for the first time, accomplishing this feat without recourse to afterburner. Other aspects of the test programme concerned weapons carriage trials which were mostly undertaken by the first prototype, while the third aircraft was assigned to the Flygvapen at a fairly early stage in its career and used for cold weather testing at Lulea, the most northerly air base in the country.

In terms of appearance, these machines conformed very closely to the production Drakens that were soon to follow, but they relied for propulsion on imported Rolls-Royce Avon Series 200 turbojet engines. These were, in fact, the only Drakens to use imported engines, Svenska Flygmotor having obtained authorisation to produce this powerplant indigenously as the RM6. Intended specifically for the Draken, the Swedish-built Avon 200 also made use of a locally designed Model 65 afterburner which bestowed a very different appearance to the aft fuselage. In consequence, the trio of prototypes possessed a tailcone unlike that of any subsequent machine.

These prototypes also utilised an extended nose pitot tube and a number of dorsal antennas that did not appear on the definitive article. Finally, the cockpit canopy fitted to the J 35 prototypes was also distinctly different to that which appeared on the J 35A when this joined the test effort in 1958.

Above: The three prototype J 35 Drakens differed from early production Drakens in their tailcones and jetpipes, and in having a slightly different canopy arrangement.

Saab 35 prototype

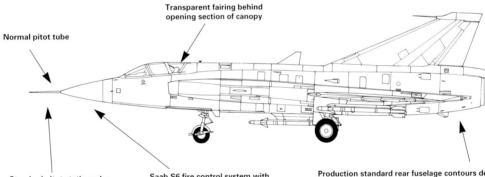

Sometimes carried non-standard dorsal antennas

Long test instrumentation boom

Small window in rear section of canopy

Imported Rolls-Royce Avon 200 engine with English afterburner

J 35A

Following on from the trio of flying prototypes and the static test specimen, the initial production model was the J 35A which made its maiden flight from Saab's Linkoping airfield on 15 February 1958. Contracts were eventually let for a total of 90 aircraft (serial numbers 35001 to 35090). In fact, the first three of these had been ordered as pre-series examples at the same time as the original prototypes, and the next 17 also fell short of full production standard for they featured a number of detail variations. As a result, it was not until the 21st J 35A appeared that a standard configuration was achieved.

Regardless of detail differences, all of these machines were powered by a Svenska Flygmotor RM6B afterburning turbojet engine. Rated at a maximum of 14,396 lb st (64 kN) with full augmentation, the RM6B was a licence-built version of the Rolls-Royce Avon 200 married to a locally designed and manufactured afterburner unit.

As it transpired, this unit was responsible for a notable change in physical appearance of the Draken. The first 62 J 35As (35001 to 35062) used a Model 65 unit in conjunction with a short tailcone and a rudimentary tail bumper to eliminate the risk of damage to the underside of the aft fuselage in the event of over-rotation on take-off or excessive angle of attack on landing. Thereafter, the remaining 28 J 35As (35063 to 35090) featured the Model 66 afterburner which was some 35 in (89 cm) longer than the original unit. This in turn

Saab J 35A early production

Normal pitot tube

Transparent fairing behind opening section of canopy

Standard pitot static probe, shorter than test instrumentation boom of prototypes

Saab S6 fire control system with Thomson-CSF Cyrano ranging radar

Production standard rear fuselage contours denoting installation of indigenous Model 65 afterburner. Last 28 aircraft fitted with Model 66 afterburner, giving revised fuselage contours like J 35B

necessitated redesign of the aft fuselage section and adoption of an extended tailcone. At the same time, the bumper was deleted in favour of a retractable twin tailwheel assembly. Retrospective modification of some of the earlier machines did bring them to the later standard, but this was not undertaken universally and 25 unmodified examples were subsequently converted to two-seat Sk 35C operational trainers.

The first Flygvapen unit to take delivery of the Draken was Flygflottilj 13 (F13 or No.

J 35A with IR sensor

Saab S6B fire control system with Thomson-CSF Cyrano ranging radar

Undernose IR sensor in square section fairing, with circular 'window' at the front

Small numbers of J 35As were fitted with undernose IR seekers late in their careers. This modification was probably only applied to aircraft built or retrofitted with the later standard J 35B-style afterburner

Below: The non-standard test instrumentation boom identifies this aircraft as one of the first J 35As, retained by Saab for test and trials work.

Above: Wearing Försökcentralen FC codes, this J 35A shows off the distinctive short original rear fuselage associated with the Model 65 afterburner. Operational J 35As went to F13 and F16.

13 Wing) at Norrkoping in March 1960 and it was joined in 1961 by F16 at Uppsala. However, the lack of compatibility with Sweden's STRIL 60 semi-automatic air defence control system resulted in the J 35A being a considerably less effective interceptor than later models. Armament for the interceptor role consisted of a pair of ADEN 30-mm cannon with 90 rounds of ammunition each and, with effect from 1961, up to four locally-produced Rb24 (AIM-9B) Sidewinder heat-seeking AAMs.

Avionics equipment initially comprised the Saab S6 fire control system, at the heart of which was a Thomson-CSF Cyrano gun-ranging radar built under licence in Sweden by L. M. Ericsson. Later, this was replaced by the S6B package which also included an

infra-red seeker but capability was impaired by the need to adopt lead-pursuit paths in order to achieve a rear-hemisphere firing position. Nevertheless, the J 35A served its purpose in allowing the Flygvapen to obtain experience of operating a modern, high-performance fighter, and it was destined to find useful work as an operational trainer after more sophisticated versions had entered the front-line inventory.

In the latter capacity, some J 35As remained in use until 1976 with the Uppsala-based F16, which served as an operational conversion unit for the Draken force until 1985, when it re-equipped with the JA 37 Viggen. As for F13, this unit disposed of its J 35As in 1965 in favour of the definitive J 35F version.

Above: The introduction of the Model 66 afterburner resulted in a slightly longer rear fuselage, projecting well aft of the brake chute fairing.

Below: F16's J 35As survived in service long enough to adopt the two-tone camouflage seen here, and some aircraft received IR seekers.

Above: A formation of early J 35As in flight. Of limited operational usefulness, the J 35As were used primarily for advanced training.

J 35B

The second major production model and the first fully operational interceptor version of the Draken, the J 35B was broadly comparable in performance terms to the J 35A, although the physical similarities masked a number of improvements. It made its maiden flight from Saab's Linkoping facility on 29 November 1959 and began to enter service with F16 at Uppsala in 1961. Other units that flew this derivative before it was retired from the inventory in 1976 were F10 at Angelholm and F18 at Tullinge.

Svenska Flygmotor's RM6B turbojet was retained for the J35B which used the Model 66 afterburner, long tailcone and tailwheel assembly from the outset. Less obvious but more important changes related to the fire-control system, this version being fully compatible with Sweden's STRIL 60 integrated air defence control system. It was also the first Draken sub-type to possess a secondary ground attack capability.

Adoption of the Saab S7 FCS greatly expanded the aircraft's potential for it permitted collision-course interceptions to

be undertaken. Cannon armament was retained, along with the Sidewinder for rear aspect lead-pursuit engagements. However, in collision-course encounters at short range, the weapon of choice was the pod-mounted 75-mm Bofors rocket projectile – carried in two pods, a maximum of 38 missiles was available so as to offer a reasonable chance of target saturation. Alternatively, when employed against ground targets, the J 35B could carry a mix

of ordnance that included 135-mm air-to-surface rockets and 100-kg or 250-kg bombs.

Despite the fact that it represented a marked improvement over the J 35A, vigorous design work by Saab soon led to the J 35D, which was a quantum leap over its predecessors. As a consequence, only some 73 J 35Bs were manufactured (serial numbers 35201 to 35273) before production turned to the next single-seat

version. None now remain in Flygvapen service, but Finland may still be operating the survivors of six aircraft acquired on lease as long ago as 1972 and purchased outright in 1975. Lacking all-weather avionics and radar, these were redesignated as J 35BSs (described separately) and assigned to HavLlv 11 at Rovaniemi.

Saab J 35B Draken

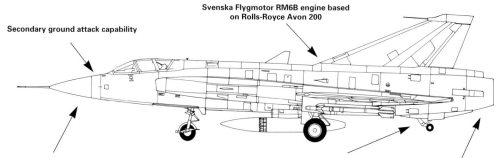

Secondary ground attack capability

Svenska Flygmotor RM6B engine based on Rolls-Royce Avon 200

Saab S7 collision-course fire control system, compatible with STRIL air defence network

Tail bumper replaced by retractable tailwheel assembly, shod with solid rubber tyres

Installation of Model 66 afterburner resulted in lengthened rear fuselage, like last 28 J 35As

Below: The J 35B was the first truly operational version of the Draken, with the Saab S7 fire control system, and equipment allowing integration with the STRIL semi-automatic air defence network.

Below: A J 35B of F16 at Uppsala. The wing transitioned from J 35As and J 35Bs to J 35Fs during 1976 and used the callsign 'Petter'.

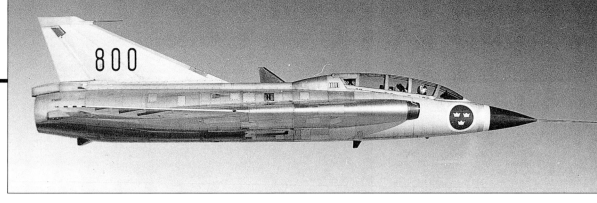

Sk 35C

Development of a two-seat trainer version of the Draken was undertaken at an early stage in the programme. This eventually became the third production derivative to fly, when the prototype Sk 35C (35800) took to the air for the first time on 30 December 1959. A tandem layout was adopted for the Sk 35C, with the student occupying the forward cockpit while the instructor was seated behind, in a slightly raised ejection seat. Accommodation for an instructor was only made possible by reduction in the size of the forward fuselage fuel cell, but this was to some extent compensated for by the provision of extra fuel capacity in the space made vacant by deletion of gun armament.

The two-seater model employed a sideways-opening arrangement for the heavily-framed cockpit canopy which was hinged on the right side to allow ingress and egress. Early experience revealed that the instructor enjoyed only limited forward visibility from the rear cockpit. This soon resulted in a stereoscopic periscope being added at about the mid-canopy point, so as to give improved vision during critical approach and landing phases of flight. In addition, an inner blast screen was positioned between student and instructor.

Like the J 35A and J 35B single-seaters, the Sk 35C prototype was powered by the RM6B turbojet engine, it also retaining the short Model 65 afterburner of the J 35A. This configuration was also adopted for the production airframes, although it should be noted that the 25 aircraft that eventually entered Flygvapen service in the early 1960s were all remanufactured J 35As. The aircraft involved were drawn from the range 35005 to 35040, but new serial numbers in the block 35801 to 35825 were

Above: The first Sk 35C prototype, 35800, was the only Sk 35C not converted from a J 35A airframe. Following completion of its flight test programme, this aircraft was used for Saab 05 air-to-surface missile development.

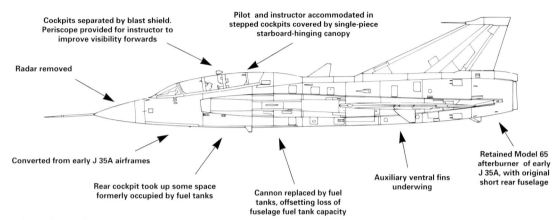

Cockpits separated by blast shield. Periscope provided for instructor to improve visibility forwards

Pilot and instructor accommodated in stepped cockpits covered by single-piece starboard-hinging canopy

Radar removed

Converted from early J 35A airframes

Rear cockpit took up some space formerly occupied by fuel tanks

Cannon replaced by fuel tanks, offsetting loss of fuselage fuel tank capacity

Auxiliary ventral fins underwing

Retained Model 65 afterburner of early J 35A, with original short rear fuselage

Saab Sk 35C

allocated following conversion to trainer standard. Unusually perhaps, no effort was ever made to fit the improved Model 66 afterburner, nor did these Drakens ever acquire the redesigned twin tailwheel of the single-seaters, relying on just a bumper to protect the underside of the aft fuselage section from damage.

Initial service use was with F16 at Uppsala, the two-seaters being primarily concerned with pilot conversion tasks as a kind of stepping stone between the basic training stage and the more advanced phases of tuition. Even though they lacked radar and gun armament, they were also sometimes used for weapons instruction, primarily with the Rb24 Sidewinder. F16 continued to operate the Sk 35C until it converted to the Viggen in 1985, but a modest number are still flown by F10 at Angelholm in order to satisfy the limited training requirement that now exists.

A diminishing need for Draken aircrew resulted in a number of Sk 35Cs being declared surplus to requirements. Some of these were sold to Finland, which acquired three in 1975 and another two in 1984. In Finnish service, these are usually referred to as the J 35CS (described separately).

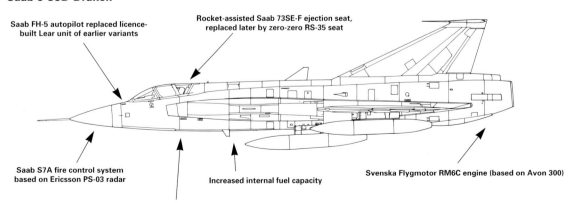

Even today, Swedish Sk 35Cs wear an overall silver or natural metal colour scheme, having never been camouflaged. Unit markings are sometimes carried, and some have carried small areas of Dayglo trim. A small number of Sk 35Cs continue in service with F10 at Angelholm, the final Flygvapen Draken wing.

J 35D

The desire for enhanced performance and combat capabilities led directly to the J 35D, which flew for the first time on 27 December 1960. The prototype was actually a modified J 35A. Major differences related to the powerplant and avionics suite installed in this version, which was longer-legged by virtue of internal fuel capacity being increased from the 493 Imp gal (2241 litres) of the J 35A/B to some 608 Imp gal (2764 litres).

Performance benefits accrued from the decision to switch to the RM6C turbojet (a licence-produced Avon Series 300) which had an initial maximum thrust rating of 17,262 lb (76.79 kN) with the benefit of full augmentation from a Model 66 afterburner unit, although later substitution of a Model 67 afterburner raised this figure to 17,637 lb (78.46 kN). Adoption of a new version of the turbojet engine was accompanied by some redesign of the air intakes, which were extended forward slightly, a feature which became standard on all subsequent members of the Draken family.

Saab J 35D Draken

Saab FH-5 autopilot replaced licence-built Lear unit of earlier variants

Rocket-assisted Saab 73SE-F ejection seat, replaced later by zero-zero RS-35 seat

Saab S7A fire control system based on Ericsson PS-03 radar

Increased internal fuel capacity

Svenska Flygmotor RM6C engine (based on Avon 300)

Redesigned engine intakes, extended forward below canopy

The most noteworthy avionics differences centred around the adoption of Saab's S7A fire-control system, a key component of which was an Ericsson PS-03 radar. The J 35D also embodied a Saab FH5 automatic flight control system instead of the licence-built Lear unit which was fitted to earlier sub-types. In addition, pilot survivability in the event of an accident was improved through the fitment of Saab's 73SE-F rocket-boosted ejection seat, which was functional at zero altitude at speeds of above 62 mph (100 km/h); later, this gave way to the RS-35 seat which possessed zero height/zero speed capability and which was fitted to the J 35F from the outset.

Armament remained essentially unchanged, with air-to-air capability resting with the Rb24 Sidewinder and Bofors rockets, while it was also compatible with the air-to-ground weaponry alluded to earlier. Original production planning anticipated the manufacture of 120 J 35Ds (serial numbers 35274 to 35393), although it seems that only 92 appeared in this form, with aircraft 35276 to 35303 being completed as S 35Es for reconnaissance tasks.

As for the remainder, these served with elements of no fewer than five wings at different times, F13 at Norrkoping claiming the honour of introducing this version to operational service in 1963. F3 at Malmslatt and F10 at Angelholm followed suit in 1964, with F4 at Froson and F21 at Lulea obtaining some J 35Ds during 1969-70 when F3 converted to the J 35F. J 35Ds continued to serve with front-line elements of the Flygvapen until 1984, when F4 and F21 re-equipped with variants of the Viggen.

Above: Checkerboard and diamond patterns in red, yellow and Dayglo have been painted on the fins and wings of various camouflaged Flygvapen Drakens, drawn from various units. They are believed to have been used as temporary exercise markings.

Right: The only Draken to wear the four-tone Viggen-style splinter camouflage was this F18 J 35D.

Two dozen former Flygvapen J 35Ds were supplied to Austria in the late 1980s. Extensively refurbished, and fitted with bulged 'J 35F-type' cockpit canopies, these were subsequently redesignated as J 35Os.

S 35E

While it may be best known as an interceptor, development of the Draken resulted in production and deployment of a specialist reconnaissance version which flew for the first time on 27 June 1963. Given the designation S 35E, this was essentially similar to the J 35D and was powered by the RM6C engine, initially with the Model 66 afterburner although most aircraft eventually acquired the Model 67 unit. Canopy design also changed during the S 35E's service life, with the original framed design giving way on some aircraft to the bulged type that was universally installed on the J 35F fighter version of the Draken. Other equipment that was common to both the J 35D and S 35E was the FH5 AFCS and the RS-35 zero-zero ejection seat which was retrofitted to the J35D.

Undoubtedly the most visible manifestation of the change in role concerned the nose section. Gone was the familiar black nosecone which housed the radar – in its place was a camera nose section which slid forward on rails to give access to the photographic equipment bay. At the beginning, this consisted of a total of seven French-designed OMERA cameras. Five of these were located in the nose, consisting of four Ska 24s (two port oblique, one downward and one starboard oblique) and a forward-facing Ska 16B – two more downward-looking Ska 24-600 cameras were buried in the wings, occupying the space that was normally taken up by cannon armament. Subsequently, as part of a sensor upgrade in the mid-1970s, 'Blue Baron' pods were

Saab S 35E Draken

Original framed canopy gave way to bulged J 35F-style canopy

Pitot static probe

Nosecone mounted on rails. Slides forward for access

Zero-zero RS-35 ejection seat

No radar

Svenska Flygmotor RM6C engine with Model 66 afterburner (some aircraft with Model 67)

Forward oblique Ska 16B camera

Nose has ports for five vertical and forward and sideways oblique cameras

Twin Ska 24 port oblique cameras

Vertical Ska 24 camera port

Pitot static probe

Forward oblique Ska 16B camera port

Single starboard oblique Ska 24 camera

Camera ports in leading edge

Left: Each wingroot of the S35E contains a French OMERA camera with a periscopic lens, allowing vertical coverage from a camera whose lens lies horizontally in the wing leading edge.

obtained, these containing three Vinten cameras that were optimised for night missions.

Production of the S 35E for service with the Flygvapen eventually totalled some 60 examples, although it should be recalled that 28 of these were originally ordered as J 35D interceptors and may well have been modified for the reconnaissance task prior to delivery. New-build aircraft from the Linkoping line were allocated serial numbers in the block 35901 to 35932. As for the J 35Ds (35276 to 35303), these

acquired new identities (35933 to 35960) as S 35Es, but the new identities were not allocated in strict numerical order (i.e., S 35E 35933 was originally J 35D 35288, other 'new/old' tie-ups being 35934/35282, 35935/35289 and 35936/35302).

Delivery of these machines began in mid-August 1965 to F11 at Nykoping which received sufficient aircraft to equip two squadrons, while the remainder were assigned to a single squadron within F21 at Lulea. They were withdrawn in June 1979, leaving a few with FMV:Prom (formerly the Försökcentralen).

Above: A young pilot poses in front of his S 35E, together with the seven cameras which formed the standard recce fit up to the 1970s.

Below: The S 35E relied on its internal camera suite until 1973, when Blue Baron pods containing British Vinten cameras arrived.

Above: The S 35E was built in small numbers (60, including conversion of J 35Ds) and was used only by two wings, F11 and F21 (seen here), and was replaced by the SF 37 Viggen in the tactical recce role from 1976.

Below: The nosecone of an S 35E slid forward to reveal the package of reconnaissance cameras mounted in the nose. This shows the unusual nosewheel mudguard of the Draken, and the original J 35A-style canopy applied to many S 35Es.

J 35F

Produced in far greater numbers than any other variant of the Draken family, the J 35F was undoubtedly the definitive interceptor version. Featuring numerous improvements over its predecessors, it was also the last model to be produced for the home market. By the time manufacture terminated, a total of 230 had been completed (serial numbers 35401 to 35630) to two basic standards. Flown for the first time in 1961, development of the J 35F relied heavily upon the services of a trio of modified J 35As, aircraft 35007 and 35008 being associated with weapons testing while 35013 more closely approximated to the eventual production configuration.

Subsequently, production standard examples of the J 35F became involved in flight test duties, clearing the way for this model to enter service in 1965. The first Flygvapen unit to operate the J 35F was F13 at Norrkoping and it eventually flew with at least eight wings (others were F1, F3, F10, F12, F16, and F17), forming the backbone of the interceptor force until about the beginning of the 1980s when it progressively gave way to the JA 37 Viggen.

Fundamentally an improved version of the J 35D, the J 35F relied on the well-proven RM6C turbojet, which was married to a new Model 67 afterburner unit to bestow a maximum augmented thrust rating of 17,637 lb (78.46 kN). Enhancement efforts were by no means limited to the engine, however, and the J 35F also introduced Saab's S7B collision-course fire control system, a key element of which was the Ericsson PS-01/A

Saab J 35F-1 *Filip Ett*

Bulged canopy without internal framework

Revised cockpit displays

Slightly refined windscreen shape

Saab S7B collision course fire control system based around Ericsson PS-01/A radar

Port wingroot cannon deleted

Svenska Flygmotor RM6C engine with Model 67 afterburner

Saab J 35F-2 *Filip Tva*

Ericsson PS-011/A radar

Undernose Hughes-developed S-71N IR sensor ball (retrofitted to some J 35F-1s)

Semi-active radar homing Rb27 carried under the fuselage

Versions of the AIM-4/-26 Falcon used as primary armament by both J 35F sub-types. IR-homing Rb28 carried underwing

Left: The J 35F introduced an entirely new fire control system and new missile armament, and was in many ways the definitive Draken. The later J 35J was produced only by conversion, and served in small numbers after the aircraft had been virtually retired. With its early style canopy this aircraft does not look like a J 35F, and may be one of the J 35Ds converted to serve as prototypes for the new version. Two J 35Ds (35007 and 35008) were used as armament trials aircraft, with a further J 35A (35013, which had already been converted to virtual J 35D standards) later joining the project as a systems testbed.

Left: The J 35F-2 introduced an undernose infra-red sensor. Produced under licence by Ericsson, the Hughes-developed sensor had a maximum range of 19 miles, high enough to be useful.

Above: An F13 J 35F-2 in flight. The J 35F and F-2 were the Flygvapen's standard interceptor fighters until the introduction of the JA 37 Jaktviggen during the early 1980s.

radar. This sensor was fitted across the fleet, whereas the Hughes-developed undernose infra-red sensor was installed more sparingly.

Produced under licence by Ericsson, the IR sensor possessed a maximum range of about 19 miles (30 km) in ideal conditions, although this could be impaired by atmospheric conditions and was also dependent upon the intensity of radiation emitted by a target. Aircraft with this item of kit (initially those with 'even-numbered' tailcodes) were referred to as J 35F-2s – those that lacked it were J 35F-1s.

Other improvements incorporated by all J 35Fs related to the nav/attack, autopilot, air data and datalink systems, while the pilot benefited by occupying a cockpit which had revised instrument displays as well as a larger bulged canopy offering better all-round vision. Internal fuel capacity was also increased, making the J 35F easily the longest-legged Draken: maximum internal load was 880 Imp gal (4000 litres), which could be increased to 1,980 Imp gal (9000 litres) with full external tanks.

Armament options were also much improved, in theory at least, since the J 35F was compatible with licence-built examples of the Hughes Falcon air-to-air missile, a weapon that had been selected for service with the Flygvapen in March 1959. Two basic versions were available, the semi-active radar-homing Rb 27 and the IR-homing Rb28, but their effectiveness is a matter for speculation. Certainly, the USA found the

Falcon disappointingly ineffective in Vietnam, but Sweden did devote a considerable amount of effort towards improving this weapon. A typical interceptor load would include two examples of each type of Falcon. The trusty Sidewinder also figured prominently in the Draken's arsenal, Sweden initially using the AIM-9B although this later gave way to the AIM-9P. Finally, up to four 19-round Bofors 75-mm rocket pods could be carried.

For the carriage of weaponry, the J 35F was fitted with a total of eight external stores stations. Two were located under the fuselage, with the remainder under the wings. Fuselage hardpoints were stressed for 1,102-lb (500-kg) loads, as were the inner wing stations to port and starboard; outer wing stations could only accommodate a 220-lb (100-kg) load. In consequence, the Rb27 SARH version of the Falcon (which weighed 262 lb/119 kg) was usually only carried on fuselage hardpoints, while the Rb28 IR model (134/61kg) went underwing, as did Sidewinder. Alternatively, in the air-to-ground role, the J 35F could have carried a mix of bombs and rockets.

Internal armament was cut to just one 30-mm cannon, situated in the starboard wingroot. Space made available was set aside for electronic equipment.

During the service life of the J 35F, many of the original J 35F-1s were upgraded with infra-red to become J 35F-2s, and the old system of odd- and even-numbered tailcodes to differentiate between the two sub-variants

fell into disuse. By the mid-1980s about 80 per cent of J 35Fs had been upgraded. Even while F10 at Angelholm progressively re-equipped with updated J 35Js, a mix of J 35F-1s and J 35F-2s remained on charge, many of the initial J 35J conversions being produced from aircraft retired from other units, or held in storage.

Although the J 35F has now virtually disappeared from the Flygvapen inventory in its original form, approximately 60 examples of the modified J 35J (all converted from J35F-2s) remain active with F10 at Angelholm. In addition, survivors of the 24 aircraft that were supplied to Finland as the J 35FS are still operational.

Below: A handful of non-IR-seeker equipped J 35F-1s remained on charge with F10 at Angelholm until replaced by the J 35J. This was one of the last J 35Fs in use.

Left: Two J 35Fs were sold to a US company for film work, starring in the movie 'Wings of the Apache' wearing this anonymous grey colour scheme. Since then, one of the pair has been sponsored by a beer company, and now wears a colourful scheme with 'Miller Genuine Draft' titles and logos.

J 35F Mod

Also sometimes referred to as the J 35F-Ny ('Ny' = new), this designation referred to an extensive update of existing J 35Fs. In the event, it was used only briefly, being replaced by J 35J (described separately).

J 35J

Like many nations, Sweden has suffered its fair share of belt-tightening with regard to defence spending, one manifestation of the need for economies being the decision to retain a single wing of Drakens until well into the 1990s, when Saab's Gripen will become available. Upgrading of these aircraft does, however, help to alleviate the worst deficiencies of continuing to utilise a 1950s-vintage design as the 21st century moves inexorably closer.

Beginning life as the J 35F Mod or J 35F-Ny, the revamped aircraft is sufficiently different to merit redesignation as the J 35J and 64 (or perhaps 66) J 35F-2 Drakens have been brought to this standard. Efforts to ensure the continued viability of the Draken include provision of extra armament capacity, with an additional stores pylon being provided under each inboard section of the double-delta wing structure, these having been strengthened to cope with the additional loads. Thus, it may operate with either four auxiliary fuel tanks and a pair of Rb24 Sidewinders, or two fuel tanks and four missiles.

In addition, attention has been given to enhancing the prime mission-related avionics systems and equipment, with the radar and infra-red sensor both being improved. The package of modifications has provided an extra transponder and a back-up altitude warning system, plus upgrades to the radar and navigation equipment and to IFF gear and cockpit instrument displays.

Expected to remain in service until 1979, production J 35Js were preceded by a

Right: The prototype J 35J conversion uses its new inboard underwing pylons to mount a pair of Rb24 Sidewinders, while still carrying four external fuel tanks under wings and fuselage.

prototype conversion of J 35F-2
35598: Testing of this aircraft in the mid-1980s cleared the way for deliveries to begin and the first two J 35Js to be subjected to the update project were formally handed over in early March 1987, with work on all 66 completed by 21 August 1991. In Flygvapen service, apart from the Försökscentralen (Research Centre) at Malmslatt, which has the prototype and one or two examples for test duties, the J 35J operates solely with F10 at Angelholm.

Known J 35J conversion include c/ns 35502, 35512, 35519, 35520, 35521, 35532, 35533, 35539, 35540, 35541, 35544, 35545, 35546, 35553, 35565, 35575, 35577, 35579, 35582, 35586, 35588, 35589, 35594, 35595, 35597, 35598 (prototype), 35602, 35604, 35605, 35606, 35607, 35608, 35609, 35610, 35612, 35615, 35616, 35617, 35618, 35619, , 35620, 35621, 35623, 35624, 35625, 35627, 35630.

In a final step towards making the surviving J 35Js look different to their predecessors, the aircraft are slowly being repainted in an air defence grey colour scheme, similar to that worn by most current JA 37 Viggens. This is applied as the aircraft come up for major overhaul, and at least five have already been resprayed.

Below: The J 35J conversion programme included structural and systems modifications. These are intended to allow the ageing Drakens to remain in service until at least 1995, and include improvements to the radar.

Left: An F10 Johann landing at Angelholm. Since the late 1970s, Swedish Drakens have had their individual two-digit identity codes repeated above the wings. On camouflaged aircraft like this one, the overwing codes are painted white.

Below: J 35Js are adopting a two-tone air superiority grey colour scheme as they undergo major overhaul.

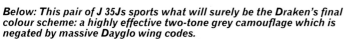

Below: This pair of J 35Js sports what will surely be the Draken's final colour scheme: a highly effective two-tone grey camouflage which is negated by massive Dayglo wing codes.

J 35J upgrade programme
Following the successful prototype conversion of a J 35F-2 (35598) to J 35J configuration, structurally upgraded and with a plethora of improvements, 66 J 35F-2 Drakens (some of which had begun life as J 35F-1s) were brought to the same standard with redeliveries beginning on 3 March 1987 and continuing until 21 August 1991. Selected aircraft were transferred to prime sub-contractor FFV at Linköping where they were split into front and rear sections. The front section was then moved to Saab, the rear section remaining with FFV. After installation of all new equipment, the airframes were reassembled by FFV, flight-tested and redelivered. As well as being reworked and rewired the aircraft were fitted with two new inboard underwing hardpoints, allowing the carriage of two tanks and four AAMs, or four tanks and two AAMs. The J 35F could carry only two missiles and two tanks, or four missiles. Other improvements included changes to the gun-firing mechanism, radar, IR seeker, and IFF, and the provision of a new altitude warning system and artificial horizon. Originating as the J 35F Mod or J 35F-Ny, the upgraded aircraft was felt to be sufficiently different from the J 35F to merit redesignation as the J 35J.

Cockpit
Remarkably, despite its age, the Draken cockpit is still a sought-after position for young Swedish fighter pilots, who prize the aircraft's performance, agility and high workload. You have to be good to fly a Draken, whereas the Viggen is perhaps more forgiving, easier to fly, and less demanding to operate. The J 35J upgrade, despite its modest scope, has restored a degree of credibility to the aircraft. Narrow, cramped and primitive, the Draken cockpit accommodates a steeply raked Saab 73SE-F rocket-powered ejection seat, with zero-zero capability. The bulged canopy gives an adequate view to the sides, but the view forward is poor, and the pilot's view of his vulnerable six is non-existent.

Radar
The Saab J 35J retains a modified version of the J 35F's Ericsson UAP 13 series radar, given the service designation PS-01/A or PS-011/A. The basic UAP 13102 was fitted to the J 35F-1, while the similar UAP 13103 (PS-011/A) was compatible with the S71N Infra Red-Search and Track set and was installed on the J 35F-2. Finnish J 35FS and J 35XS fighters use the UAP 13104. Operating in the I/J-band, the UAP 13 is a simple pulse radar which can illuminate targets for semi-active radar homing missiles like the Hughes AIM-4 Falcon. Earlier Drakens were fitted with Ericsson PS-03 (J 35D) or Thomson-CSF Cyrano (J 35A) radars, the latter being a simple ranging radar set. The proposed J 35H for Switzerland was to have had a British Ferranti AIRPASS radar, similar to that fitted to the contemporary Lightning.

IRST set
The J 35J is fitted with a modified version of the J 35F-2's S71N Infra-Red Search and Track set. This has a range of about 16 miles under normal conditions, making it a useful emission-free supplement to the radar.

Saab J 35J Draken

This J 35J wears the colourful markings applied to the F10 display pilot's aircraft. Because he is assigned to the 3rd Division, that squadron's swordfish-like creature (reportedly a dragon) adorns the upper and lower surfaces of the wings. Flygflottilj 10 (10 Wing) at Angelholm, known as the 'Skanska Flygflottilj', is Sweden's last Draken wing, operating a handful of two-seat Sk 35Cs and the modernised J 35J in two squadrons alongside a single squadron of Viggens. The decision to retain a Draken wing, pending introduction of the JAS 39 Gripen, was made on economic grounds, because procurement of an interim fighter would be prohibitively expensive and because there were insufficient Viggens to form an extra wing. In the event, the end of the Cold War did allow a reduction in Flygvapen front-line strength, and F6 was disbanded, but many older Viggens were becoming structurally 'tired' and were retired, leaving only enough 'extra' aircraft to equip one of F10's Draken squadrons. By the early 1980s, the Draken was clearly obsolescent, and it was obvious that any aircraft retained for service into the 1990s would have to be upgraded, as well as being reworked. In 1980, Sweden still had five wings of J 35Fs, and two of J 35Ds, so there were plenty of airframes available for continued service. Naturally enough, it was decided to upgrade a number of low-houred J 35Fs, whose more advanced fire control system, RM6C engine and Model 67 afterburner made it the more capable variant. The best, lowest-houred surviving examples were therefore gathered within F10 (the wing selected for continued service) prior to conversion, allowing the wing to remain operational as its aircraft were cycled through the upgrade.

Gun
The J 35J is fitted with a single belt-fed ADEN M/55 30-mm cannon in the starboard wing root, well aft of the engine intake in a position which makes it easily accessible to the ground crew, and easy to boresight. Gun gas ingestion is not a problem. The J 35D and previous single-seat variants had two guns.

Missile armament
J 35Fs and J 35Js can carry Falcon missiles as well as AIM-9 Sidewinders. The IR-homing AIM-4D is designated Rb28 in Sweden, while the larger semi-active radar homing AIM-26B is designated Rb27. The AIM-4D is limited to tail aspect engagements, but Swedish missiles may have been upgraded to a more advanced standard with a measure of all-aspect capability. The heavier SARH missile is usually carried under the fuselage, with the IR-homing missiles underwing.

Undercarriage
The Draken is fitted with a hydraulically retractable tricycle undercarriage, with single wheels on each unit. The narrow track of the main gear allows operation from highway strips, and does not prevent the carriage of underwing stores even quite close to the wingroot. To protect the rear fuselage the aircraft has a retractable, non-steerable twin-wheel tail undercarriage unit. Each wheel is shod with a solid rubber tyre and is supported by its own strut and cantilevered axle. These are joined to a single hydraulic actuator.

GRANT RACE.

Saab 35 Draken Export Variants

J 35H

Saab activity in the export market has for the most part been subject to governmental supervision and, while the Draken might have achieved greater success had it originated in any other country, Sweden's desire to adhere to its policy of neutrality has been a limiting factor. Nevertheless, well over 100 new-build and second-hand aircraft were supplied to other air arms between 1971 and 1989, and not all of those customers were neutral.

The first attempt at obtaining success in the export market actually predated Denmark's purchase of the Draken by almost a decade and resulted in the appearance of the J 35H ('H' for Helvetia), which was developed to satisfy a Swiss requirement for a new interceptor to replace outdated and obsolescent de Havilland Vampires. In this instance, no obstacle was placed in Saab's way by the Swedish government, but the Draken submission was by no means the only one for this potentially worthwhile contract and it came up against fierce and determined opposition

from a number of other contenders, such as Lockheed's F-104 Starfighter and Dassault's Mirage III.

As part of the sales effort, a single J 35A (35011) was modified to serve as a demonstrator, incorporating the British Ferranti AI.23 Airpass collision-course radar as installed in the RAF's Lightning. Trials in Sweden paved the way for a series of evaluations in Switzerland during the summer of 1960 but, despite generally encouraging results, the Swiss authorities eventually opted for the hugely successful Mirage III, which was to be produced locally

under the terms of a licence agreement. As it turned out, cost overruns and scandal plagued the Mirage programme and the first squadron did not attain operational status until March 1968, close to five years later than first planned and, ironically, at almost the same moment that Saab succeeded in securing its first export order for the Draken.

As for the J 35H demonstrator, on completion of the test programme this was apparently returned to J 35A standard for further service with the FFV and then as an instructional airframe.

A 35XD

Although it had failed to secure an order from the Swiss for the J 35H, Saab was well aware that later development meant that it had an excellent product and the company was obviously keen to capitalise on the Draken's export potential. During the mid-1960s Saab set about developing a version that might prove attractive to foreign customers. The result was the Model 35X, which was based on the J 35F, but with extra fuel capacity and a more robust structure that could carry more payload.

Governmental authorisation was eventually forthcoming for sales presentations to neighbouring Denmark, even though the latter was part of the NATO military alliance. Although there were some who probably construed the export effort as compromising Sweden's avowed policy of neutrality, Saab duly succeeded in winning an initial contract for 20 examples of the single-seat A 35XD ('X' for export, 'D' for Denmark) fighter and three two-seat combat proficiency trainers on 29 March 1968.

Fundamentally similar in appearance to the definitive J 35F, though lacking fire control radar, the A 35XD was the first of three versions to be obtained by Denmark, with the 20 aircraft involved (serial numbers A-001 to A-020, construction numbers 351001 to 351020) being delivered to Esk. 725 at Karup between September 1970 and May 1971 as replacements for the long-serving North American F-100D Super Sabre. Esk. 725 continued to operate the Draken until it disbanded on 1 January 1992, leaving a modest number of survivors to continue in service with Esk. 729 alongside some RF 35s and TF 35s.

The primary role of the F 35, as it became known in Danish service, is ground attack, with armament options encompassing a pair of internal wing-mounted ADEN 30-mm cannon and a respectable external payload. The latter can be carried on no fewer than 11 hardpoints located beneath the wings and centre fuselage section; these should not be confused with the pair of outboard 'bullet' fairings which are understood to house radar warning receiver and other electronic equipment. No provision was made for carriage of the Hughes Falcon air-to-air missile in either IR- or radar-guided form, although the Sidewinder is compatible with this version of the Draken and is viewed primarily

as a defensive weapon.

Subsequent modification in the mid-1980s centred around updating of avionics equipment, in the form of a Lear-Siegler nav/attack computer, Singer-Kearfott inertial navigation system, Marconi Series 900 head-up display and other refinements, all intended to extend the operational life of the surviving

machines until well into the 1990s. Part of this programme embraced the fitment of a Ferranti Laser Rangefinder and Marked Target Seeker (LRMTS) in a modified nose section that is similar to that of reconnaissance-dedicated aircraft, although it does not contain any camera equipment.

Saab A 35XD (F 35) - (early configuration)

- Based on J 35F, with same engine, intakes and bulged cockpit canopy
- No radar, but little change to nose contours
- More robust structure
- No auxiliary dorsal fin
- RWR retrofitted
- 30-mm ADEN cannon mounted in each wingroot

Saab A 35XD (F 35) - (late configuration)

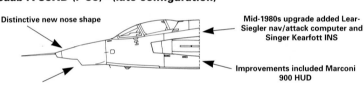

- Distinctive new nose shape
- Ferranti LRMTS in undernose fairing
- Mid-1980s upgrade added Lear-Siegler nav/attack computer and Singer Kearfott INS
- Improvements included Marconi 900 HUD

Below: The Saab 35XD prototype wore Flygvapen markings during its initial flight test programme. The aircraft was optimised for the fighter-bomber role, lacking radar and being delivered as a replacement for the F-100 Super Sabre in Royal Danish Air Force service. The aircraft could carry up to six 1,000-lb bombs, plus two underwing fuel tanks. It made its maiden flight on 31 October 1969, and was finally delivered to the Danish air force on 29 January 1970, the first of 20 single-seat fighter-bombers.

Above: The Danish Drakens were delivered in an overall dark green camouflage scheme, and lacked the distinctive auxiliary dorsal fin of Swedish Drakens.

Above: Danish Drakens underwent a major modification programme during the 1980s which totally altered their nose shape, adding an LRMTS fairing below a shallow proboscis.

S 35XD

The second major combat-capable version of the Draken to enter service with Denmark was the RF 35 (company designation S 35XD) which specialises in tactical reconnaissance. As with the F 35, the June 1968 contract covered just 20 aircraft (serial numbers AR-101 to AR-120 inclusive, c/ns 351101 to 351120) and a trio of trainers. These were allocated to Esk. 729 at Karup over a period of about a year starting in May 1971, as replacements for the Republic RF-84F Thunderflashes supplied by the USA under MDAP. Today, Esk. 729 still operates the Draken, with the RF 35 having been joined by some F 35s in the wake of Esk. 725's demise on 1 January 1992.

Unlike the Swedish-operated S 35E, which featured cameras in the wing bays as well as the nose, the RF 35 retains cannon armament and relies almost entirely on nose-mounted cameras (a maximum of five can be installed) as the principal day reconnaissance tool. However, night capability was added in 1975 when 'Red Baron' pod-mounted infra-red imagery equipment was obtained. These aircraft also benefited from some aspects of the avionics upgrade undertaken in the mid-1980s and may well possess a secondary ground attack role, hence the retention of cannon armament and provision of 11 hardpoints for carriage of external stores.

Right: Danish reconnaissance Drakens gained all-weather capability in 1975, when Red Baron IR pods were acquired, as seen on the outboard underwing pylons of this aircraft. The nose contours of the RF 35 are extremely similar to those of the updated F 35, making differentiation difficult.

Saab 35XD (RF 35)

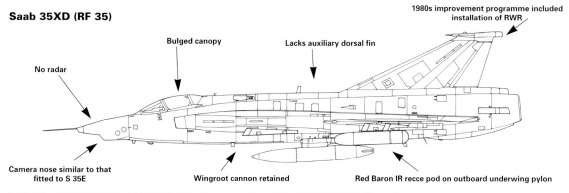

1980s improvement programme included installation of RWR

Bulged canopy

Lacks auxiliary dorsal fin

No radar

Camera nose similar to that fitted to S 35E

Wingroot cannon retained

Red Baron IR recce pod on outboard underwing pylon

Sk 35XD

Employed as an operational proficiency trainer and possessing combat capability comparable to the F 35, a total of 11 examples of the two-seat TF 35 (company designation Sk 35XD) was purchased by Denmark in three separate batches. The original F 35 contract was extended to include three TF 35s (serial numbers AT-151 to AT-153 inclusive, c/ns 351151 to 351153), as was the RF 35 purchase (AT-154 to AT-156, c/ns 351154 to 351156). All six of these machines were delivered to Denmark between June 1971 and April 1972, and were eventually joined in 1976-77 by five more two-seaters (AT-157 to AT-161, c/ns

351157 to 351161) which had been ordered in November 1973. Denmark's trainers are fitted with a single 30-mm cannon in the starboard wing. They also adopted improved avionics and the 'stepped nose' LRMTS modification which appeared across the F 35 fleet in the latter half of the 1980s. In service, the aircraft were distributed fairly evenly between the two Draken squadrons until the beginning of 1992; since then, a handful of two-seaters continued in operation with Esk. 729 and seemed likely to soldier on until the end of the century until defence cuts forced a premature disbandment.

Saab Sk 35XD (TF 35)

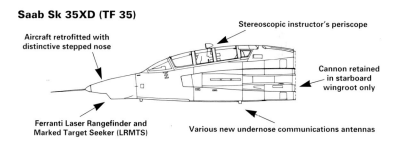

Stereoscopic instructor's periscope

Aircraft retrofitted with distinctive stepped nose

Cannon retained in starboard wingroot only

Ferranti Laser Rangefinder and Marked Target Seeker (LRMTS)

Various new undernose communications antennas

Left: With their RM6C engines and single 30-mm cannon, Danish two-seat TF 35s were the most powerful and best armed of any two-seat Drakens, and were unique in being newly built derivatives of the J 35F rather than conversions from redundant J 35A airframes. Matt dark green paint was replaced by gloss during the Draken's career in Denmark, and the two-seaters were gradually modernised in the same way as the single-seaters, receiving RWRs before they received the undernose LRMTS. Two-seat Drakens served with both Danish Draken squadrons, recce-assigned Esk. 725 (which disbanded on 1 January 1992) and Esk. 729 which was prematurely disbanded as an economy measure at the end of 1993.

Left: Denmark's two-seat TF 35s were the only cannon-armed two-seaters, retaining an ADEN in the starboard wingroot. Since they were based on the airframe of the A 35XD they also had the long tailcone associated with the RM6C engine. The survivors of the 11 delivered underwent the same avionics improvement programme as the F 35s during the late 1980s, gaining the same LRMTS and its associated stepped nose, as well as the tail-mounted RWR. Denmark finally retired the last of its Drakens at the end of 1993.

Saab 35 Draken Variants

J 35BS

Pending the availability of the dozen Valmet-assembled aircraft that were ordered in spring 1970, training of an initial batch of Finnish personnel was accomplished at Tullinge in Sweden. The Ilmavoimat also concluded an agreement with Sweden covering the lease of six former Flygvapen J 35Bs (35265, 35261, 35266, 35214, 35243 and 35257) in order that operations might begin earlier than would otherwise have been possible. Delivery of these aircraft was effected from May 1972, when entered service with HavLlv 11 (No. 11 Squadron), which continues to operate from Rovaniemi. In Finnish service, the principal mission is that of air defence and the primary weapon is the heat-seeking AIM-9 Sidewinder.

All-weather avionics and equipment were deleted prior to delivery of the J 35BS, as the type was subsequently designated, with the six aircraft adopting even-numbered identities in the block DK-202 to DK-212. Of these, the original DK-206 (35266) was damaged in an accident in 1974 and subsequently relegated to ground instructional duties with the identity 'DK-942'. To make good the shortfall, a replacement 'DK-206' was acquired from Sweden in the form of J 35B 35245.

Eventually, the lease agreement was supplanted by outright purchase in autumn 1975, at the same time that Finland opted to buy an additional batch of former Flygvapen Drakens.

Above: Wearing HavLlv's traditional badge, large white codes and large national insignia, this J 35BS shows off the camouflaged colour scheme adopted by Finnish Drakens in place of the overall silver originally used.

J 35CS

Also sometimes referred to as the J 35C, this is basically the Sk 35C two-seat trainer obtained from surplus Flygvapen stocks and refurbished for Ilmavoimat service. A total of five examples has been obtained, with the initial batch of three (serial numbers DK-262, DK-264 and DK-266, formerly 35823, 35820 and 35803 respectively) being ordered in 1975 for HavLlv 11 at Rovaniemi. Almost a

decade later, the decision to acquire more Draken interceptors to equip HavLlv 21 at Tampere was accompanied by a repeat order for an extra pair of trainers (DK-268 and DK-270, formerly 35807 and 35812 respectively), both of which were delivered in June 1984. Differences are likely to be minimal and may be confined to the installation of Finnish communications and navigation equipment.

Left: Like Swedish Draken two-seaters, Finland's five J 35CS trainers wear a natural metal colour scheme. This one has reduced-size codes and national insignia, indicating that the photograph is a recent one.

Above: These are Finland's first two J 35CS trainers. Their former Swedish air force codes (91 for DK-262 and 89 for DK-264) can still be faintly discerned on the tailfins. Initially Finland took delivery of three two-seaters, acquiring a further pair in the mid-1980s.

J 35FS

Experience gained during the early period of Draken operation was an influential factor in persuading Finland's Ilmavoimat to place repeat orders in October 1975 and March 1984. As with the J 35BS model, these were acquired from Flygvapen stocks rather than directly from the production line but these follow-on contracts were for the later and much improved J 35F version, which became known as the J 35FS in Finnish service.

The first batch of six aircraft (35460, 35412, 35489, 35449, 35445 and 35493) adopted odd serial numbers in the sequence DK-261 to DK-271 on entering service with HavLlv 11 in the latter half of the 1970s. The final Finnish buy was also the largest, covering 18 more J 35FSs (with

Right: Finland's J 35FS is a refurbished, zero-timed ex-Flygvapen J 35F, and batches of six and 18 were acquired, the first six to augment HavLlv 11's J 35BS and J 35XS fighters at Rovaniemi, the second batch to equip HavLlv 21 at Tampere.

odd serial numbers in the range DK-225 to DK-259) to equip HavLlv 21 at Tampere with effect from June 1985. In the case of the latter batch, these were 'zero-timed' in Sweden and then shipped to Valmet for final fitting out with communications and navigation equipment. Respective previous identities for the batch of 18 aircraft were 35431, 35425, 35443, 35432, 35417, 35444, 35446, 35447, 35448, 35450, 35451, 35441, 35455, 35458, 35462, 35483, 35487 and 35499.

In Finnish service, limitations on the number of front-line combat aircraft have resulted in the Drakens being dual-roled as both air defence interceptors and as fighter-bombers.

Left: To reduce conspicuity, Finland has toned down its front-line fighters, reducing the size of the blue and white roundel and replacing large black codes with small white ones.

J 35Ö

Another non-aligned state that has previously looked to Sweden as a source of military aircraft is Austria which, after an inordinately lengthy consideration of types such as the BAe Lightning, Dassault-Breguet Mirage III, IAI Kfir and Northrop F-5E, eventually elected to obtain two dozen former Flygvapen J 35Ds in April 1985. The first example was formally handed over in Sweden in June 1987, but several months were set aside for pilot training and it was not until May 1988 that they began to arrive in Austria. By August 1989, all 24 Drakens had been flown to Austria, presently operating with units at Zeltweg (No. 1 Staffel) and Graz-Thalerhof (No. 2 Staffel).

Each of the 24 aircraft was the subject of major overhaul before delivery, with the nature of this work being sufficiently extensive to merit allocation of new construction numbers (351401 to 351424). They were subsequently redesignated as J 35Ös, but apart from Austrian national insignia, the most visible evidence of the transformation concerns the fitment of J 35F-type bulged canopies. In selecting the Draken, Austria secured a deal that also encompassed provision of pilot training in Sweden as well as spare parts and ground support equipment. There was some talk of Rb24 Sidewinders being part of the package but this evidently lapsed, and the only armament carried to date has been the standard pair of ADEN cannon.

Possibility of adopting missile armament has again emerged in recent times, in the light of repeated air space violations by Yugoslavian warplanes. As a first step, Austria has been seeking to buy missile rails from Sweden and was expected to invite proposals from industry for a suitable weapon by the end of 1992. In view of the fact that the Drakens are already wired for Sidewinder, this looks like being the ideal solution, although the technical obstacles may be the least of the problem since Austria is forbidden by international law from carrying air-to-air missiles on its aircraft.

As far as identity markings are concerned, national insignia is displayed on nose and wings but the only other aid to identification is a two-digit numerical code carried on the fin. These run in the sequence from '01' to '24' and correlate to the construction numbers mentioned earlier, with former Flygvapen identities being 35313, 35314, 35315, 35317, 35323, 35324, 35328, 35335, 35336, 35338, 35340, 35341, 35342, 35347, 35351, 35360, 35368, 35370, 35373, 35378, 35382, 35384, 35386 and 35393.

Right: J 35Ds destined for export to Austria lined up at Linköping prior to conversion to J 35Ö standard. This conversion involved a major overhaul and comprehensive rework. The Austrian national insignia has been crudely applied but the aircraft at this stage retained their F4 wing identity .

Below: Seen after delivery is a J 35Ö, with a J 35F-type bulged cockpit canopy, and a smart new air superiority grey colour scheme. The Austrian air force reportedly preferred the Lightning offered by BAe, but politics intervened.

J 35XS

Finland's April 1970 decision to purchase the Draken was partly driven by the desire to undertake local assembly, and the first contract covered a batch of 12 brand-new J 35XS ('X' for export, 'S' for Suomi or Finland) models, all of which were to be supplied in kit form to Valmet. As it transpired, although this version was the first to be ordered by the Finns it was not the first to enter service, being preceded by the batch of leased J 35BSs mentioned earlier.

The maiden flight of a Valmet-assembled Draken took place on 12 March 1974, with deliveries being accomplished between late April of that year and mid-1975. All were assigned to HavLlv 11 at Rovaniemi and odd-numbered serials in the range DK-201 to DK-223 were allocated to these aircraft (c/ns 351301 to 351312). Fundamentally similar to the J 35F, the aircraft lacked compatibility with the Hughes Falcon missile, relying on the Sidewinder as the primary missile system. Other notable differences concerned the internal armament, which comprised two cannon rather than the one installed on Swedish J 35Fs. An undernose infra-red detector set was fitted as standard and these aircraft probably also feature a revised navigation/communications suite, evidence to support this contention being provided by a quite different antenna configuration on the upper centre fuselage section, this being common to all of the Drakens that have seen service with the Ilmavoimat.

Above: Finland's original interest in the Draken was inspired by its desire to assemble the aircraft locally, and the initial contract covered the supply of 12 aircraft in kit form to Valmet. These were actually preceded into service by a batch of leased J 35BS fighters (later purchased outright and described earlier) and were soon augmented by further refurbished ex-Swedish aircraft.

Left: The J 35XS originally wore an overall silver colour scheme, as shown here, later being camouflaged. Externally similar to the J 35F-2, Finnish aircraft lacked a datalink, and were not compatible with the Falcon missile, although they are fitted with an undernose IR sensor. The J 35XS entered service with HavLlv 11 during 1974.

Offutt's White-tops
The special Boeings of the 55th Wing

Offutt AFB is located on the outskirts of Omaha in eastern Nebraska. The facility has been synonymous with the head-quarters of Strategic Air Command until the organisation was dissolved at the end of May 1992. Despite this, the underground complex from which the unmanned Intercontinental Ballistic Missile and the manned bomber fleets could be ordered to retaliate against a nuclear aggressor is still in operation. No bombers or ICBMs are stationed at Offutt, as the base houses the remaining airborne command posts and some of the reconnaissance assets which were previously operated by SAC – now managed by Air Combat Command. The base and flying squadrons are controlled by the 55th Wing which almost exclusively operates Boeing products, including the E-4B National Emergency Airborne Command Post. Further along the large flightline are two rows of Boeing aircraft with RC-135s on one side and EC-135s on the other. The Wing has a complement of approximately 40 aircraft, although less than half are present at any one time as many are on duty overseas, while others are receiving upgrades to their onboard equipment or are on major overhaul. Operations are frequently conducted far from home and quite often close to the territorial boundary of a potential enemy. Therefore to ply their trade in international airspace the aircraft of the 55th Wing need to be clearly identified. To this end they are finished in a high visibility gloss white and grey paint scheme with the US flag prominently displayed on the fin. In line with Air Combat Command practice, the wing's aircraft have adopted the 'OF' tailcode.

Left: An RC-135V Rivet Joint from the 55th Wing's Sigint-gathering fleet. A total of 14 Rivet Joints is on strength, forming the backbone of the US Air Force's electronic reconnaissance effort. From Offutt they deploy around the world, with regular detachments to England, Crete, Saudi Arabia and Okinawa. For many years they were primarily concerned with monitoring the Soviet Union and its allies, but today the world climate has changed, and target areas such as former Yugoslavia and Iraq are now of equal importance. The V model is readily distinguished from the otherwise externally similar RC-135W by the auxiliary airscoop above the outboard engines.

OFFUTT IN THE 1960s

Period shot (below) of the flightline at Offutt AFB sometime prior to July 1967 when the aircraft were all natural metal finish with the blue and white SAC star-spangled banner around the fuselage. On the left are six RC-135Cs which have just entered service after the fitment of the Airborne Instruments Laboratory (AIL) AN/USD-7 surveillance system and the AIL/Melpar/GTE AN/ASD-1 electronic reconnaissance system as their primary mission equipment. The contractor for the overall modification programme was Martin Aircraft Corporation at Baltimore, Maryland. Nearest the camera is RC-135C 63-9792 which was further modified to an RC-135U before receiving the Rivet Joint Block III suite to become an RC-135V. It appears 63-9792 was the equipment test bed for an interim Block II system which was not pursued as the Block III system followed shortly afterwards. Adjacent to 63-9792 are the first five RCs from the fiscal year 1964 order, serials 64-14841 to 14845. Barely visible at the end of the RC-135 ramp are two RB-47Hs, while a third is positioned behind the RCs. The right-hand side of the flight line contains three Looking Glass EC-135Cs, which operated a continuous airborne relay posture for more than 25 years. The four aircraft at the end of the ramp are of primary interest. Nearest is KC-135R 59-1465 with a huge towel bar positioned atop the fuselage. Four aircraft were allocated this designation, including the next aircraft in the row (55-3121) with an identical towel bar antenna. The first section of the towel bar was for the AN/ALC-101 Long Range Air Navigation (LORAN) system, while the remaining sets supported mission equipment. Third in line is KC-135A 59-1472, which may well have been just a 'plain Jane' tanker on loan to the 55th SRW, as it was later assigned to the 97th BW at Blytheville AFB, Arkansas. The final airframe is KC-135R 59-1514.

RECONNAISSANCE

RC-135V Rivet Joint

63-9792 was originally ordered as the first RC-135B in 1963 in a batch of its own, and was followed by a further nine aircraft in 1964 (64-14941 to 14849). All ten were redesignated RC-135C before delivery to the Air Force. 63-9792 was accepted in May 1964 and transferred to the Martin Corp. at Baltimore, Maryland, for installation of the AN/ASD-1 reconnaissance suite. The aircraft received a new reconnaissance system during the late-1960s, changing designation to RC-135U. 63-9792 was the forerunner of the Combat Sent programme with 64-14847 and 14849 receiving the same modifications between 1969 and 1972. The successful introduction into service of the latter two enabled 63-9792 to be refitted with the Rivet Joint Block III system between late 1975 and early 1977, becoming an RC-135V. The cheeks fitted to the eight RC-135V models were the original Martin design and extended as far as the flight crew access door, whereas those on the six RC-135W aircraft were developed by E-Systems and were slightly longer, partially covering the hatchway. These were originally designed for fitment to the RC-135M as they were modified to RC-135W Rivet Joint Block III standard. The FY64 RC-135Vs were refitted with the new enlarged cheeks, which are lighter and stronger, permitting heavier antennas to be installed. 63-9792 had yet to receive them in late 1993.

The cheeks contain the antennas of the Elint reconnaissance system which include the Automatic Elint Emitter Locator System (AEELS). Although the term 'cheeks' has been used, they are actually a series of flat direction-finding interferometers with signal deciphering super-heterodynes housed in a 200-sq ft (18.6 m²) raised area on either side of the fuselage. The cheeks contain numerous antennas feeding automatic, programmable receivers which collectively cover the majority of electronic signals which can be intercepted. The data obtained is recorded in either digital or analog format with direction finders pinpointing the precise location of the signals source. The intercepted signals are relayed automatically to a Raven operator seated in the cabin. With millions of signals in the air at any one time, the equipment can be programmed to differentiate between the mass of unwanted data and the small quantity of useful pulses. Once a signal has been identified other special detection equipment can be activated to break down a radar or data pulse and look inside to analyse the capabilities of the emitter and any special featurers of the signal.

The 'hog' nose which is unique to the RC-135S, V and W models was formed by an extension of 90 in (2.28 m) to accommodate an additional SIGINT collection antenna. The forward bulkhead was enlarged by 24 in (0.6 m) in diameter with the radome faired over additional stringers to the basic aircraft contour to ensure a smooth surface. The cantilevered structure attached to the bulkhead was also reworked to install the extra electronic equipment. The radomes were contructed of fibreglass honeycomb and designed to withstand weather conditons and loads likely to be encountered by high performance jet aircraft. They were designed to allow signal transmission with minimum distortion and attenuation. At the front of the nosecone is a standard APN-59E radar unit as installed in all KC-135s.

Located beneath the nose and fuselage are a variety of aerials and antennas of differing sizes. A trio of blade aerials are positioned under the nose, ahead of five smaller stub UHF communications antennas beneath the cheeks. Forward of the wingroot are four large black inverted T-shaped disc antennas. Aft of the wingroot are nine more of varying shapes and sizes

The 55th Wing Sigint fleet consists of eight RC-135Vs (above), six RC-135Ws and two RC-135Us (right).

including one with the end turned horizontally in a similar manner to those fitted to the superpods of U-2s. The majority of these underside antennas are known as MUCELS, whose capabilities and functions are highly classified. Finally a double lobe antenna fairing is positioned beneath the rear fuselage to house two spinning direction finding systems. A recent additional modification to the latter fairing is the circular housing containing one of the new direction finding systems. Developed by Condor Systems, the small circular CS-2010 Raven Hawk feeds the AEELS II and manual ELINT sysytems. The circular dome corrects antenna attenuation problems with the new Condor unit. Above the fuselage are various High Game and Low Game SATCOM and communications antennas.

The RC-135S and W versions are powered by Pratt and Whitney TF33-P5 engines while the RC-135U and V models have the slightly different TF33-P9 turbofans. Both are rated at 18,000 lb (80.1 kN) thrust, although only the P-5 versions are fitted with thrust-reversers. The bullet shaped fairing attached to the engine mounting above the exhaust outlet is the Loral Magnavox AN/APR-17 infra-red missile jamming system known as Have Siren.

The Air Force announced during the late eighties that two RC-135s were to be withdrawn from service as a cost cutting measure although to date only the RC-135X Cobra Eye has fallen to budgetary constraints. Operations Desert Shield and Desert Storm resulted in a huge increase in Rivet Joint requirements. Subsequently the small fleet of RC-135s has been extremely busy at various worldwide locations. The 82nd RS at Kadena AB, Okinawa, and the 922nd RS at

An RC-135W cleans up departing from Mildenhall on a mission to Bosnia. Note the Have Siren IR jammers above each jetpipe.

RAF Mildenhall, England, have a small number of aircraft detached at any one time, while Det 1/922nd RS at Souda Bay, Crete, has at least one aircraft in residence. A sizeable contingent of RC-135s is located at Riyadh, Saudi Arabia, to continue monitoring the ever-present threat posed by the Iraqi regime of Saddam Hussein. Other potential trouble spots in the world require the intelligence-gathering services of the RC-135, including the Balkan region with Bosnia-Herzegovina and Serbia high on the list of priorities.

RC-135W Rivet Joint

Comparison with the RC-135V shows there are scarcely any differing features externally between the two versions of Rivet Joint aircraft. The six RC-135Ws (62-4131, 4132, 4134, 4135, 4138, 4139) were converted from RC-135Ms, featuring the E-Systems cheek fairings from the outset. The major external difference now that the RC-135Vs have similar fairings concerns the W's lack of auxiliary air scoops above the engine cowlings.

RC-135U Combat Sent

The two RC-135Us (64-14847 and 14849) are radically different from the Rivet Joints and obviously perform a different role. The aircraft are known as Combat Sent with their patch intimating a 'scientific and technical' role. The cheeks are similar to those of the RC-135V with the same raised rectangular antennas. The RC-135U features a small airscoop on the lower section of the leading edge of the starboard cheek, which the other versions lack. Mounted beneath the nose are two small black canted panels each with four antennas. Identical panels are mounted on both wing tips and on

a special extension to the rear fuselage. Collectively these are known as PPMS (an abbreviation for Precision Power Measurement System) and give the sensor operator 360-degree coverage. The large black circular antenna beneath the cheek fairings is a QRC-501 Gap Filler and ALR-46 antenna for signal direction finding. Apart from this antenna the underside of the aircraft is remarkably aerial-free.

The RC-135U was fitted with an Emerson MD-7 radar mounted at the rear of the upper surface of the tail which was formerly fitted to the B-58A Hustler, although this system was removed in 1990/1991. The aircraft is fitted with a modified double lobe fairing beneath the rear fuselage with the middle section featuring a flat underside. A KA-59 camera was installed in this position on the RC-135C, although this was removed sometime prior to 1980. The aircraft was later fitted with a turret containing an infra-red system and a television camera although these were removed in 1991. No cameras are now carried. An antenna fairing similar to those of Rivet Joint will be fitted during the next depot modification planned for the middle of the decade. The primary mission of Combat Sent is technical Elint.

Until recently, the RC-135Us carried a towel-rail antenna above each cheek fairing.

RC-135X Cobra Eye

The most recent reconnaissance version of the C-135, the Cobra Eye was a surplus EC-135B ARIA space-tracker modified by E-Systems with a large optical sensor mounted in the forward cabin. A hatch in the starboard fuselage covered the sensor when not in use, sliding backwards to reveal it for operation. The sensor was obviously used for some kind of space vehicle/missile tracking, and it is known that the Cobra Eye operated on Strategic Defense Initiative sorties. However, the precise nature of its tasks remains unknown. After a brief operational period with the 6th SW, the RC-135X was transferred to Offutt AFB for a short time before being withdrawn from service and flown to E-Systems at Greenville, Texas, in February 1993 for removal of equipment prior to storage.

RC-135S Cobra Ball

One of the most highly classified aircraft in the Air Force inventory, the RC-135S is universally known as Cobra Ball. 61-2662 was initially operated by MATS as a C-135B at Travis AFB, California, until the mid-1960s when it joined Air Force Systems Command performing a variety of test work. These included evaluating satellite communication systems contained in a large black radome mounted aft of cockpit. However following the loss of 6th SW RC-135S 61-2664 Cobra Ball II at Shemya AFB, Alaska in March 1981, 61-2662

was earmarked as its replacement. The reconnaissance suite was installed by E-Systems Greenville Division Inc at Majors Field, Greenville, Texas in 1982. The precise nature of the equipment installed remains classified, although it is known that Cobra Ball performs missions related to the interception of telemetry data from Russian, Chinese, North Korean and Indian Intercontinental Ballistic Missile (ICBM) and theatre ballistic missile tests. The suite includes receivers tuned to missile and rocket telemetry signals, together with optical sensors fitted to the starboard side of the forward fuselage. These optical sensors are specially designed to collect data on the re-entry of warheads under test. Until 1992 missions were operated by the 24th Strategic Reconnaissance Squadron, 6th Strategic Wing, primarily from Eielson AFB but also from the remote site at Shemya AFB (since renamed Eareckson AFB and better known for obvious reasons as 'The Rock'). 61-2662 and its sister-ship 61-2663 were reassigned to Offutt AFB in October 1992, thereby centralising all reconnaissance C-135s under a single wing. Consideration was given to deploying an RC-135S to Saudi Arabia during Desert Storm to help detect Iraqi Scud missiles, although in the event they were not required.

Prior to Cobra Ball, the programme was known as Rivet Ball with the fitment of a huge sliding hatch protecting a massive glass panel. According to one source the glass panel covered a spectrometer to measure and analyse the wavelength, energy and intensity of particles in the atmosphere following Soviet nuclear and ICBM tests. The original equipment

The sole RC-135X Cobra Eye maintained the 6th SW tradition of having the starboard wing painted black to reduce glare for photography. The aircraft was recently retired to storage.

included Ballistic Framing Camera Systems (BFCS) adjacent to a Medium Resolution Camera System (MRCS). Positioned inside the rear fuselage just forward of the tail was a darkroom enabling wet film to be processed while airborne. However the equipment was replaced by the four smaller windows during the early 1980s as a more advanced suite was developed.

The two sensors in the second window from the left, with three sensors in the second from the right together form the Real Time Optical System (RTOS). The far left window covers a single sensor which is the Large Aperture Tracking System (LATS), while that on the far right has no discernible equipment visible, housing the Multiple Object Discrimination System (MODS) when fitted. The four elongated High and Low Slot antennas positioned beneath the windows are shown to good effect. Mounted above the window is a single dipole antenna which until recently was also a feature on either side of the RC-135U. Visible beneath the fuselage are some of the small aerials including a TACAN antenna, UHF Command Radio Antenna, and pilot's low range radio antennae.

The old system needed the wings painted black to reduce glare, although the new sensors are no longer affected by sun glint. The black sections were retained for some time to further the Cobra Ball 'mystique', but are now being removed.

Right: Two RC-135S Cobra Balls serve with the 55th Wing, optimised for the analysis of missile launches. In addition to the telemetry information gathering systems, the aircraft is fitted with optical tracking and recording systems, which peer through the four large windows in the starboard side. With the need to monitor foreign nuclear missile tests decreasing, the Cobra Ball aircraft may pick up a theatre missile-detection mission following the coalition's experiences with Iraqi 'Scuds' during Desert Storm.

COMMAND POSTS

EC-135A 61-0287

Ownership of the aircraft was officially transferred from Strategic Air Command to the Offutt AFB Museum on 10 February 1992. Having prepared the EC-135 for display, personnel at Offutt had to wait for the ground adjacent to the main gate to freeze during mid-winter in order to tow '287 to its final resting place without it sinking into the earth. The EC-135A was one of five which provided Airborne Command Post mission support with the 4th ACCS, 28th BW at Ellsworth AFB, South Dakota. Amongst the equipment installed were an Airborne Launch Control Centre and enhanced communications systems for the World Wide Airborne Command Post programme. The majority of this equipment was removed prior to display. While the basic colour scheme was that applied during its period of assignment to the 28th BW, the nose inscription and tail markings are completely erroneous. The inscription 'Belle of Bellevue' relates to the town adjacent to Offutt AFB. The five EC-135As were the first operational airborne command posts operated by SAC and were assigned to the 34th Air Refuelling Squadron at Offutt AFB until the purpose built EC-135Cs commenced delivery in 1964.

E-4B NEACP

Four E-4s were ordered to support the National Emergency Airborne Command Post by providing relay of command, control and communications (C3) in the event of the United States being under attack by outside forces. The aircraft were originally designed to provide an alternative headquarters for the National Command Authority and the Joint Chiefs of Staff during time of threat or attack. Three E-4As were upgraded to E-4B standard with the fitment of additional communications systems inside the huge dome atop the forward fuselage. This houses a 33-in (0.84-m) computer-controlled steerable dish which links the super high frequency Defence Satellite Communications System (DSCS 2). In addition the E-4 employs Low and Very Low Frequency communications systems transmitted by means of a 25,000-ft (7620-m) trailing wire extended from the rear fuselage. A drogue device provides stability for the trailing wire which has an anti-jam capability and is compatible with the Navy's E-6 TACAMO ballistic missile submarine system. The E-4 itself is hardened against the effects of nuclear explosions including electromagnetic pulse. The E-4s are capable of being inflight refuelled, thereby extending range indefinitely;

the only factor limiting their endurance being crew fatigue. An advanced on-board electrical system is designed to power the mass of communications suites installed. The system is capable of a direct link with commercial telephone and radio networks enabling broadcasts to the general population. More recently the aircraft have received an upgraded data-processing capability together with a more survivable C3 system including initial Milstar modification. Unlike the EC-135s, the E-4s do not carry the 'OF' tail code or any unit/command emblems externally. Whenever the President of the United States travels overseas an E-4 accompanies his personal aircraft 'Air Force One' to

Offutt's museum EC-135A began its career at the base, but spent the majority of its active life at Ellsworth, supporting the PACCS system.

provide the communications link to Washington. The E-4 remains in a secure area at an appropriate US military facility with the crew on standby to make a rapid departure if necessary.

The NEACP E-4Bs are the most comprehensively equipped aircraft in the world in terms of communications. They are colloquially referred to as the 'kneecap' aircraft.

EC-135C Looking Glass

SAC initiated a continuous airborne alert posture on 3 February 1961 under the project name Looking Glass. The mission was flown by EC-135A aircraft on eight-hour relays with various prescribed routes over the central United States. The role was simply to assume overall command of SAC assets in the event of the SAC HQ underground command centre at Offutt AFB being destroyed. Amongst the duties placed upon the battle staff aboard the EC-135s were the assessment of battle damage, communications and radioactive fallout, and the location and strength of surviving forces with which to mount a retaliatory strike. The success of the operation soon became apparent, with SAC placing an order for five EC-135Cs in 1962 and a further twelve in 1963. Amongst the highly sensitive electronic equipment installed were an Acoustic System Signal Processor, a Westinghouse AN/ARC-96 transmitter and low frequency receiver, AN/ASQ-121 Control Indicator and Teleprinter, together with HF, VHF and UHF radios. Subsequently a secure teletypewriter system was fitted. Communications were enhanced by the fitment of three AFSATCOM/AS-3062A antennae along the upper section of the fuselage. Additional antennas have been fitted to various external parts of the fuselage as ongoing development of command post systems have become operational. Among these are the Westinghouse AS-1909 Very Low Frequency black saddle antenna atop the central fuselage and, attached to the side of the rear fuselage, the white Westinghouse AS-3521 which receives low frequency signals from other airborne command posts. Mounted beneath the fuselage is the trailing wire antennae which extends to 28,500 ft (8687 m) when the aircraft is at altitude. However the extended length determines the frequency to be transmitted. The two airscoops on the forward fuselage are designed to enhance the flow of cooling air to some of the electronic apparatus installed in the fuselage.

The continuous airborne relay ceased on 24 July 1990, just seven months short of its thirtieth year of operation, and was replaced by regular daily sorties. EC-135Cs of the 2nd ACCS periodically deploy to Europe to support the Commander in Chief of US European Command. By mid-1993 three EC-135Cs had been retired from service, with two going into storage with AM&RC and the third joining the SAC Museum at Offutt AFB. A study is to be carried out to evaluate the possibility of EC-135Cs performing the Airborne Battlefield Communications Command and Control (ABCCC) role.

The most recent modification programme has involved the installation of the AN/ARC-208(V) Milstar transition satellite communications system with the primary sensor housed in a large oval fairing aft of the cockpit. Milstar is being developed jointly by Lockheed Missiles and Space Co, TRW and Hughes to produce the next generation Extreme High Frequency (EHF) satellite communications system to provide worldwide, jam resistant, survivable command and control communications for US tactical and strategic forces. The major contractor for the terminals is the Raytheon Corporation. Only four aircraft have received the modification, as plans to operate Milstar have changed with the system due to be installed in the E-6A Mercury, with the Navy taking over responsibility for secure communications in the future.

Below and right: Four EC-135Cs are equipped with the Milstars satcom fairing on the spine.

EC-135J

Although basically similar to the EC-135C, the EC-135J has only recently joined the 55th Wing at Offutt AFB. Three EC-135Js were ordered in 1963 for the 1st ACCS at Andrews AFB to perform the National Emergency Airborne Command Post (NEACP). These were replaced by the E-4A in 1975 with the EC-135Js joining the Pacific Air Force at Hickam AFB, Hawaii, for ABNCP duties with the 9th ACCS. These were joined by a former 55th SRW EC-135C which was redesignated as an EC-135J when it joined PACAF during the early 1980s. During service with the 9th ACCS the aircraft were known as project Blue Eagle and, unlike Stateside based ABNCPs, were crewed by battle staff from all branches of the US Armed Services. However the withdrawal of ACPs from overseas locations during 1992 resulted in the four EC-135Js returning to the USA with two being placed in storage with AMARC while the other two joined the 55th. 62-3584 was damaged beyond economical repair during a landing accident at Pope AFB, North Carolina, on 29 May 1992. 63-8055 remaining in operational service until October 1993, when it was flown to Davis Monthan AFB for storage with AM&RC, thereby ending the career of the J-models.

The ex-PACAF EC-135Js joined the 2nd ACCS briefly before retirement.

TRAINERS

TC-135W 62-4129

The 38th RS operates a single TC-135W for proficiency training of Rivet Joint aircrew. The aircraft has been modified with many of the external features associated with the RC-135V and W models. The TC-135W has the 'hog' nose radome extension common to the RC-135S, V and W models, together with the E-Systems cheeks. However the cheeks are simply aerodynamic shapes designed to give realistic training for transitioning aircrew. The aircraft lacks the High Frequency probe antennas mounted on a small rail above the outer wingtip, but retains the conventional aerial as fitted to the KC-135 fleet. Small 'High Game' SATCOM dishes are mounted atop the fuselage, while the double lobe antenna fairing is positioned beneath the rear fuselage in the same location as the refuelling boom housing on tanker aircraft. Surprisingly, considering the aircraft is dedicated to the training role, it is fitted with the Have Siren infra-red missile jamming device above the engine exhaust. The usage of the TC-135W enables new aircrew to receive specialist 'hands-on' conversion training without spending all flight hours in vaulable mission aircraft.

TC-135S 62-4133

Following the tragic loss of RC-135T 55-3121 near Valdez, Alaska, on 25 February 1985, the 24th RS, 6th SW urgently needed to acquire a replacement trainer aircraft to support the RC-135S Cobra Ball. Aeronautical Systems Division at Wright Patterson AFB, Ohio, made C-135B 62-4133 available for conversion by E-Systems at Majors Field. The aircraft was officially on strength with the 6th SW by July 1985. The TC-135S has the extended radome and the probe antennas mounted on a small rail above the outer wingtip. No sensors are fitted to the starboard side although the engines and wing are painted matt black in the same manner as Cobra Ball. When Rivet Joint operations were

Above: At first glance this aircraft appears to be a standard Rivet Joint, but closer examination reveals the lack of mission antennas. This is the sole TC-135W, used as a trainer for the Rivet Joint fleet.

Above: Training for the Cobra Ball/Cobra Eye fleet was accomplished using the TC-135S, and it continues in this role at Offutt. The 'North Star' artwork is retained from its days with the 6th SW, and the starboard wing is painted black to imitate the operational aircraft, although it has no mission equipment. During Desert Storm the TC-135S was loaned to the 55th and was heavily utilised on crew shuttle duties between Offutt and Riyadh.

terminated at Eielson AFB it became much more cost effective to consolidate the RC fleet at Offutt AFB. Centralisation of RC-135 operations was completed in 1992 with the 24th RS being reassigned to the 55th Wing along with the two RC-135Ss and their TC-135S trainer, the 6th SW deactivating.

Below: Dedicated to training OC-135B crews, the TC-135B was similarly converted from a surplus WC-135B weather recon aircraft.

TC-135B 61-2667

The 55th Wing accepted delivery of the unique TC-135B early in 1993. The aircraft performed weather reconnaissance with MATS and MAC as a WC-135B for the majority of its carrer, but was later employed briefly as a base hack with the 513th ACCW at RAF Mildenhall, providing training and proficiency flying with the 10th Airborne Command and Control Squadron [Silk Purse European Airborne Command Post programme]. For this latter duty much of the weather monitoring equipment was removed, although the two airscoops mounted on the fuselage side above the wingroot were retained. These have now been deleted with the appropriate holes sealed. The TC-135B has the specific duty of training personnel destined to implement the Open Skies Treaty with three specially modified OC-135Bs. Whereas the OC-135s themselves are fitted with KS-87B oblique-mounted and KA-91A vertical-mounted panoramic cameras, the trainer is not fitted with any additional sensors.

OPEN SKIES & WEATHER
WC-135B

The planned conversion of three WC-135Bs to OC-135B configuration to monitor the Open Skies Treaty resulted in the remaining WC-135B airframes being reassigned from the 55th Weather Reconnaissance Squadron at McClellan AFB, California to the 55th Wing. Ten aircraft were modified for the role of long range, high altitude weather reconnaissance during the mid-1960s although gradually the requirement was reduced enabling five aircraft to be transferred to other units for alternative duties including VIP transport and aircrew training. Five aircraft were officially transferred from the 55th Wing on 1 October 1993 consisting of 61-2665 and 61-2670 plus the three examples which will be reconfigured to OC-135B 61-2672, 61-2673 and 61-2674. Amongst the external modifications to the WC-135Bs was an air scoop positioned on both sides of the fuselage above the wing. These have been removed from all five aircraft along with the tail band containing the legend 'WEATHER'. Shortly after arrival at Offutt AFB the aircraft received tail code 'OF' and a tactical-style serial presentation.

OC-135B

Three former WC-135Bs are being converted to OC-135B configuration to implement the Open Skies Treaty. The Treaty itself was signed in March 1992 by 25 nations to verify the military activities of the signatories by teams of observers. Each nation signing the Treaty has agreed to permit 42 annual observation flights. Amongst the participants are the US, Canada, all NATO countries in Europe, former Warsaw Pact nations, and several CIS members including Russia, Belarus, Georgia, Kazakhstan and Ukraine.

The three aircraft have been modified with the installation of photographic sensors including a KA-91A vertical-mounted panoramic camera for photography above 26,000 ft (7925 m), together with two KS-87B oblique-mounted framing cameras and a KS-87 vertical-mounted camera for low altitude imagery. Some of these cameras have been removed from surplus RF-4C Phantoms. Modification work was completed earlier in 1993 with evaluation performed by the 4950th Test Wing at Wright Patterson AFB, Ohio. The OC-135s can accomodate 38 crew, maintenance personnel, foreign representatives and members of the On-Site Inspection Agency (OSIA). The latter Agency will provide the

Further consolidating the special C-135 fleet at Offutt was the transfer of three WC-135Bs from McClellan AFB, California, to the 55th Wing in October 1993.

sensors and linguists for all operational Open Skies sorties, and will escort overseas based observation aircraft conducting missions over the United States.

The aircraft were assigned to the 55th Weather Reconnaissance Squadron at McClellan AFB, California, under Air Mobility Command until 1 October when they were transferred to Air Combat Command and relocated to the 24th Reconnaissance Squadron, 55th Wing at Offutt AFB, Nebraska. The majority of Offutt based aircraft display the unit's 'OF' tail code, although the OC-135Bs will not have this marking. Instead they will have 'OPEN SKIES' across the tail band, together with the Open Skies emblem on the fin.

Adapting to the new world, the elderly C-135 airframe has been modified for a 1990s mission in the form of the OC-135B, three of which will be used for photographic inspection of military facilities in nations that have signed the treaty.

SUPPORT AIRCRAFT
C-135A 60-0378

The CSA machines are the only 55th Wing C-135 aircraft to display the units' legend 'Fightin 55th' on the fin tip. The three are completely different models (respectively Boeing 717-100A, 717-157 and 717-158) and therefore create problems for maintenance personnel who need a separate Technical Order for each. 60-0378 was originally purchased for the airlift role with Military Air Transport Service. Following the delivery of the C-141 Starlifter, the MATS C-135s found secondary roles with other Commands. 60-0378 was operated briefly by Air Force Systems Command, before being bailed to NASA from 1969 to 1973 for weightlessness flights, performing over 14,000 parabola flight profiles. There then followed a period of assignment with Headquarters Air Force Communications Service and an assignment to Andrews AFB, Maryland, with the 89th MAW, before being moved to Offutt with the 55th SRW by September 1978.

Below: The second C-135 built, this aircraft enjoyed a long and fruitful career on test duties before passing to the 55th CSA fleet. It still carries the NKC-135A designation.

Above: The three Command Support Aircraft (CSAs) lined up at Offutt. C-135A 60-0378 has been a stalwart of the Offutt fleet since 1978. It retains the original J57 turbojets.

Below: In its first period of 55th service, 59-1514 had the far more interesting role of electronic reconnaissance (as a KC-135R). Now re-engined as a KC-135E, it serves today as a utility transport.

KC-135E 59-1514

The KC-135E conversion programme was exclusively for the Air National Guard and Air Force Reserve with the exception of two aircraft, one of which (59-1514) was the first to be re-engined with the TF33 turbofan. The other active duty KC-135E (57-2589) is used as the CINCSTRATCOM command aircraft. Both aircraft have inflight refueling capability. 59-1514 served the 55th at Offutt AFB originally as a KC-135R (R for reconnaissance) during the late 1960s and later as a KC-135A until January 1982, when conversion to KC-135E standard was completed and it returned to the Wing. The KC-135E frequently ferries replacement RC-135 air and ground crews between the USA and overseas operating locations, such as Kadena AB, Okinawa, RAF Mildenhall, UK, Souda Bay AB, Crete and Riyadh, Saudi Arabia. It was highly active during the Gulf War shuttling between Offutt and Riyadh. These operating areas are considered to be low risk and the aircraft does not have any specialist threat warning equipment. Clearly evident is the stress on the lower part of the fuselage caused by 33 years of service, as the aircraft had accumulated more than 24,000 flight hours by mid-1993!

NKC-135A 55-3119

The second KC-135A built, 55-3119 spent much of its operational career as a test airframe based at Wright Patterson AFB, Ohio, with the designation NKC-135A. With the reduction of test programes, it was transferred to Headquarters Strategic Air Command at Offutt AFB as a Command Support Aircraft (CSA). The small number of CSA aircraft was assigned to the 55th SRW (redesignated 55th Wing) for convenience. The primary duty was to ferry high ranking SAC personnel between facilities in the USA. However when SAC was deactivated on 1 June 1992 the majority of its assets were divided between Air Combat Command (ACC) and Air Mobility Command (AMC). Responsibility for long range targetting policy and command and control of nuclear weapons was vested in Strategic Command, a unified organisation staffed by Air Force, Navy and Army personnel and located in the former HQ SAC complex. The C-135s continued to support the new command, although they have now been either retired or reassigned. Despite retaining the designation NKC-135A, 55-3119 had its refuelling boom removed.

C-21A

The 55th Wing activated the 11th Airlift Flight on 1 May 1993 to operate the C-21A Learjets formerly assigned to Detachment 1, 458th Airlift Squadron of Air Mobility Command. These were stationed at Offutt AFB on a tenancy basis, but transferred to ACC to streamline responsibility of assets to the host Wing.

Offutt's hottest aircraft are the four T-38As assigned to provide additional flight experience for flight-crew. These were detached to former SAC tanker, recon and bomber bases from training units, but are now permanently assigned within the wing structure. The Offutt machines now proudly wear the 'Fightin 55th' fin-stripe.

Above: A standard C-135B, 62-4130 spent many years as part of the 89th MAW's staff/VIP transport fleet. It serves in a similar role at Offutt.

Below: Originally MAC aircraft detached to Offutt for fast courier work, the C-21As at the Nebraska base are now assigned directly to the parent wing.

C-135B 62-4130

The third of the three CSA aircraft, C-135B 62-4130 was originally in service with MATS at McGuire AFB, New Jersey, before being modified for VIP duties as a VC-135B for service with the 89th MAW at Andrews AFB, Maryland. After ten years of ferrying VIPs from the nation's capital, the aircraft was transferred to Offutt AFB by September 1978 for similar duties with HQ SAC. However the demise of the Command has resulted in some, if not all of the CSA aircraft being reassigned or retired.

T-38A Talon

The 55th Wing assumed responsibility for the four T-38As which perform the companion trainer role at Offutt AFB, providing additional flight time for pilots. The Talons were previously assigned to Air Training Command, but detached to Offutt on a permanent basis from the 12th FTW at Randolph AFB, Texas. The Talons have adopted the 55th Wing 'OF' tail code and 'Fightin 55th' tail band. At least one Offutt based T-38A has been painted light grey overall with black markings including a subdued national insignia.

Turkey

Turkey continues to field very large armed forces, since its position as a bridge between Europe and Asia has resulted in a need to defend not only against the USSR, but also against its Islamic neighbours Iraq, Iran and Syria, and against Bulgaria and Greece, the country's longest-standing enemy. Ethnic tensions with Bulgaria continue to this day, while control of water reserves continues to prevent normal relations with Syria. The problem of Kurdistan continues to create tension between Turkey, Iran and Iraq, while Turkish participation in Operation Desert Storm further intensified difficulties with the latter nation. Relations between Greece and Turkey have always been difficult, more recently exacerbated by the 1974 Turkish invasion (and continuing occupation) of Northern Cyprus.

Türk Hava Kuvvetleri (Turkish Air Force)

The Turkish air force has for many years been regarded as a large and professional force, albeit one equipped largely with semi-obsolescent cast-offs from other NATO air arms. In recent years, this image has been furthered by the air arm's extensive use of the F-104G Starfighter, and by the current re-equipment of many units with ex-USAF and ex-Luftwaffe Phantoms. In fact this is a gross over-simplification, for while the Turkish air force continues to rely on elderly types to boost front-line strength, it also fields squadrons of the latest F-16Cs, many of which have been indigenously assembled or built under licence at Mürted.

Turkish military aviation dates back to the Balkan Wars of 1912-1913 and gained experience during World War I and in the War of Independence (1919-22), although the country was neutral during World War II. Initially organised under army command, the air arm grew from three company-sized units to three regiments in 1934, and to three brigades in 1941, each consisting of three four-company regiments. In 1943 the air arm became a corps in its own right, with three divisions. Such a large organisation deserved the independence which it achieved on 31 January 1944.

By late 1944 the air force had two full divisions in the west, each with a bomber regiment, an attack regiment, and a fighter regiment. The third large formation remained a brigade, although it was of similar composition to the two divisions. Recce and transport units were attached but reported directly to air force HQ. Lend-Lease deliveries later in the war were combined with aircraft bought from both sides, and this brought about an unusual mix of types, which included Fw 190s, Spitfires, Hurricanes and Kittyhawks, as well as Battles, Baltimores, Blenheims and Liberators. Large-scale US aid to Turkey began in 1948, as the Cold War intensified, and resulted in the gradual replacement of the country's predominantly British-supplied aircraft (including large numbers of Spitfires and Mosquitos) with more modern US types (and also with some similarly vintage P-47s and B-26s). Considerable sums were allocated to Turkey annually under the Foreign Military Sales

and Mutual Assistance Programs, with West Germany adding further aid in consecutive 18-month programmes running from 1964. Large numbers of Turkish pilots were sent to the USA and Germany for jet training, and two T-33As were delivered to Balekesir in the summer of 1951 to equip a 'jet training detachment'. In June 1952 the first 25 (of an eventual 360) F-84Gs were delivered aboard the carrier *Corregidor*. Turkey was suddenly seen as a useful bulwark against the Soviet Bloc in the strategically important Eastern Mediterranean, especially with its decisive control over the historically vital Dardanelles, through which the mighty Soviet Black Sea Fleet had to pass. Turkey became a member of NATO during 1952, its air arm becoming as a result a truly independent strike force, rather than being little more than a mere close-support air arm of the army, as it had previously been. On 14 October 1953 NATO activated its Sixth Allied Tactical Air Force, to be responsible for air operations in the region.

Cold War improvements

During the next 15 years the Turkish air force infrastructure was radically improved, with the construction of 12 new air bases and the establishment of a brand new early warning system. Since 1950 the air force had been re-organised into two tactical air forces, with four strike and one interceptor wing. In 1951 the transport units were formed into a single Air Base Command. Re-equipment of the fighter-bomber wings with F-84Gs was the highest priority, and it was not until 1954 that the interceptor wing was able to trade its ancient Spitfires for North American F-86E Sabres. This allowed the formation of a three-squadron Air Defence Command on 17 June 1953 from the remnants of the former 2nd Tactical Air Force at Balikesir. This later moved to Ankara. Reconnaissance was the next role to be modernised, B-26s being relegated to target-towing duties and replaced by RT-33As and, in 1957, by RF-84Fs. Considerable efforts were also made to ensure that the air force was fully self-sufficient, and programmes were instituted which resulted in the establishment of maintenance units that could overhaul all types in the

inventory, and of a pilot training scheme which eventually allowed Turkey to pull out of the NATO training scheme in 1956.

The F-84Gs suffered heavy attrition and fatigue problems. These difficulties were partially offset by deliveries of second-hand aircraft from other NATO air forces, including 28 from Belgium alone, and others from the USAF, Netherlands and France between 1955 and 1959. Modernisation of the fighter-bomber force also resulted in the delivery of F-100Fs and F-100Ds, and of surplus French F-84Fs during the late 1950s. Air defences were strengthened when Nike-Ajax SAMs were deployed in 1959, joining Air Defence Command's manned interceptors, three (later seven) Radar Control Groups and the 12th Transport Base. Further F-84Fs (modified to F-84FQ standard) were delivered between 1962 and 1966, including 19 each from the USAF and Netherlands air force, and 164 from the Luftwaffe. This allowed the last straight-winged F-84Gs to bow out in 1965, but Turkey clearly needed a more modern strike aircraft in substantial numbers, since the F-84F could never be any more than an interim type.

The F-104G Starfighter was then entering service with other NATO air arms in large numbers, and was becoming virtually the standard alliance fighter-bomber. It was a natural choice for Turkey, which first received the F-104G during 1963 with the delivery of 55 single-seaters and eight TF-104Gs funded through MAP. These were later augmented in 1972 by eight F-104Gs and two TF-104Gs retired by Spain, and by further aircraft supplied by Italy following the 1974 invasion of Cyprus and by other NATO nations during the early 1980s.

The same modernisation plan which brought about the delivery of the first F-104Gs was also responsible for Turkish air force induction of another new fast-jet type, the Northrop F-5. Twenty single-seat F-5As and two F-5B two-seat trainers were delivered in late 1964. Seventy-five F-5As and 13 F-5Bs were eventually funded by MAP, and further aircraft were transferred from Libya (about 10, perhaps via Pakistan), and later from the USAF, Netherlands and Norway. All the new aircraft were still being built or

This Dakota serves with the communications unit of the First Tactical Air Force, which is based at 1 Ana Jet Üs.

Eskisehir has two colourfully marked gate guardians, an F-86 and this F-84F, both of which wear this 'Thunderbirds' style scheme.

Eskisehir hosts two units which operate the T-33. Some are on the strength of the Base Liaison and Training Squadron, others are with the 1 TAF communications.

Many of the recent ex-USAF F-4Es delivered still retain their old ANG squadron markings; here a 141st TFS tiger's head.

113 Filo operates the RF-4E in the tactical reconnaissance role. More RF-4Es are being delivered from surplus German stocks.

Turkish F-4Es wear a variety of colour schemes, from USAF-style Vietnam-era camouflage, to lizard camouflage (here on a 112 Filo aircraft) or air superiority grey.

The second Phantom wing of the First TAF is based at 3 Ana Jet Üs at Konya. This 131 Filo F-4E carries an underwing target.

The two 3 Ana Jet Üs Phantom squadrons (one temporarily stood down) are augmented by the F/NF-5As of 133 Filo.

Even at 4 Ana Jet Üs at Konya, home to Turkey's most high-tech warplane, the Base Liaison and Training Flight operates the venerable Lockheed T-33A!

Time is running out for the F-104Ss of 191 Filo, due to begin conversion to the F-16 during late 1993/early 1994. Some aircraft may then transfer to 8 Ana Jet Üs.

The flying units of 9 Ana Jet Üs at Balikesir, including the T-33 equipped BLTS, have been detached to Akhisar while their home base is prepared for F-16 operations. 192 Filo did not move, deploying instead to Mürted for F-16 conversion.

The General Dynamics F-16C, built under licence in Turkey, is becoming the mainstay of the First Tactical Air Force. Three squadrons at 4 Ana Jet Üs, and two at 6 Ana Jet Üs, have already converted, and the three squadrons of 9 Ana Jet Üs are following suit. Turkey eventually plans to have 12 F-16 squadrons.

delivered as the Turkish air force was called upon to fly operational sorties for the first time, however.

Cyprus, which has historically had a large Turkish minority population in the north of the island, gained its independence from Britain in 1960, after a long campaign by Greek Cypriot terrorist groups. The UK continues to maintain military bases (The Sovereign Base areas) on the strategically important island to this day. Following independence, friction between the Greek and minority (30 per cent) Turkish communities grew until clashes broke out in 1963. Turkey's air force was finally sent into action in December 1963 , when it flew 'demonstration of force' sorties at rooftop height over Cyprus. The two communities were separated by UN forces, but these were inadequate to prevent further problems, four fighter-bomber squadrons having to be sent into action against Greek forces which attacked Turkish Cypriot villages during August 1964. Topel and Erkilet air bases are named after pilots killed in the action.

The Air Defence Command transferred all of its flying units to the two tactical air forces in 1965 (the third then redesignating as the Second Tactical Air Force), while a new transport command, the Hava Ulastirma Komutanligi (Air Transport Command), was established reporting directly to the Air Force HQ. This operated a variety of types, including five newly delivered C-130E Hercules. To free up the F-104s for strike duties, in 1968 Turkey received 41 F-102As and seven TF-102s to equip two air defence squadrons. These were based at Mürted and Diyarbakir.

Huns into service

The withdrawal of the F-100 Super Sabre from combat in Vietnam freed large numbers of these aircraft for export to Turkey, with 27 F-100Ds being delivered in 1969-70, and 74 F-100Cs (upgraded to D standards) following during 1972-74. This revolutionised the fighter-bomber arm. The last F-84Fs were replaced by the newer aircraft during 1974, although they remained in storage into the 1980s, and a handful of RF-84Fs remained in service in the reconnaissance role even longer. This was because the 20 RF-5As delivered in 1969 proved deficient in range, and only re-equipped one of the two tactical reconnaissance squadrons, while RF-84Fs were retained for longer range missions.

Modernisation did not only affect the front line. The Hava Ulastirma Komutanligi received 20 Transall C.160Ds (redesignated C.160T) from Germany during 1970, while three new C-130s were delivered during 1971-74. Despite this, C-47s remained in widespread use. T-6 Texans were replaced by 30 Cessna T-41Ds in the training role and ageing VIP C-54Ds were replaced by three Vickers Viscounts during 1972. Base flights began exchanging their T-6s and AT-11s for Lockheed T-33s, and some also received odd examples of the Bell UH-1, but the process was leisurely, and the last AT-11s were still active during 1982.

Trouble in Cyprus flared up again during 1974. Turkish allegations of Greek atrocities against their villages were followed by demands that Britain, as guarantor of the fragile constitution, should intervene. On 20 July Turkish F-100s and F-104s attacked Greek forces on

Cyprus, and this was followed by helicopter-borne commando assaults and a full-scale parachute landing (from C-47s and C.160 Transalls). The conflict lasted for more than a month, and some aircraft were lost, but not (claim the Turks) to enemy action. Turkish fighter-bombers proved quite effective, but unfortunately managed to sink one of their own navy's destroyers, which was mistaken for a Greek vessel.

The invasion of Cyprus led to a four-year suspension of US military aid and weapons deliveries, and this halted the re-equipment of units with the F-4 Phantom and had a disastrous effect on the serviceability of the F-102 fleet. Fortunately, Turkey's other NATO partners stepped in to fill the breach. Germany and Norway delivered much-needed spares, while Italy supplied 18 or 20 Aeritalia F-104Ss to meet a 1974 order, augmenting these with a further batch of 22 similar aircraft. These were used by Nos 191 and 192 Filos for interception duties, the latter squadron later re-equipping with F-104Gs. The Starfighter was eventually to become a mainstay of the Turkish air force, with large numbers of surplus aircraft being delivered as Western European nations retired their F-104s. Belgium supplied 17 F-104Gs during 1980-83, the Netherlands 43 F-104Gs and RF-104Gs with 10 TF-104Gs during the same period, and Norway 12 F-104Gs and one TF-104G in 1981. From October 1980 Germany supplied 118 F-104Gs and 30 TF-104Gs, the last of these arriving in 1988. Canada donated 50 CF-104Gs, 30 refurbished by MBB in Germany, the remaining 20 being delivered for use as spares. Interestingly, the Belgian Starfighters suffered serviceability problems and were soon replaced by German and Dutch machines. The Turkish F-104 era is due to end during 1994 or 1995 when 8 Jet Base re-equips with F-16Cs and F-16Ds.

The 1980s were a period of major expansion, and an order for the Panavia Tornado at one time seemed likely, though the UK government's unwillingness to provide credit support undermined this deal. The possibility of Tornados as part of a German military aid package re-emerged in 1985, and remained under consideration for several years, but the attractiveness of cheap second-hand Phantoms to bulk-out overall numbers, with locally-built F-16s to provide a high-quality 'tip-of-the-spear', proved too great.

Just as it received surplus NATO F-104Gs to augment its original MAP Starfighters, the 1980s saw Turkey receiving surplus Norwegian (35 F-5As and six RF-5As), USAF (four F-5Bs) and Dutch (60) Freedom Fighters to supplement the original MAP-funded aircraft, and those transferred from Libya.

Drive for self-sufficiency

Even before the Cyprus operation, Turkey was realising that total reliance on other nations for its weaponry might be unwise, and in 1973 began allocating about 10 per cent of each annual defence budget to the so-called Reorganisation and Modernisation Plan (REMO), aiming at eventual self-sufficiency in many types of arms production. This included ambitious plans for the establishment of an indigenous aviation industry, encouraged by the success of indigenous construction of aircraft like the Miles Magister during the 1940s. This resulted in successive plans for the licence-manufacture of Alpha Jets,

M.B.339s and then F-5Es. Eventually the TUSAS (Turk Ucak Sanayi Ananim Sirketi) factory at Mürted and the TUMSAS factory at Eskisehir were established to participate in the Peace Onyx I plan for the supply of F-16s to Turkey. Under the offset agreements underlining this plan, General Dynamics contracted the new TUSAS Aerospace Industries to co-produce 152 of the 160 F-16Cs and F-16Ds involved, and to produce rear and centre fuselage sections and wings for USAF F-16s. The first eight aircraft (two F-16Cs, six F-16Ds) were supplied complete from Fort Worth. Initial Mürted-built aircraft were to F-16C Block 30 standards, but the final 101 single-seaters and 15 two-seaters were to Block 40 standard with provision for LANTIRN pods. An order for Loral Rapport III ECM was announced in late 1988. Eighteen Turkish F-16s were deployed to Ghedi in Italy for use in Deny Flight air exclusion zone operations during late 1992.

As well as F-16s, TAI has received orders for 10 SF-260Ds (to be followed by 24 more), the first four of which were delivered in 1991. The company is also assembling and producing parts for 50 of the Airtech CN-235s on order for the air force. The first Turkish-assembled aircraft made its maiden flight on 24 September 1992, and was delivered on 13 November. The company is also involved in co-production of the Sikorsky Black Hawk.

NATO command

The Turkish air force today reports to Supreme Allied Commander Europe (Mons, Belgium), in a chain of command which runs via Allied Forces Southern Europe (Naples), Allied Air Forces Southern Europe (Naples) and the Sixth Allied Tactical Air Force (SIXATAF) headquartered at Sirinyer Garrison at Izmir.

The peacetime mission of SIXATAF is the full-time air defence of Turkey, while maintaining its assigned units at a high state of readiness through regular evaluations and exercises. In wartime, the role would expand to include tactical air support to NATO land and naval forces. In time of war, command of the Turkish First and Second Tactical Air Forces would pass, following national approval, to the SIXATAF commander. SIXATAF headquarters is manned by officers from Turkey, the USA, Britain and Italy, and in wartime the organisation could be reinforced by other NATO air forces, perhaps including USAF F-15s, F-16s and other types, Dutch F-16s, RAF Jaguars, and other rapid-reaction and mobile units. This massive potential wartime expansion has been made possible by much investment (often funded by NATO) in air base infrastructure.

Turkey won itself greater influence and goodwill through its help in the Gulf War, during which USAF aircraft operated from Incirlik, and through its ongoing participation in Operation Deny Flight, enforcing the 'No-Fly Zone' over Bosnia. These operations have served to finally lay to rest American reservations about supplying arms to Turkey, which were originally occasioned by the invasion of Cyprus and ongoing tension with fellow NATO ally Greece. The US base agreement had been formally renewed in March 1980, and military aid was then resumed, albeit on a limited scale, and with MAP/FMS allocations of between $490 million and $714

An F-5A of 5 Ana Jet Üs stands outside its hardened aircraft shelter. Turkey is seeking to upgrade its Freedom Fighters for continued service into the next century.

Despite its age and simplicity, the Northrop F-5A Freedom Fighter remains a cost-effective and popular fighter-bomber, and equips one full wing at 5 Ana Jet Üs, Merzifon, and single squadrons at Konya and Diyarbakir.

Among the Second Tactical Air Force's flying units are the F-4E squadrons at 7 Ana Jet Üs, Erhac. Even when F-16 deliveries are complete, the F-4E will retain a vital role.

The sharkmouth on the nose identifies this 7 Ana Jet Üs F-4E as having previously served with the 110th TFS, Missouri Air National Guard.

A 7 Ana Jet Üs F-4E touches down at Erhac in a cloud of blue smoke. Turkey wants to upgrade its F-4Es to keep them viable into the next century. An upgrade programme similar to the German F-4F ICE modification, with a new radar and BVR missile, is the favoured option.

8 Ana Jet Üs at Diyarbakir will be the last home of the F-104 in Turkish service. Due to re-equip with F-16s in 1994/95, it may then swap over with one of the 1st TAF F-4 wings.

The third squadron at 8 Ana Jet Üs, 184 Filo, operates the RF-5A Freedom Fighter. These aircraft may be replaced by the RF-4E Phantoms being delivered from Germany.

CF-104Gs of 8 Ana Jet Üs line up at Diyarbakir. Once expected to serve for many more years, Turkey's F-104s will have disappeared by the end of 1995, replaced by brand new F-16s and more versatile F-4Es. This will leave Italy as the final NATO operator of the Starfighter. F-104s also serve in Taiwan.

million during the 1980s.

A new wave of re-equipment has already begun, and Turkey is also taking advantage of the cascading process which has inevitably accompanied the US defence drawdown following the end of the Cold War. Under this, older front-line types are passed to friendly nations to avoid cuts of newer aircraft, or cancellation of new projects. Most important is the USA's promise to supply about 50 surplus Fairchild A-10A Thunderbolt IIs, which will represent a major increase in CAS capability. The Army have also been offered 25 surplus AH-1Es and AH-1Ps to augment the AH-1Ws being diverted from USMC contracts. While the USA is passing surplus equipment to Turkey, Germany, another long-term donor of equipment, checked supplies due to its concerns over Turkish policy relating to Kurdish rebels. Authorisation for the delivery of 46 ex-Luftwaffe RF-4Es (14 for spares) was thus delayed until 23 September 1992, with deliveries following in April 1993. The 32 aircraft for service were refurbished by MBB at Ingolstadt. The Phantom looks set to remain an important element in the Turkish air force for many years, despite the massive influx of more modern F-16s. In an effort to keep the Phantom fleet viable and competitive, Turkey is seeking to significantly increase the type's air-to-air and air-to-ground capability. Rockwell, IAI and MBB are competing to carry out such an upgrade, which will include provision of a new radar, new EW equipment and upgraded avionics. MBB

seem to be the front runners for the contract, offering an upgrade package which will bring Turkish Phantoms up to the same standards as German F-4F ICE modified aircraft.

A similar upgrade package is being sought for Turkey's surviving 135 F-5 Freedom Fighters. IAI, teamed with Singapore Aerospace, and Northrop/Allied Signal, DASA/Fokker/Sierra, Rockwell/Bristol Aerospace and GEC Marconi/Sogerma are competing for the contract .

New equipment on order

Turkey is not only receiving and upgrading second-hand aircraft in the present re-equipment, modernisation and expansion process. A further 40 F-16Cs and F-16Ds are on order under Peace Onyx II, and contracts have been placed for long lead-time articles for a further 40. This would bring total Turkish F-16 procurement to 240, in 12 squadrons. The front line is also being strengthened by the incorporation of AH-1W Cobra attack helicopters into the Army. Staying with rotorcraft, Turkey has ordered 95 Sikorsky S-70A-28 Black Hawks for the paramilitary Jandarma (the first five) and armed forces. The last 50 will be co-produced by TUSAS. These aircraft augment six S-70A-17s delivered to the Jandarma in December 1988 and six more (two in VIP configuration) to the national police in late 1990.

One might have expected that the massive Black Hawk order would fulfil Turkey's transport helicopter requirement, but surprisingly 20

Eurocopter AS 532UL Cougars were ordered in October 1993, and a number of Mil Mi-17s have reportedly also been ordered. Other recent orders have included a Gulfstream IV (delivered in 1993 for VIP duties) and two similarly configured Citation VIIs. Turkey has also ordered a single Pilatus Britten-Norman/Westinghouse BN2T-4R MSSA (Multi-Sensor Surveillance Aircraft). This is based on the Defender 4000, but has a nose-mounted AN/APG-66 radar with a 360° rotating antenna, as well as a WF-360 FLIR, LTN-92 ring laser gyro, dual V/UHF radios, a real-time video datalink and high resolution multi-function displays. Four more are required.

Today the Turkish air force is divided into two Taktik Hava Kuvveti Komutabligi (tactical air forces), and two independent direct-reporting Komutanligi (commands). Units are gathered in Ana Jet Üs (jet bases) or Ana Üs (bases) which function as operational wings. Aircraft assigned to these wings carry codes consisting of the numerical base code followed by a three number suffix. Sometimes one or more squadrons assigned to an Ana Jet Üs will be based (permanently or temporarily) at a subsidiary or satellite airfield, but while they remain under the command of the main base, they retain its code. Each base usually has between two and three operational filos (squadrons), whose designations consist of a three-digit number, the second numeral indicating the base identity. Each base also has a communications unit, referred to as a Base Liaison and Training Squadron and abbreviated as BLTS.

1ci Taktik Hava Kuvveti Komutabligi (First Tactical Air Force)

Activated in 1950, during the major reorganisation of the Turkish Air Force, the First Tactical Air Force is one of two components committed to NATO's SIXATAF and is headquartered at Eskisehir, east of Istanbul. It consists of a versatile mix of fighter-interceptor, strike-attack and reconnaissance units, with air defence radar and missile units providing an integrated electronic ground environment. Eskisehir's three front-line squadrons are respectively assigned to the interdiction, air defence and reconnaissance roles, Konya's to interdiction and close air support (133 Filo only) and Mürted's to interdiction, air defence and F-16 type conversion. At Bandirma the squadrons are respectively assigned to CAS and air defence, while at Balikesir the F-104 units are re-equipping with F-16s and will assume defence responsibilities.

First Tactical Air Force

UNIT	TYPE	BASE
HQ Flight	C-47, UH-1H, T-33A	Eskisehir
1 Ana Jet Üs, Eskisehir		
111 Filo	F-4E Phantom	Eskisehir
112 Filo	F-4E Phantom	Eskisehir
113 Filo	RF-4E Phantom	Eskisehir
BLTS	T-33A/RT-33A	Eskisehir
3 Ana Jet Üs, Konya		
131 Filo	F-4E Phantom	Konya
132 Filo	F-4E Phantom	Konya
(temporarily disbanded 1990-)		
133 Filo	NF-5A/B	Konya
BLTS	T-33A, UH-1H	Konya
4 Ana Jet Üs, Mürted		
141 Filo	F-16C/D	Mürted
142 Filo	F-16C/D	Mürted
Oncel Filo	F-16C/D	Mürted
HQ Flight	T-33A	Mürted

Mürted's base flight is officially the HQ Liaison and Training Squadron, serving as the communications squadron for the Turkish air force HQ at Ankara.

6 Ana Jet Üs, Bandirma		
161 Filo	F-16C/D	Bandirma
162 Filo	F-16C/D	Bandirma
BLTS	T-33A, UH-1H	Bandirma
9 Ana Jet Üs, Balikesir		
191 Filo	F-104S/TF-104G	Akhisar
192 Filo	*F-16 conversion at Mürted late '92*	
193 'Sahin' Filo	TF/F-104G	Akhisar
BLTS	T-33A/RT-33A	Akhisar

Balikesir's flying units moved to Akhisar during late 1992 to see out the F-104 era except 192 Filo, whose pilots began F-16 conversion at Mürted. The base was meanwhile prepared for F-16 operations and the return of its squadrons.

15th Missile Base, Alemdag		
1 Filo	Nike-Hercules	Alemdag
2 Filo	Nike-Hercules	Alemdag
3 Filo	Nike-Hercules	Alemdag
4 Filo	Nike-Hercules	Alemdag
5 Filo	Nike-Hercules	Fenertepe
6 Filo	Nike-Hercules	Fenertepe
7 Filo	Nike-Hercules	Fenertepe
8 Filo	Nike-Hercules	Fenertepe

Although the SAM units are described here as being based at only two locations they are believed to be more widely dispersed, with only squadron headquarters and maintenance facilities at Alemdag and Fenertepe.

2ci Taktik Hava Kuvveti Komutabligi (Second Tactical Air Force)

The Second Tactical Air Force was created in 1972 by the redesignation of the Third Tactical Air Force, which in turn had been redesignated in 1950, having previously been the Third Air Division, first created in 1947. It is headquartered at Diyarbakir, in southeastern Turkey. The Second Tactical Air Force is considerably smaller than the First, with only three assigned bases.

Merzifon's squadrons are tasked with close air support, and also include the F-5 OCU (153 Filo). Erhac houses the F-4 OCU (173 Filo) and F-4 interdictor and air defence squadrons. Diyarbakir's F-104 squadrons are assigned to CAS, with the F-5 unit providing recce capability. Each base has a liaison unit, with a mix of aircraft types assigned. Some reports suggest that

the Second Tactical Air Force will gain two squadrons of F-4s from the First to replace its F-104s, these in turn being replaced by F-16s. This would concentrate the most modern aircraft types in the First Tactical Air Force, which would have only F-16s and one wing of the most recently acquired F-4Es, while the older F-4s and F-5s would all be assigned to the Second.

Turkey's Transalls wear a variety of styles of 'Turk Hava Kuvvetleri' logos. This aircraft has one with italic script.

Turkey operates only a handful of examples of the versatile Hercules, a mix of C-130Bs and C-130Es. These equip 222 Filo.

The Douglas Dakota serves with several units, including some liaison units, and three of the four 12 Ana Üs Filos. This aircraft wears a modern lizard-type camouflage.

This Dakota has a non-standard nose profile, and several extra blade antennas, perhaps indicating that it has an Elint role.

Despite its drive for modernisation, the Turkish air force remains a major Dakota operator. Some even fly VIP missions.

One of 224 Filo's Vickers Viscounts. Three were taken on charge, transferred from Turk Hava Yolari in 1971. 224 Filo at Etimesgut also operates C-47s and helicopters.

Turkey's training organisation has not undergone the same modernisation as the front line, and T-33s remains vitally important.

Thirty Northrop T-38s augment the survivors of 70 T-33s with 121 Filo, the advanced flying training squadron.

A small number of Bell UH-1Hs are used by the air force for search and rescue and medevac duties. Exactly how they fit into the wing and squadron structure is uncertain.

Unusually, the T-37s of 122 Filo wear a squadron badge – in this case a scorpion insignia.

Primary flying training is undertaken mainly on the Cessna T-41D with 123 Filo at Gaziemir. The aircraft are painted in an attractive grey colour scheme. The squadron reports to 2 Ana Üs at Cigli, hence the 2- prefix codes.

A handful of ageing Beech T-34As serve alongside the Cessna T-41Ds with 123 Filo at Gaziemir. Its tandem seating makes it more suitable for the later stages of the primary training course. Trainee pilots progress on to the T-37 before undergoing advanced training on the T-38 and T-33.

Second Tactical Air Force

UNIT	TYPE	BASE
HQ Flight	C-47, UH-1H, T-33A	Diyarbakir

5 Ana Jet Üs, Merzifon

151 Filo	F-5A	Merzifon
152 Filo	F-5A	Merzifon
153 'Safak' Filo	F-5A/B	Merzifon
BLTS	T-33A, UH-1H	Merzifon

7 Ana Jet Üs, Erhac

171 Filo	F-4E Phantom	Erhac
172 Filo	F-4E Phantom	Erhac
173 'Simsek' Filo	F-4E Phantom	Erhac
BLTS	T-33A, UH-1H	Erhac

8 Ana Jet Üs, Diyarbakir

181 Filo	F-104G/TF-104G	Diyarbakir
182 Filo	CF-104G/CF-104D	Diyarbakir
184 Filo	RF-5A	Diyarbakir
BLTS	T-33A/RT-33A	Diyarbakir

Hava Ulastirma Komutanligi (Air Transport Command)

Reporting directly to THK headquarters in Ankara, Air Transport Command is centred on two bases, with the second (Etimesgut) subordinate to the first. Thus Etimesgut's aircraft wear 12- prefixed codes, although they are not based at 12 Ana Üs, and form the semi-independent Etimesgut Ulastirma Grubo (Etimesgut Transport Group). Erkilet/Kayseri houses the tactical airlift units (two squadrons, one of 20 Transall C.160Ts, one of six C-130 Hercules and two C-47s), while Etimesgut hosts most of the remaining C-47s (being replaced by CN-235s),

Vickers Viscounts, Citation IIs and Bell UH-1s. A Gulfstream III was acquired in mid-1987 but was written off on 9 June 1987 and returned to Savannah for repair and resale. Two Gulfstream IVs have since been delivered for VVIP duties, one of them civil registered. Turkey takes the assault transport role particularly seriously, having already used paratroops during the invasion of Cyprus. The large number of Transalls in use reflects the high degree of aid received from Western Germany.

Second Tactical Air Force

UNIT	TYPE	BASE
12 Ana Üs, Erkilet/Kayseri		
221 Filo	C-160T	Erkilet/Kayseri
222 Filo	C-47, C-130	Erkilet/Kayseri
223 Filo	C-47	Etimesgut
224 Filo	C-47, Viscount, UH-1H, Citation II	Etimesgut

Häva Okullari Komuntanligi (Air Training Command)

Another direct-reporting organisation is Air Training Command, whose major flying training operation operates from Cigli. Although a member of the NATO pilot training scheme until 1956, Turkey began training its own pilots from an early stage. An independent Air Training Command was established on 30 August 1956. The Miles Magisters then in use were replaced by their indigenous derivative, the Ugur 5106, by 24 ex-Canadian Beech T-34As, and by some 66 ex-NATO Texans and Harvards. RT-33As were absorbed by the command when they proved too underpowered for sustained operational use in hot-and-high conditions. The success of these aircraft in the training role led to the procurement of many more standard T-33 trainers. Today the primary flying school (123 Filo) flies Beech T-34As and mainly Cessna T-41Ds, giving student pilots a brief 10/15-hour course before they move to Cigli. Here students progress to the Cessna T-37B and T-37C (20 and 50 respectively acquired new and from USAF stocks) for a 90/100-hour course with 122 Filo, before moving to 121 Squadron for advanced training on the T-33 and/or T-38.

Thirty ex-USAF T-38s were acquired in late 1979 but plans for a second batch have so far come to nothing. The T-38 can therefore only be used for giving potential fast-jet pilots some experience of real high-performance flying at the end of their training course. The backbone of the advanced flying training school remains the elderly T-33, with aircraft coming from a wide variety of sources, wearing various colour schemes. Turkey originally acquired 74 J33-engined T-33s under MAP, followed by 54 ex-RCAF Nene-engined T-33s (delivered between 1958 and 1973) and 31 French aircraft, some of them Nene-powered. The final T-33s to arrive were 12 ex-USAF aircraft in 1988. Until late 1986 or early 1987 pilots then went on to 3 Ana Üs at Konya for advanced training on the F-100. The base then transferred out of Air Training Command and its squadrons converted to F-4s, and pilots now go straight to fast-jet OCUs for type conversion and role training, transitioning directly to the F-16, F-104, F-5 or F-4 from the T-38, and with the bulk of their hours flown on the T-33. 124 Filo is the flying instructor's school and borrows its aircraft from other units at Cigli as required.

Air Training Command

UNIT	TYPE	BASE
HQ Flight	C-47, UH-1H	Gaziemir
Air Force College		Istanbul
Air Warfare School (Hava Harp Okulu)		Istanbul
Air Defence School		Istanbul
Electronics & Communications School		Gaziemir
Technical Training School		
2 Ana Üs, Cigli		
121 Filo	T-33A, T-38A	Cigli
122 Filo	T-37C	Cigli
123 Filo	T-34A, T-41D	Gaziemir
124 Filo	Aircraft borrowed from 121 and 122 Filos as needed	Cigli
BLTS	C-47, UH-1H	Cigli
Air Force College flying school	Cessna T-41D	Yesilkoy
Air Warfare School (Hava Harp Okulu) flying unit	C-47, UH-1H, T-41D	Yesilkoy
Unidentified unit	C-47	Erzurum

Türk Donanma Havaciligi (Turkish Naval Aviation)

Dormant since 1946, when a flying-boat squadron at Guzelyali near Izmir was disbanded, naval flying resumed in 1971, with the delivery of eight S-2A and two TS-2A Trackers from the Netherlands, later augmented by 12 ex-US Navy S-2Es. These formed an ASW squadron at Bandirma, with air force pilots and ground crew, and navy electronics operators. These original Trackers are being replaced or augmented by 18 refurbished ex-US Navy S-2Es. Plans to re-engine an eventual 30 Trackers with a turboprop powerplant were abandoned during late 1993 after bids were solicited from Marsh Aviation,

Grumman and Conair. Three AB 204ASs formed an ASW detachment at Karamursel until 1973, when both units moved to a long inactive airfield near Istanbul, resurrected under the name Topel. The naval aviation element, the Turk Cumhuriyet Bahrya (Turkish Naval Aviation), is today a tiny force, having lost its fixed-wing S-2 Trackers to the air force during the mid-1970s. This left it with only three land-based AB 204ASs for ASW operations, augmenting these from 1977 with 16 AB 212ASWs which can be deployed aboard 'Berk'- and 'MEKO 2000'-class frigates. The first six aircraft were equipped

with SMA APS-705 radar, the later aircraft having Ferranti Sea Spray and BAeD Sea Skua missiles. The Navy retains some degree of operational control over the ageing Trackers, which therefore appear under the naval order of battle.

Turkish Naval Aviation

UNIT	TYPE	BASE
301 Filo	S-2E Tracker	Topel
351 Filo	AB 204AS, AB 212ASW	Topel

The **Cessna T-41** is used for basic flying training. Its side-by-side seating and docile handling characteristics make it ideal for the early stages of such training.

The **Bellanca Citabria** is used for screening potential trainee pilots, and for primary flying training. It is simple, rugged and robust, and cheap to operate.

The **Cessna U-17** is used for basic training, its taildragger configuration and powerful engine making it quite a handful for the trainee pilot to master. Like most Turkish army aircraft, it wears drab colours, with small roundels. Red spinners are common on trainers.

For multi-engine training, and for occasional liaison work, the Army Aviation School fleet includes the **Beech T-42A (Baron)**. Only a handful are in the inventory.

Below: Tip-tanks identify this aircraft as one of three Cessna 421B Golden Eagles.

Above: One of Turkey's Robinson R22s, used for basic helo training.

Above: The Schweizer/Hughes 300 is the primary army training helicopter, the Enstrom TH-28 and R-22 having proved troublesome and unpopular.

Below: One of three Super King Air 200s used by the Army in the liaison role.

Türk Kara Ordusu Havaciligi (Turkish Army Aviation)

Able to field some 540,000 men (including only 45,000 regular troops) the Turkish Army (Kara Kuvvetleri – or Army Forces) is NATO's second largest, and its aviation element, the Turk Kara Ucak Komutanligi (Turkish Army Aviation), is correspondingly large. An Army Aviation School (Kara Havacilik Okulu) was established at Polatli in 1948, using 15 ex-US Army L-4J Cubs. L-18B Super Cubs entered service in October 1949, and two of these aircraft (of 149 eventually delivered) saw active service in Korea, where Turkish army pilots also flew the L-19. In 1958 the Army Aviation School moved to Güvercinlik, its present home.

The expansion of the army's aviation element was leisurely, Cessna L-19 Bird Dogs being taken on charge in 1963, Cessna U-17 Skywagons (100) and Do 27s (five) from 1964, and Do 28Bs and Do 28Ds (six and 15) from 1965. A single DHC-2 Beaver was also delivered.

The Bell UH-1B was the first rotary-wing type taken on charge by the Army, arriving in 1966 in Italian-built AB 205A form. Batches of AB 205As eventually totalled 156, with further AB 212s and some 70 UH-1Hs coming directly from Bell and through FMS. Some 60 ex-Heer Alouette IIIs were delivered in 1982, some of them for the police. Further helicopter deliveries have included 10 Robinson R22 Betas for training and a number of Enstrom TH-28s. The organisation became an independent main branch of the army during 1986.

All aircraft are controlled by the Central Army Aviation Establishment at Güverncinlik, which is also the largest single base and home to the Kara Havacilik Okulu (Army Aviation School). Army pilots are screened using the 40 Bellanca Citabria 150s delivered from 1979, in a 12-hour grading phase, before progressing to a two-stage (15 hours each) preliminary training course. Instrument flying and multi-engine training follows on the Beech T-42 Baron and Dornier Do 28B. Helicopter pilots then went on to the TH-13T, though the last of these were retired prematurely, being grounded on 2 December 1991 following a crash. No such fate has befallen the 30 Hughes 300Cs delivered in late 1982 and early 1983. Preliminary helicopter training is now undertaken by the Robinsons. Communications and liaison duties are performed by recently delivered Beech Super King Air 200s, Cessna 421B Golden Eagles (three delivered from 1975), a Cessna 421C (delivered in 1977), and perhaps still a single Cherokee Six dating from 1972.

The Turkish Army's search for an attack helicopter began during the 1970s, and a $50 million order for six AH-1Ss was authorised in late 1983, though this may have later lapsed. Some confusion exists, not least because the Turkish Army is today certainly an operator of the AH-1F (hitherto known as the Modernized AH-1S). Regardless of when these Cobras were delivered, deliveries of another Cobra variant, the USMC AH-1W, are less shrouded in secrecy. Five of these were delivered in 1990, diverted from USMC orders, and another five were taken on charge in 1993. Häva Bölük (aviation companies) are attached to Army ground units at kolordu (corps), tümen (division), tüguy (brigade), tabur (battalion) or alay (regiment) level, and to training units like the Parasütcü Okülo (paratroop school) and the Diyade Okülo (infantry school) at Gebze. Other main bases include Horasan, Konya, Koskekoy and and Sinop, but the exact order of battle is unknown.

The location of individual aviation units remains unknown, and any further information should be addressed to the editors.

Türk Jandarma Teskilati (Turkish Gendarmerie)

The 120,000-strong Jandarma is controlled in peacetime by the Ministry of the Interior and functions as a para-military police force. In wartime control would revert to the Ministry of Defence, and the Jandarma would act as a military police force. The force operates its own helicopters, and deliveries have included at least 20 AB 204Bs, 56 AB 205A-1s, 15 AB 206 JetRangers (eight remain), 12 AB 212s, two Do 28s and a single Rockwell Aero Commander 690. Six Sikorsky S-70A-17s have been delivered. The civil police is also a helicopter opera-

tor, with a number of ex-German Alouette IIIs. Main operating bases for Jandarma aviation units are Güverncinlik and Diyarbakir.

The order of battle and location of other Jandarma units remains unknown, and any further information should be addressed to the editors.

Türk Hava Kurumu (Turkish Air League)

The Turkish Air League is an auxiliary flying training and air experience organisation. Bases include Yalova and Inönü. Aircraft types in use include the LET L-13 Blanik, Fournier RF-5 motor glider, and SIAT 223K-1 (MBB Flamingo) and Slingsby T-67M lightplanes used as glider tugs and trainers. Other aircraft on strength include Cessna T-41Ds, Cessna 150As, Cessna 180Ds, Cessna 207s, a Cessna 402, PZL Wilgas, and Antonov An-2s. The organisation provides screening for potential Turkish Air Force pilots, giving 12 hours of instruction and 10 parachute jumps, and also performs liaison, crop-spraying and survey duties.

The order of battle and location of individual Air League units remains unknown, and any further information should be addressed to the editors.

Polis (Police)

The civil police force uses a handful of ex-Heer Alouette IIIs, as well as two Sikorsky S-70As and a handful of Aérospatiale Pumas.

The location of individual police aviation units remains unknown, and any further information should be addressed to the editors.

Despite its wire cutters and fuselage-mounted Minigun, this aircraft is a Bell 206 and not an OH-58 Kiowa. The type is not in widespread service, but has proved popular.

Very little is known about the Turkish Army's AH-1Ps (which may be old surplus US Army AH-1S airframes with new canopies). They seem to have been delivered since the first AH-1Ws were taken on charge, and retain a US Army style olive drab colour scheme.

The S-70A-28 is rapidly becoming one of the mainstays of Turkish army aviation, and will eventually fully replace the ageing UH-1 and its derivatives.

Many Army helicopters, including this UH-1H, have lost their roundels and 'KK' markings and have gained Turk Kara Kuvvetleri (Turkish Army Forces) titles instead.

Today the UH-1B is used primarily for advanced rotary-wing training, though a handful may survive in front-line use in outlying areas. This aircraft was photographed at the Army Aviation School at Güvercinlik.

Among the Genelkurmay fleet are at least two specially equipped Do 28Ds with prominent ventral and chin radomes. The role of these aircraft remains unknown.

This anonymous-looking S-70A-17 belongs to the General Staff of the Turkish Army, as is signified by the Genelkurmay Baskanligi titles. Turkish Army Black Hawks are broadly equivalent to the UH-60L.

One of Turkey's new AH-1Ws. These aircraft wear brown, green and black camouflage, carrying a rocket pod and empty TOW tubes. The wingtip carries an overwing chaff/flare dispenser, as fitted to current USMC Cobras.

INDEX

INDEX

Picture acknowledgments

Front cover: Peter Steinemann. **4:** Robert Hewson, Jan Jørgensen. **5:** Yves Debay, via Paul Jackson. **6:** Ralf Hupfeld, David Donald. **7:** Jon Lake (two). **8:** Richard L. Ward, Paul Jackson. **9:** Jan Jørgensen, Stefan Luechinger. **10:** Graham Robson, Carey Mavor. **11:** Beechcraft, Michel Fournier. **12:** Bob Archer (two). **13:** McDonnell Douglas, Paul Carter. **14:** James Benson. **15:** Chris A. Neill, Paul Carter, Bob Archer. **16:** David Draycott. **17:** McDonnell Douglas, Mike Reyno, Loral. **18:** Combat Camera Deployed. **19:** Combat Camera Deployed, Bon Alessandro. **20:** Combat Camera Deployed (three), Marco Amatimaggio, Tim Ripley. **21:** Tim Ripley (two). **22:** David Donald, IAI. **23:** IAI, Conair, David Donald. **24-26:** Jon Lake. **30:** Jon Lake. **31:** Jon Lake (two), Sergei Skrynnikov/AviaData. **32-34:** Jon Lake. **35:** Jon Lake, Sergei Skrynnikov/AviaData. **36:** Richard Cooper. **38:** Richard Cooper, Robert Hewson. **39-41:** Jon Lake. **42:** Gordon Upton. **43:** Stefan Petersen, Jon Lake (two). **44:** Robert Hewson, Jon Lake (two). **45:** Gerard Keysper. **46-47:** Herman Potgieter. **48:** via Paul Jackson (two). **49:** Dassault (two). **50:** Paul Jackson, SIRPA/AIR. **51:** Dassault. **52:** via Paul Jackson, Dassault. **53:** Dassault, Jean-Jacques Petit, via Paul Jackson. **54:** Paul Jackson (two), Herman Pieterse, Jean-Jacques Petit. **55:** Dassault, René J. Francillon. **56:** Peter Steinemann, Herman Potgieter. **57:** Herman Potgieter. **60:** Dassault (four), Salvador Mafé Huertas, John Blackman. **61:** Dassault (two). **67:** Dassault, Paul Jackson (three), Salvador Mafé Huertas. **68:** Dassault (three), Ben J. Ullings. **69:** Paul Jackson (two), MATRA (four), Salvador Mafé Huertas. **70:** Herman Potgieter. **71:** Jean-Jacques Petit, SIRPA/AIR via René J. Francillon. **74:** Dassault, Dirk Lamarque. **75:** Herman Potgieter, B. Colin via René J. Francillon. **76:** Dassault, via Paul Jackson. **77:** via Salvador Mafé Huertas, Yves Debay. **78:** Ray Sumner, Peter R. Foster. **79:** Martin Baumann, Paul Jackson, Ben J. Ullings. **80:** Paul Jackson (three), Jean-Jacques Petit (two). **81:** Paul Jackson (two), Chris Ryan, David Donald, Hans Nijhuis. **82:** Robbie Shaw (four), Bruno Cowet, C. Jacquet via René J. Francillon. **83:** Gasztych (two), Michel Fournier (two), Martin Baumann. **84:** Ray Sumner (three), Ben J. Ullings, Robbie Shaw. **85:** Ben J. Ullings, Antione J. Givaudon, John Blackman, Michel Fournier. **86:** Dassault, John Blackman (three), Martin Baumann, Yves Debay. **87:** Jean-Jacques Peiti (three), via Paul Jackson. **88:** Peter Steinemann (two), Hans Nijhuis, Salvador Mafé Huertas. **89:** Peter R. Foster, Jean-Jacues Petit (three). **90:** via Paul Jackson, Jean-Jacques Petit (two), Peter Steinemann (two). **91:** William J. Mondy (three), Jean-Jacques Petit (two). **92:** US Navy, Jean-Jacques Petit (three), Paul Jackson. **93:** Paul Jackson, Peter Steinemann (two), Robbie Shaw, Achille Vigna. **94:** Achille Vigna, Louis J. Vosloo, Chris Lofting, Michel Fournier, Gerd Kromhout. **95:** Michel Fournier, Peter R. Foster. **96-107:** Peter Steinemann. **108-115:** Warren Thompson. **116:** Anders Nylén (two), Saab. **117:** Anders Nylén. **118-120:** Saab. **121:** Anders Nylén. **122-123:** Saab. **124:** Saab (three), Bruce Robertson. **125:** Saab, Peter R. Foster. **126:** Chris Brooks/Aerophoto, Peter Liander. **127:** Saab (three), Peter Liander (three), Anders Nylén, Danielsson. **128:** Saab (two), Peter R. Foster, Werner Münzenmaier. **129:** Peter Liander (three), Anders Nylén, Danielsson. **132:** Saab, Peter R. Foster, Chris Ryan. **133:** Chris Ryan, Jelle Sjoerdsma. **134:** Saab, via Jon Lake (two), via Michael Stroud. **135:** Saab (two), Chris Lofting. **136-137:** Joe Bruch Collection. **138:** Ted Carlson/Fotodynamics, Bob Archer. **139:** Bob Archer, Joe Bruch. **140:** James Benson. **141:** Joe Bruch (two), US Air Force. **142:** Joe Bruch (two). **143:** Joe Bruch Collection. **145:** Joe Bruch, Robert R. Bennett, Joe Bruch. **146:** Joe Bruch (two), Bob Archer. **147:** Joe Bruch (two), Don Logan. **149:** Robbie Shaw (seven), Peter Steinemann (two), Yves Debay, Herman Sixma, Hans Nijhuis. **151:** Robbie Shaw, Peter Steinemann (two), Carmine de Nardi, Stuart Lewis, Ton van Dreumel, Peter R. Foster, Yves Debay. **153:** Hans Nijhuis (eight), Herman Sixma (two), Gary Jennings, Peter Steinemann. **155-157:** Peter Steinemann.